McGraw-Hill
netw⦿rks™
A Social Studies Learning System

Discovering World Geography

QUIZZES
AND TESTS

Mc
Graw
Hill
Education

Bothell, WA • Chicago, IL • Columbus, OH • New York, NY

www.mheonline.com/networks

Send all inquiries to:
McGraw-Hill Education
8787 Orion Place
Columbus, OH 43240

ISBN: 978-0-07-664934-1
MHID: 0-07-664934-2

Printed in the United States of America.

1 2 3 4 5 6 7 8 9 RHR 18 17 16 15 14 13

Table of Contents *continued*

Table of Contents *continued*

Table of Contents *continued*

Table of Contents *continued*

Unit Test

The World

networks

DIRECTIONS: True/False Indicate whether the statement is true (T) or false (F).

_____ **1.** The physical features of Earth never change.

_____ **2.** Earth has three layers: the core, the mantle, and the crust.

_____ **3.** A tsunami is a tall mountain.

_____ **4.** Migration is a primary reason that urbanization occurs.

_____ **5.** Standard of living is a measure of what is produced and what is required to produce it.

DIRECTIONS: Matching Match each item with its description.

_____ **6.** city with an extremely large population

_____ **7.** average weather conditions in an area over a long time

_____ **8.** important outward display of culture

_____ **9.** imaginary lines running north to south

_____ **10.** thin layer of gases that envelop Earth

A. longitude

B. atmosphere

C. climate

D. megalopolis

E. customs

DIRECTIONS: Multiple Choice Indicate the answer choice that best answers the question.

_____ **11.** What is a landscape?

    A. picture   **C.** portion of Earth's surface

    B. chart   **D.** printed sheet

_____ **12.** What imaginary line of latitude circles the middle of Earth?

    A. Tropic of Capricorn   **C.** Tropic of Cancer

    B. Equator   **D.** Prime Meridian

_____ **13.** Which item is part of the human system element in the study of geography?

    A. water cycle   **C.** environment

    B. wind current   **D.** language

_____ **14.** What event occurs around September 23 of each year?

    A. autumnal equinox   **C.** summer solstice

    B. vernal equinox   **D.** spring solstice

_____ **15.** What causes Earth's plates to move?

    A. erosion

    B. moon's pull on Earth

    C. heat from deep within Earth

    D. weathering

_____ **16.** What are the two types of water found on Earth's surface?

    A. sulfur water and freshwater

    B. mineral water and sulfur water

    C. salt water and mineral water

    D. freshwater and salt water

_____ **17.** If the global birthrate is more than the death rate, how would this affect the world's population?

    A. There would be more demand on resources and more pollution.

    B. There would be no changes in the global population.

    C. Males would live longer than females.

    D. The global population would decrease.

_____ **18.** What effect did the industrial age have on where people lived?

    A. The number of farmers increased.

    B. The populations of cities increased.

    C. The populations of rural areas increased.

    D. Many people left the cities to find jobs elsewhere.

_____ **19.** Which country is a dictatorship?

    A. Mexico

    B. North Korea

    C. United Kingdom

    D. Canada

_____ **20.** What is the environment?

    A. the natural surroundings of a place

    B. the shape and nature of the land

    C. the average weather in a place over a long period of time

    D. places that are close to one another and share characteristics

Lesson Quiz 1

networks

The Geographer's World

DIRECTIONS: True/False Indicate whether the statement is true (T) or false (F).

_____ **1.** History is the study of Earth and its peoples, places, and environments.

_____ **2.** Geographers study how places change over time.

_____ **3.** People can affect the environment, but the environment cannot affect people.

_____ **4.** Understanding how to use geography helps people make good decisions about the world.

_____ **5.** If you use Google Maps to help you find a nearby pizza parlor, you are using a geography skill.

DIRECTIONS: Multiple Choice Indicate the answer choice that best answers the question.

_____ **6.** What is one type of physical feature that can be used to describe locations on Earth?

    A. population

    B. climate

    C. economic activity

    D. land use

_____ **7.** What is the difference between absolute and relative location?

    A. Absolute location is the exact location of something.

    B. Absolute location cannot be identified using lines of latitude and longitude.

    C. Absolute location describes where something is compared to another place.

    D. Absolute location describes the characteristics of a place.

_____ **8.** Which of the following two places belong to the same region?

    A. Canada and England

    B. Lake Michigan and the Mediterranean Sea

    C. Los Angeles, California, and San Diego, California

    D. Mount Everest and Mount McKinley

_____ **9.** Which of the following is an example of a landform?

    A. mountain   **C.** coal mine

    B. city   **D.** bridge

_____ **10.** When a geographer studies how people make laws, what is she is studying?

    A. the world in spatial terms   **C.** physical systems

    B. places and regions   **D.** human systems

Lesson Quiz 2

networks

The Geographer's World

DIRECTIONS: True/False Indicate whether the statement is true (T) or false (F).

_____ 1. Each half of Earth is called a hemisphere.

_____ 2. You use a map's scale bar to determine how many miles in the real world each inch on the map represents.

_____ 3. All map projections show the correct size of areas in relation to one another.

_____ 4. Satellites use remote sensing to gather information about Earth from far away.

_____ 5. GPS stands for Geographical Positioning System.

DIRECTIONS: Multiple Choice Indicate the answer choice that best answers the question.

_____ 6. Which of the following divides Earth into Northern and Southern Hemispheres?

    A. Prime Meridian

    B. International Date Line

    C. Equator

    D. Tropic of Capricorn

_____ 7. What is one way in which maps and globes differ?

    A. Maps are easier to store and carry.

    B. Globes tend to show more kinds of information than maps.

    C. Maps are more accurate than globes.

    D. Globes distort physical reality.

_____ 8. Carlos does not understand what the blue lines on his map represent. What should he look at to find the answer?

    A. map key   **C.** compass rose

    B. scale bar   **D.** map title

_____ 9. Which type of map would show the boundaries of countries?

    A. vegetation map   **C.** land-use map

    B. political map   **D.** elevation map

_____ 10. Which of these tools provides practical information about the locations of physical and human features?

    A. political maps   **C.** storm tracking technology

    B. thematic maps   **D.** geospatial technology

Chapter Test, Form A

networks

The Geographer's World

DIRECTIONS: True/False Indicate whether the statement is true (T) or false (F). If the statement is false, rewrite it to make it true.

_____ **1.** Lines of latitude run east to west; lines of longitude run north to south.

_____

_____ **2.** A map is more accurate than a globe because it does not distort physical reality.

_____

_____ **3.** The map feature that indicates north, south, east, and west is the map key.

_____

_____ **4.** Geographers look at how people, products, ideas, and information move from one place to another.

_____

_____ **5.** Geographers can use satellite information to look for changes in the shape of the land.

_____

DIRECTIONS: Matching Match each item with its description.

_____ **6.** the shape and nature of the land

_____ **7.** refers to Earth's features in terms of their locations, shapes, and relationships to one another

_____ **8.** the difference between the elevation of one feature and the elevation of another nearby feature

_____ **9.** the relationship between distances on a map and on Earth

_____ **10.** portions of Earth's surface that can be viewed at one time and from one location

A. spatial

B. relief

C. landscapes

D. scale

E. landforms

Chapter Test, Form A *cont.*

netw⊙rks

The Geographer's World

DIRECTIONS: Multiple Choice Indicate the answer choice that best answers the question.

_____ **11.** What is the name for unique locations on Earth that are defined by both physical and human characteristics?

    A. landscapes

    B. places

    C. vistas

    D. environments

_____ **12.** What is climate?

    A. the average weather in a place over a long period of time

    B. the day-to-day state of Earth's atmosphere

    C. the combination of temperature, humidity, precipitation, cloudiness, and wind

    D. the natural surroundings of a place, including its landforms and resources

_____ **13.** Which of the following geographical tools is a visual display of numerical information?

    A. map

    B. diagram

    C. graph

    D. table

_____ **14.** Which of the following maps would most likely show the location of your house and the nearby streets?

    A. large-scale map

    B. thematic map

    C. small-scale map

    D. physical map

_____ **15.** Which of the following would most likely be explained by the key on an elevation map?

    A. the kinds of plants that grow in different areas

    B. the amount of annual rainfall each color represents

    C. the locations and names of cities

    D. what height above or below sea level each color represents

Chapter Test, Form A *cont.*

networks

The Geographer's World

Map 1

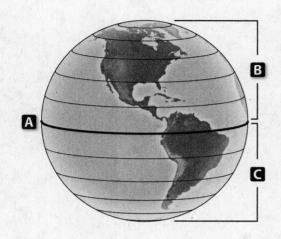

Map 2

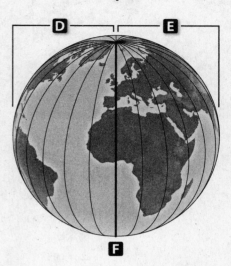

_____ **16.** What does Line A on Map 1 represent?

  A. line of latitude   **C.** line of longitude

  B. meridian line   **D.** dateline

_____ **17.** What does Line F on Map 2 represent?

  A. Equator   **C.** Prime Meridian

  B. International Dateline   **D.** Tropic of Cancer

DIRECTIONS: Short Answer Answer each of the following questions.

18. Give two examples of how people affect the environment. Then give two examples of how the environment affects people.

_____

_____

_____

19. Explain why globes are more accurate than flat maps.

_____

_____

DIRECTIONS: Essay Answer the following question on a separate piece of paper.

20. What do you think would happen if geospatial technologies such as the Global Positioning System or remote sensing suddenly stopped working for a week or two? How would society be affected? Explain your answer.

Discovering World Geography

Chapter Test, Form B

network

The Geographer's World

DIRECTIONS: True/False Indicate whether the statement is true (T) or false (F). If the statement is false, rewrite it to make it true.

_____ **1.** Absolute location uses the cardinal directions—north, south, east, and west.

_____

_____ **2.** When you grab a jacket for your walk to the mall because you notice the seasons are changing, you are using geography.

_____

_____ **3.** Forests and oil are examples of resources.

_____

_____ **4.** General-purpose maps usually show both the human-made features of an area and its natural features.

_____

_____ **5.** A geographic information system is a powerful tool because it links data about all kinds of physical and human features with the locations of those features.

_____

_____ **6.** A large-scale map focuses on a smaller area.

_____

DIRECTIONS: Matching Match each item with its description.

_____ **7.** a map that shows a wide range of information about an area

_____ **8.** the starting point for measuring longitude

_____ **9.** a map that shows specialized information about an area

_____ **10.** the starting point for measuring latitude

A. Equator

B. general-purpose map

C. Prime Meridian

D. thematic map

Chapter Test, Form B *cont.*

networks

The Geographer's World

DIRECTIONS: Multiple Choice Indicate the answer choice that best answers the question.

_____ **11.** Which of the following are geographers most likely to study?

    A. events that occur over time and how those events are connected

    B. people and the world in which they live mainly in terms of space and place

    C. how living things survive and relate to one another

    D. the production, distribution, and consumption of goods and services

_____ **12.** Why do geographers study particular regions?

    A. to describe the physical beauty and complexity of places

    B. to understand the most general physical features of places

    C. to identify the broad patterns of larger areas

    D. to analyze the location and size of things

_____ **13.** What human feature might be used to define a unique location on Earth, or place?

    A. land use

    B. landforms

    C. vegetation

    D. climate

Map 1

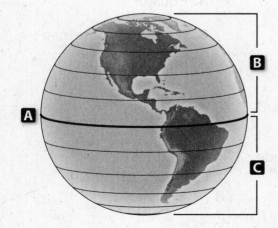

Map 2

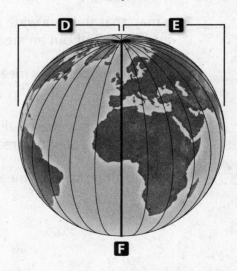

_____ **14.** What does Area B on Map 1 show?

    A. Northern Hemisphere   **C.** Northern Tropics

    B. Southern Hemisphere   **D.** Northern Temperate Zone

Discovering World Geography

_____ **15.** What does Area D on Map 2 show?

      A. Northern Hemisphere   **C.** Western Hemisphere

      B. Eastern Hemisphere   **D.** Equatorial Zone

_____ **16.** Which of the following is most likely to be shown on a map but not a globe?

      A. political boundaries

      B. election results

      C. major landmasses

      D. bodies of water

_____ **17.** What is another name for mapmakers?

      A. projectionists

      B. calligraphists

      C. graphic designers

      D. cartographers

_____ **18.** What part of a map is shown in the above graphic?

      A. map title

      B. compass rose

      C. scale bar

      D. map key

_____ **19.** If you were looking at a map, what would the map element shown above help you determine?

      A. the elevation of Mt. Everest

      B. the absolute location of New York City

      C. the distance between Los Angeles and San Francisco

      D. the relative location of Toronto, Canada, compared to your hometown

DIRECTIONS: Essay Answer the following question on a separate piece of paper.

  20. What do you think would happen if geospatial technologies such as the Global Positioning System or remote sensing suddenly stopped working for a week or two? How would society be affected? Explain your answer.

Lesson Quiz 1

networks

Physical Geography

DIRECTIONS: True/False Indicate whether the statement is true (T) or false (F).

_____ **1.** Earth's atmosphere has more nitrogen than oxygen in it.

_____ **2.** The sun remains directly overhead in areas outside the tropics.

_____ **3.** Movements of air are called winds.

_____ **4.** Rain generally falls on the side of the mountain facing the ocean.

_____ **5.** Earth has five basic climate zones.

DIRECTIONS: Multiple Choice Indicate the answer choice that best answers the question.

_____ **6.** What is the source of all energy on Earth?

    A. the wind

    B. the sun

    C. Earth's coal

    D. Earth's oxygen

_____ **7.** What causes the seasons to change on Earth?

    A. the North and South Poles

    B. Earth's distance from the sun

    C. the wind currents

    D. the Earth's tilt as it revolves around the sun

_____ **8.** How many layers make up the inside of Earth?

    A. two

    B. three

    C. four

    D. five

_____ **9.** What is the correct term for Earth's completion of one full trip around the sun?

    A. orbit   **C.** revolution

    B. axis   **D.** circle

_____ **10.** What term describes the increase in the average temperature of Earth's atmosphere?

    A. climate zones   **C.** climate warming

    B. global change   **D.** global warming

Discovering World Geography

Lesson Quiz 2

networks

Physical Geography

DIRECTIONS: Matching Match each item with its description.

_____ **1.** a process by which water, wind, or ice moves bits of rock elsewhere

_____ **2.** a giant ocean wave

_____ **3.** a small ice mass that spreads outward on a land surface

_____ **4.** a long, narrow band of volcanoes around the Pacific Ocean

_____ **5.** a large, continuous mass of land

A. continent

B. Ring of Fire

C. tsunami

D. erosion

E. glacier

DIRECTIONS: Multiple Choice Indicate the answer choice that best answers the question.

_____ **6.** How many continents are found on Earth?

A. 10   **C.** 7

B. 4   **D.** 15

_____ **7.** What causes earthquakes and volcanoes?

A. plate movement

B. the moon's pull on the Earth

C. solar flares

D. the Earth's tilt

_____ **8.** What process works with weathering to change Earth's surface?

A. change in seasons

B. gravity

C. solar flares

D. erosion

_____ **9.** Which is the largest type of ice mass?

A. glacier   **C.** ice sheet

B. ice cap   **D.** avalanche

_____ **10.** What force has caused the fastest change in Earth's environment in the last 50 years?

A. erosion   **C.** weathering

B. human actions   **D.** volcanic eruptions

Lesson Quiz 3

networks

Physical Geography

DIRECTIONS: True/False Indicate whether the statement is true (T) or false (F).

_____ 1. Plains are never found along coastlines.

_____ 2. Continents are a type of landform surrounded by water.

_____ 3. The Dead Sea is a freshwater sea.

_____ 4. Earth's oceans are actually connected and form one global ocean.

_____ 5. Acid rain can damage Earth's environment.

DIRECTIONS: Multiple Choice Indicate the answer choice that best answers the question.

_____ 6. What does elevation describe?

  A. how far above sea level a landform or location is

  B. how deep an ocean is

  C. how many square miles of land a country has

  D. how much erosion has occurred

_____ 7. What is the name for a long, narrow, steep-sided cut in the ground or on the ocean floor?

  A. a continental shelf

  B. a ridge

  C. the Continental Divide

  D. a trench

_____ 8. What percentage of Earth's water is salt water?

  A. 45   **C.** 83

  B. 52   **D.** 97

_____ 9. By which process is liquid water turned into water vapor?

  A. condensation

  B. erosion

  C. evaporation

  D. weathering

_____ 10. What is the name given to the regular movement of water?

  A. water cycle   **C.** rainfall

  B. condensation   **D.** water supply

Discovering World Geography

Chapter Test, Form A

networks

Physical Geography

DIRECTIONS: True/False Indicate whether the statement is true (T) or false (F). If the statement is false, rewrite it to make it true.

_____ **1.** The sun's heat causes Earth to constantly orbit around it.

_____

_____ **2.** One measure for comparing climates is the average daily temperature.

_____

_____ **3.** Earth's crust is made up of seven enormous tectonic plates.

_____

_____ **4.** Ice sheets cover most of Greenland and Australia.

_____

_____ **5.** Water contained inside Earth's crust is called groundwater.

_____

DIRECTIONS: Matching Match each item with its description.

_____ **6.** imaginary line running through Earth's center

_____ **7.** underwater plain that borders a continent

_____ **8.** narrow strip of land connecting two larger land areas

_____ **9.** occurs on or about June 21 in the Northern Hemisphere

_____ **10.** a biome

A. isthmus

B. tundra

C. axis

D. continental shelf

E. summer solstice

Chapter Test, Form A *cont.*

networks

Physical Geography

DIRECTIONS: Multiple Choice Indicate the answer choice that best answers the question.

_____ **11.** What is it called when day and night in both hemispheres are of equal length?

    A. summer solstice

    B. axis

    C. equinox

    D. winter solstice

_____ **12.** What is the center of Earth called?

    A. mantle

    B. core

    C. crust

    D. lithosphere

_____ **13.** Who was the scientist who invented a system that divided Earth into climate zones?

    A. Albert Einstein

    B. Sir Isaac Newton

    C. Boris Karloff

    D. Wladimir Köppen

_____ **14.** How long does it take plates to move enough to create landforms?

    A. thousands of years

    B. millions of years

    C. hundreds of years

    D. around 100 years

_____ **15.** Which two continents are completely surrounded by water?

    A. Australia and Antarctica

    B. Asia and Africa

    C. Europe and Africa

    D. Europe and Asia

_____ **16.** Which of the following correctly lists Earth's oceans from smallest to largest?

    A. Southern, Indian, Arctic, Atlantic, and Pacific

    B. Pacific, Atlantic, Southern, Indian, and Arctic

    C. Arctic, Southern, Indian, Atlantic, and Pacific

    D. Atlantic, Pacific, Arctic, Southern, and Indian

Discovering World Geography

Chapter Test, Form A *cont.*

networks

Physical Geography

DIRECTIONS: Short Answer Answer each of the following questions.

> "There was a great rattle and jar. . . . [Then] there came a really terrific shock; the ground seemed to roll under me in waves, interrupted by a violent joggling up and down, and there was a heavy grinding noise as of brick houses rubbing together."
>
> —from Mark Twain, *Roughing It*

17. Based on the excerpt, list some words that Mark Twain used to describe how an earthquake sounded and felt to him.

_____

_____

_____

_____

18. How do you think Mark Twain felt during the earthquake? How can you tell by reading the excerpt?

_____

_____

_____

_____

19. What other natural disasters or events can earthquakes trigger? Give an example of a recent event.

_____

_____

_____

_____

DIRECTIONS: Essay Answer the following question on a separate piece of paper.

20. Explain how human actions have damaged the world's water supply. What can people do to prevent further damage to this precious resource?

Chapter Test, Form B

networks

Physical Geography

DIRECTIONS: True/False Indicate whether the statement is true (T) or false (F). If the statement is false, rewrite it to make it true.

_____ **1.** A year is defined as 368 days.

_____

_____ **2.** Cold temperate climates have a long summer season.

_____

_____ **3.** A glacier is the smallest of the ice masses.

_____

_____ **4.** The Panama Canal connects the Atlantic and Arctic oceans.

_____

_____ **5.** Condensation turns water vapor into a denser liquid or a solid state.

_____

DIRECTIONS: Matching Match each item with its description.

_____ **6.** an area located at the mouth of a river

_____ **7.** melted rock

_____ **8.** a climate zone

_____ **9.** subsystem that consists of Earth's water

_____ **10.** process that produces safe drinking water

A. desalination

B. hydrosphere

C. desert

D. magma

E. delta

DIRECTIONS: Multiple Choice Indicate the answer choice that best answers the question.

_____ **11.** Why do places on Earth have daily periods of daylight and darkness?

    A. because of Earth's North and South poles

    B. because Earth rotates once every 24 hours

    C. because of Earth's tilt

    D. because of Earth's distance from the sun

_____ **12.** What percent of Earth's surface is water?

    A. 71 percent

    B. 90 percent

    C. 85 percent

    D. 75 percent

_____ **13.** Why are cities often warmer than areas in the countryside?

    A. Cities have more parks.

    B. Cities consume more water.

    C. Cities have more lights.

    D. Cities have more metal, asphalt, and concrete surfaces.

_____ **14.** Where are you more likely to see an ice sheet?

    A. in the Rockies

    B. at the North Pole

    C. in Bryce Canyon

    D. along the Equator

_____ **15.** Which mountain range is under water?

    A. Mount Everest   **C.** Blue Ridge Mountain

    B. Mariana Trench   **D.** Mid-Atlantic Ridge

A peninsula is a long, narrow area that extends into a river, a lake, or an ocean. Peninsulas at one end are connected to a larger landmass. An isthmus is a narrow strip of land connecting two larger land areas. One well-known isthmus is the Central American country of Panama. Panama connects two massive continents: North America and South America. . . . It is the narrowest place in the Americas. . . .

—from *Discovering World Geography*

_____ **16.** Based on the excerpt, why do you think the country of Panama was chosen as the site for what is known as the Panama Canal?

    A. It extends into both rivers and lakes.

    B. It connects North America and South America.

    C. It is the narrowest place in the Americas.

    D. It is both long and narrow.

_____ **17.** Based on the excerpt, what is a peninsula?

    A. A peninsula is a landmass that extends into a man-made canal.

    B. A peninsula is a landmass that extends into natural waters.

    C. A peninsula is a landmass that is completely surrounded by water.

    D. A peninsula is a narrow strip of land that connects two other landmasses.

Year (AD)	Event
79	Mount Vesuvius erupts
1556	Deadly earthquake strikes northern China
1906	Earthquake, fire devastate San Francisco
1931	Floods in China leave 80 million homeless
2005	Hurricane Katrina strikes southeastern United States
2010	Haiti earthquake kills more than 220,000 people
2011	Earthquake, tsunami near Japan triggers nuclear accident

_____ **18.** Based on the table and what you have learned in this chapter, which statement below would be the best conclusion?

   A. Earthquakes only occur in North America and South America.

   B. Volcanic eruptions rarely occur.

   C. Disasters occur worldwide.

   D. China has more earthquakes than Haiti does.

_____ **19.** Based on the table and what you have learned in this chapter, which ocean has the most earthquakes?

   A. Atlantic Ocean

   B. Arctic Ocean

   C. Indian Ocean

   D. Pacific Ocean

DIRECTIONS: Essay Answer the following question on a separate piece of paper.

20. Explain how human actions have damaged the world's water supply. What can people do to prevent further damage to this precious resource?

Lesson Quiz 1

networks

Human Geography

DIRECTIONS: True/False Indicate whether the statement is true (T) or false (F).

_____ **1.** One major cause of population growth is a falling death rate.

_____ **2.** On a global scale, rapid population growth can harm the environment.

_____ **3.** In most countries, population is typically distributed evenly.

_____ **4.** Migration is one of the main causes of population shifts in our world today.

_____ **5.** A huge cluster of cities with an extremely large population is called a metropolis.

DIRECTIONS: Multiple Choice Indicate the answer choice that best answers the question.

_____ **6.** Suppose a country has a population of 6 million in 2015, 9 million in 2025, and 12 million in 2035. What is the doubling time for that country's population?

    A. 5 years   **C.** 15 years

    B. 10 years   **D.** 20 years

_____ **7.** Which of the following describes areas with large, fast-growing populations?

    A. There are usually plenty of jobs for everyone.

    B. It is not hard for people to find good housing.

    C. Disease can spread rapidly.

    D. Crime rates are typically very low.

_____ **8.** What is the main reason people choose to settle in one area and not in another?

    A. They want to get away from major transportation centers.

    B. The area has sufficient resources to meet their basic needs.

    C. They want to live close to friends and family.

    D. The area has deep religious significance to them.

_____ **9.** Which of the following illustrates a push factor—something that drives people from an area?

    A. Anu moves from India to the United States to be with her family living there.

    B. Peter moves from his small town to Nashville to find a job in the music industry.

    C. Amit moves to Turkey from his home in India after an earthquake destroys his village.

    D. Bethany moves from her home in Ohio to go to school in France.

_____ **10.** Which of the following means to enter and live in a new country?

    A. immigrate   **C.** emigrate

    B. urbanization   **D.** migrate

Lesson Quiz 2

Human Geography

DIRECTIONS: True/False Indicate whether the statement is true (T) or false (F).

_____ **1.** Everyone belongs to one—and only one—culture.

_____ **2.** An ethnic group consists of all the people who live in a particular region or community.

_____ **3.** Religion is one of the major influences on how people of a culture see the world.

_____ **4.** Cultural regions can be large or relatively small.

_____ **5.** Technology is rarely responsible for cultural change.

DIRECTIONS: Multiple Choice Indicate the answer choice that best answers the question.

_____ **6.** Which of following are the two largest ethnic minority groups in the United States?

   A. Hispanic Americans and Asian Americans

   B. Hispanic Americans and African Americans

   C. African Americans and Asian Americans

   D. Asian Americans and Native Americans

_____ **7.** In some parts of the United States, a carbonated drink is called *soda*; in other parts, it is called *pop*. What is this regional language difference an example of?

   A. urbanization   **C.** syntax

   B. ethnic group   **D.** dialect

_____ **8.** Which of the following statements describes a custom?

   A. doing your homework   **C.** shaking hands when you greet someone

   B. not littering   **D.** studying geography

_____ **9.** Which of the following describes a monarchy?

   A. The government is run by the people.

   B. A king or queen rules over the country.

   C. One person has absolute power to rule the government, people, and economy.

   D. The citizens elect the government officials.

_____ **10.** Which statement about globalization is correct?

   A. Globalization is always a smooth and easy process.

   B. Because of globalization, only a handful of world cultures now exist.

   C. Globalization helps spread ideas and innovations.

   D. Virtually everyone around the world welcomes globalization.

Lesson Quiz 3

networks

Human Geography

DIRECTIONS: True/False Indicate whether the statement is true (T) or false (F).

_____ **1.** To obtain the things you want and need, you use both natural and human resources.

_____ **2.** A country's decision about what to produce determines its economic system.

_____ **3.** In developing countries, most of the population lives in poverty.

_____ **4.** One disadvantage of trade is that it can sometimes create unemployment.

_____ **5.** When a country focuses on sustainability, it attempts to produce all of its own goods without relying on trade at all.

DIRECTIONS: Multiple Choice Indicate the answer choice that best answers the question.

_____ **6.** Which of the following is an example of a nonrenewable resource?

    A. water   **C.** trees

    B. coal   **D.** wind

_____ **7.** Which of the following are all factors of production?

    A. land, labor, and gross domestic product

    B. labor, service industries, and capital

    C. land, labor, and capital

    D. capital, service industries, and labor

_____ **8.** In which type of economy are most of the means of production privately owned?

    A. traditional economy

    B. command economy

    C. mixed economy

    D. market economy

_____ **9.** Which of the following is an example of a job in the primary sector, which produces raw materials and basic goods?

    A. auto mechanic   **C.** farmer

    B. physician   **D.** banker

_____ **10.** In economics, what is meant by the term *productivity*?

    A. a measure of what is produced and what is required to produce it

    B. the level at which a person, group, or nation lives

    C. the percentage of the labor force that is employed

    D. the total dollar value of all final goods and services produced in a year

Chapter Test, Form A

networks

Human Geography

DIRECTIONS: True/False Indicate whether the statement is true (T) or false (F). If the statement is false, rewrite it to make it true.

_____ **1.** On any given day around the world, more deaths than births occur.

_____

_____ **2.** The most common reason why people move to cities is to find jobs.

_____

_____ **3.** Dance, music, visual arts, and literature are all important elements of culture.

_____

_____ **4.** People who live in a representative democracy often have few rights.

_____

_____ **5.** The process by which nations, cultures, and economies become integrated is called globalization.

_____

_____ **6.** The United States has a command economy.

_____

DIRECTIONS: Matching Match each item with its description.

_____ **7.** to send goods to another country

_____ **8.** the geographic pattern of where people live on Earth

_____ **9.** the average number of people living within a square mile or square kilometer

_____ **10.** to bring in goods from another country

A. population distribution

B. population density

C. import

D. export

DIRECTIONS: Multiple Choice Indicate the answer choice that best answers the question.

_____ **11.** Which of the following accurately describes the global population growth rate?

    A. It has been level for the past 50 years.

    B. It is gradually slowing.

    C. It has fallen sharply over the past 20 years.

    D. It is increasing rapidly.

Major World Religions		
Buddhism	Siddhãrtha Gautama, the Buddha	Suffering comes from attachment to earthly things, which are not lasting. People become free by following the Eightfold Path, rules of right thought and conduct. People who follow the Path achieve nirvana—a state of endless peace and joy.
Christianity	Jesus Christ	The one God is Father, Son, and Holy Spirit. God the Son became human as Jesus Christ. Jesus died and rose again to bring God's forgiving love to sinful humanity. Those who trust in Jesus and follow his teachings of love for God and neighbor receive eternal life with God.
Hinduism	No one founder	One eternal spirit, Brahman, is represented as many deities. Every living thing has a soul that passes through many successive lives. Each soul's condition in a specific life is based on how the previous life was lived. When a soul reaches purity, it finally joins permanently with Brahman.
Islam	Muhammad	The one God sent a series of prophets, including the final prophet Muhammad, to teach humanity. Islam's laws are based on the Quran, the holy book, and the Sunnah, examples from Muhammad's life. Believers practice the five pillars—belief, prayer, charity, fasting, and pilgrimage—to go to an eternal paradise.
Judaism	Abraham	The one God made an agreement through Abraham and later Moses with the people of Israel. God would bless them, and they would follow God's laws, applying God's will in all parts of their lives. The main laws and practices of Judaism are stated in the Torah, the first five books of the Hebrew Bible.
Sikhism	Guru Nanak	The one God made truth known through 10 successive gurus, or teachers. God's will is that people should live honestly, work hard, and treat others fairly. The Sikh community, or Khalsa, bases its decisions on the principles of a sacred text, the Guru Granth Sahib.

_____ **12.** Based on the chart above, what is one thing that Islam, Judaism, and Christianity have in common?

 A. They all believe suffering comes from attachment to earthly things.

 B. They all consider the Bible as their holy book.

 C. They all believe in one God.

 D. They all accept the principle of reincarnation.

_____ **13.** Based on the chart above, which religion teaches that God the Son became human?

 A. Christianity **C.** Sikhism

 B. Hinduism **D.** Judaism

Chapter Test, Form A *cont.*

networks

Human Geography

_____ **14.** What is the most likely reason that the population in Egypt is concentrated along the Nile River?

    A. The views of the river are quite beautiful.

    B. Egyptians consider the Nile to be a sacred river.

    C. The Egyptian government forces the people to live there.

    D. The river provides water, food, and fertile soil for growing crops.

_____ **15.** What is the best definition of *culture*?

    A. the total population of a particular country

    B. the spread of ideas from one region to another

    C. all of the beliefs, behaviors, and traits shared by a particular group

    D. the physical characteristics of a specific population

_____ **16.** Which of the following is one of the three basic economic questions?

    A. What goods and services will be produced?

    B. Where should factories be located?

    C. How much should employees be paid?

    D. How should government reduce inflation?

_____ **17.** An increase in productivity would probably have which of the following effects?

    A. It would have no effect on the employment rate.

    B. It would cause an increase in a country's gross domestic product.

    C. It would cause a decrease in a country's standard of living.

    D. It would have little impact on per capita income.

DIRECTIONS: Short Answer Answer each of the following questions.

18. Summarize the effects of rapid population growth on the environment.

_____

_____

19. How is language related to culture?

_____

_____

DIRECTIONS: Essay Answer the following question on a separate piece of paper.

20. What economic system is used in the United States? Give specific examples to support your answer.

Discovering World Geography

Chapter Test, Form B

Human Geography

networks

DIRECTIONS: True/False Indicate whether the statement is true (T) or false (F). If the statement is false, rewrite it to make it true.

_____ **1.** Population growth rates are the same in all areas of the world.

_____

_____ **2.** Cultural blending is a positive effect of migration.

_____

_____ **3.** Members of a culture sometimes have special roles or positions as part of their cultural traditions.

_____

_____ **4.** A physical region is a geographic area in which people have certain traits in common.

_____

_____ **5.** Human rights are different for people in different cultures.

_____

_____ **6.** Employees are an example of capital.

_____

DIRECTIONS: Matching Match each item with its description.

_____ **7.** to leave one's home to live in another place

_____ **8.** a tax added to the cost of imported products

_____ **9.** to enter and live in a new country

_____ **10.** a limit on the amount of a good that can be imported

A. emigrate

B. immigrate

C. tariff

D. quota

DIRECTIONS: Multiple Choice Indicate the answer choice that best answers the question.

_____ **11.** Which of the following is the largest megalopolis in the Americas?

A. Toronto, Canada

B. Los Angeles, California

C. Mexico City, Mexico

D. Chicago, Illinois

_____ **12.** What are fair treatment before the law and the right to marry and have children examples of?

A. customs

B. human rights

C. traditions

D. legal rights

_____ **13.** Which of the following is an example of an ethnic group?

    A. everyone who goes to your school

    B. all of the people who live in a specific country

    C. the people who attend your church

    D. members of the Cherokee nation

_____ **14.** When Americans celebrate Independence Day, which element of culture is being observed?

    A. history   **C.** the arts

    B. religion   **D.** literature

_____ **15.** Which term is defined as the total dollar value of all final goods and services produced in a country annually?

    A. standard of living   **C.** gross domestic product

    B. per capita income   **D.** productivity index

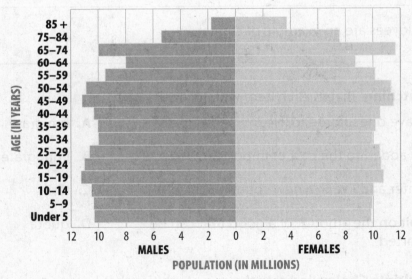

Source: U.S. Census Bureau,
Statistical Abstract of the United States: 2012

_____ **16.** Based on the population pyramid, what do you find when you compare the female U.S. population to the male U.S. population?

    A. boys age 9 and under far outnumber girls age 9 and under

    B. there are fewer men than women over the age of 75

    C. girls age 9 and under far outnumber boys age 9 and under

    D. there are fewer women than men over the age of 75

_____ **17.** Based on the data in the population pyramid, which of the following is a reasonable conclusion?

 A. The overall population of the United States will decrease greatly by 2100.

 B. Men seem to live longer than women in the United States.

 C. The population of people 10 and under is growing rapidly in the United States.

 D. Women seem to live longer than men in the United States.

In recent years, nations have become more interdependent, or reliant on one another. As they draw closer together, economic and political ties are formed. The World Trade Organization (WTO) helps regulate trade among nations. The World Bank provides financing, advice, and research to developing nations to help them grow their economies. The International Monetary Fund (IMF) is a group that monitors economic development. The IMF also lends money to nations in need and provides training and technical help. One well-known policy and organization that promotes global trade is the North American Free Trade Agreement (NAFTA). NAFTA encourages free trade among the United States, Canada, and Mexico.

—*Discovering World Geography*

_____ **18.** Based on the passage above, how are the World Bank and the International Monetary Fund alike?

 A. They both help regulate world trade.

 B. They both lend money to developing nations.

 C. They both promote increased urbanization.

 D. They both attempt to reduce tariffs.

_____ **19.** Based on the passage above, which of the following is true about relationships between nations in recent years?

 A. Nations have become less reliant on one another.

 B. The relationships between nations have not changed.

 C. Nations have become more reliant on one another.

 D. Fewer economic and political ties have been formed.

DIRECTIONS: Essay Answer the following question on a separate piece of paper.

20. What economic system is used in the United States? Give specific examples to support your answer.

Unit Test

North America

DIRECTIONS: True/False Indicate whether the statement is true (T) or false (F).

_____ **1.** To aid in their study, geographers often divide countries into large areas called regions.

_____ **2.** Europeans were the first humans to settle in North America.

_____ **3.** The climate in southern Alaska is mild.

_____ **4.** The United States and Canada share the Gulf of St. Lawrence.

_____ **5.** Mexico City is one of the largest cities in the world.

DIRECTIONS: Matching Match each item with its description.

_____ **6.** Canadian administrative units similar to states

_____ **7.** smaller river that flows into a larger river

_____ **8.** referring to a people who move about, rather than settle in one place

_____ **9.** foods that are eaten regularly, such as corn and squash

_____ **10.** "living or occurring naturally in a particular place"

A. tributary

B. indigenous

C. nomadic

D. provinces

E. staples

DIRECTIONS: Multiple Choice Indicate the answer choice that best answers the question.

_____ **11.** Which is a true statement about the New England subregion?

    A. It is located in the northwestern corner of the United States.

    B. It is where many of the first English colonists settled.

    C. It includes Maryland as part of the subregion.

    D. It is the largest subregion of the United States east of the Mississippi River.

_____ **12.** Which position is part of the tourism industry?

    A. hotel desk clerk   **C.** banker

    B. attorney   **D.** insurance agent

_____ **13.** Which U.S. state is the largest in land area?

    A. Oklahoma   **C.** Alaska

    B. Texas   **D.** California

_____ **14.** What effect did railroads have on the population west of the Mississippi River?

    A. The population declined; people moved back east.

    B. The population at first increased but then declined.

    C. The population did not change.

    D. The population boomed.

_____ **15.** Desalination is a possible answer to what challenge facing the western states?

    A. eliminating soil pollution

    B. maintaining an adequate water supply

    C. attracting tourists

    D. attracting people to move there

_____ **16.** Which of the following statements about the climate in Canada's northern lands is accurate?

    A. Most of Canada's north is extremely cold all year.

    B. Most of Canada's north has short, cold days and long, cold nights.

    C. Most of Canada's north has mild winters and hot summers.

    D. Most of Canada's north has cold winters and mild summers.

_____ **17.** Which city is the capital of Canada?

    A. Toronto   **C.** Ottawa

    B. Montreal   **D.** Vancouver

_____ **18.** With which nation does Canada traditionally have the most cultural ties?

    A. Britain   **C.** France

    B. United States   **D.** Spain

_____ **19.** Which body of water borders Mexico on the west?

    A. Gulf of Mexico   **C.** Atlantic Ocean

    B. Pacific Ocean   **D.** Caribbean Sea

_____ **20.** What is the dominant religion in most Central American countries?

    A. Protestantism

    B. Judaism

    C. Roman Catholicism

    D. Islam

Lesson Quiz 1

networks

The United States East of the Mississippi River

DIRECTIONS: True/False Indicate whether the statement is true (T) or false (F).

_____ **1.** The United States east of the Mississippi River is divided into four subregions.

_____ **2.** The Great Lakes border the United States and Mexico.

_____ **3.** The Ohio River has had the most impact on the nation's history.

_____ **4.** Coastal areas tend to have mild climates.

_____ **5.** Cotton grows well in sandy soils.

DIRECTIONS: Multiple Choice Indicate the answer choice that best answers the question.

_____ **6.** Where did many of the first English colonists settle during the 1600s?

    A. Mid-Atlantic

    B. Midwest

    C. New England

    D. Southeast

_____ **7.** Which is the largest subregion in the eastern United States?

    A. Midwest

    B. Southeast

    C. New England

    D. Mid-Atlantic

_____ **8.** In which state does the Mississippi River begin?

    A. Minnesota   **C.** Ohio

    B. Illinois   **D.** Michigan

_____ **9.** What two well-known mountain ranges are part of the Appalachian Mountain system?

    A. Rocky Mountains and Great Smoky Mountains

    B. Blue Ridge Mountains and Great Smoky Mountains

    C. Rocky Mountains and Blue Ridge Mountains

    D. Sierra Mountains and Great Smoky Mountains

_____ **10.** What has caused the mountains in the Appalachian Mountain system to wear down over time?

    A. glaciers   **C.** strong winds

    B. earthquakes   **D.** erosion

Lesson Quiz 2

networks

The United States East of the Mississippi River

DIRECTIONS: Matching Match each item with its description.

_____ **1.** relocation of people from the South to the North

_____ **2.** an early settlement in Florida

_____ **3.** U.S. claim to lands in the Ohio Country

_____ **4.** first to settle in North America

_____ **5.** forced migration of thousands of Cherokee

A. Land Ordinance of 1785

B. Native Americans

C. Trail of Tears

D. Great Migration

E. St. Augustine

DIRECTIONS: Multiple Choice Indicate the answer choice that best answers the question.

_____ **6.** How did the first Native Americans come to North America?

A. They migrated from what is now Mexico.

B. They crossed a land bridge from Asia.

C. They arrived by ships.

D. They arrived by horseback.

_____ **7.** What was the first permanent European settlement in what is now the United States?

A. Jamestown

B. Plymouth

C. New Haven

D. St. Augustine

_____ **8.** Why did settlers want to move inland and away from the coastal areas?

A. They wanted to move closer to their families.

B. Places inland had more opportunities.

C. Towns along the coastal areas were too crowded.

D. Life would be easier for them in inland areas.

_____ **9.** Which invention increased harvests and profits for cotton farmers?

A. gasoline-powered tractor

B. cotton picker

C. steam-powered plow

D. cotton gin

_____ **10.** Why did settlers pour into the southern states during the 1830s?

A. They went to look for gold.

B. They were tired of the harsh New England winters.

C. They went to look for work.

D. They wanted a safer place to live.

Discovering World Geography

Lesson Quiz 3

networks

The United States East of the Mississippi River

DIRECTIONS: True/False Indicate whether the statement is true (T) or false (F).

_____ 1. The Boston-Washington corridor has a population of about 50 million people.

_____ 2. During the Civil War, Atlanta was a supply depot for the Union army.

_____ 3. The U.S. government has three parts: legislative, executive, and judicial.

_____ 4. The Supreme Court is the most powerful court in the United States.

_____ 5. Organic farming produces foods that are filled with toxins.

DIRECTIONS: Multiple Choice Indicate the answer choice that best answers the question.

_____ 6. What is the term for a supersized city?

    A. megalopolis

    B. triopolis

    C. biopolis

    D. metropolis

_____ 7. What are the two largest metropolitan areas east of the Mississippi River?

    A. Philadelphia and New York

    B. Boston and Chicago

    C. New York and Chicago

    D. New York and Boston

_____ 8. Which term best describes the government of the United States?

    A. monarchy

    B. independent

    C. democracy

    D. commonwealth

_____ 9. What is the name of the legislative branch of government?

    A. House of Representatives   **C.** Senate

    B. Supreme Court   **D.** Congress

_____ 10. Which group is the second largest ethnic group in the Unites States after Caucasians?

    A. Asian Americans   **C.** African Americans

    B. Hispanics   **D.** Native Americans

Chapter Test, Form A

networks

The United States East of the Mississippi River

DIRECTIONS: True/False Indicate whether the statement is true (T) or false (F). If the statement is false, rewrite it to make it true.

_____ **1.** The Ohio River divides the United States into two main regions.

_____

_____ **2.** The Appalachian Mountain system stretches from Alabama to Canada.

_____

_____ **3.** At times, groups of Native Americans fought over land and resources.

_____

_____ **4.** Trade between the United States and other countries began in port cities.

_____

_____ **5.** The president cannot set aside land for use as a national park.

_____

DIRECTIONS: Matching Match each item with with its description.

_____ **6.** basic rights that belong to all citizens

_____ **7.** stretches from northeastern U.S. to Mexico

_____ **8.** income generated by businesses

_____ **9.** gated passageways between the Great Lakes and St. Lawrence River

_____ **10.** areas where many factories closed

A. revenue

B. "Rust Belt"

C. locks

D. civil rights

E. Atlantic coastal plain

DIRECTIONS: Multiple Choice Indicate the answer choice that best answers the question.

_____ **11.** Into which river do the waters of the Great Lakes flow?

    A. Ohio River

    B. Mississippi River

    C. St. Lawrence River

    D. Missouri River

_____ **12.** What type of fuel is coal?

    A. fossil   **C.** mineral

    B. dark   **D.** natural

_____ **13.** Which of the following can be said about Native Americans?

  A. They only settled in areas east of the Mississippi River.

  B. They are indigenous to North America.

  C. They settled North America following the arrival of the Europeans.

  D. They wore clothing made of cotton.

_____ **14.** What was the Dutch colonial port city that became New York originally named?

  A. Jamestown

  B. New Netherlands

  C. New Haven

  D. New Amsterdam

_____ **15.** Which federal agency provides aid to people affected by disasters?

  A. OSHA

  B. CIA

  C. FEMA

  D. NASA

"Employment of software developers is projected to grow . . . much faster than the average for all occupations. . . . The main reason . . . is a large increase in the demand for computer software. Mobile technology requires new applications. Also, the healthcare industry is greatly increasing its use of computer systems."

—from the *Occupational Outlook Handbook*

_____ **16.** Based on the excerpt, which of the following is one of the reasons why employment of software developers is expected to grow?

  A. The tourist industry is increasing its use of computers.

  B. There is a large increase in the demand for computer software.

  C. New applications are not needed for mobile technology.

  D. There is a decrease in the demand for computer software.

Discovering World Geography

_____ **17.** Based on the excerpt, what has most likely caused the increase in computer use by the healthcare industry?

    A. The U.S. population is decreasing and needs fewer medical services.

    B. The U.S. population is getting poorer and cannot afford medical services.

    C. Fewer medical workers require more computers.

    D. The U.S. population is aging and needs more medical services.

DIRECTIONS: Short Answer Answer each of the following questions.

18. Where did the first English colonists settle when they came to North America? How did the population and settlements in the colonies change from the early 1600s to the mid 1700s? Explain your answer.

_____

_____

_____

_____

_____

_____

19. How did the Great Migration affect the population of the North?

_____

_____

_____

_____

_____

_____

DIRECTIONS: Essay Answer the following question on a separate piece of paper.

20. Compare how the environment shaped the lives of Native Americans and the early colonists.

Chapter Test, Form B

networks

The United States East of the Mississippi River

DIRECTIONS: True/False Indicate whether the statement is true (T) or false (F). If the statement is false, rewrite it to make it true.

_____ **1.** The state of New York is in the New England subregion.

_____

_____ **2.** The Great Lakes is a cluster of five huge lakes.

_____

_____ **3.** The Great Migration had ended by 1900.

_____

_____ **4.** New Orleans is an important commercial trade center.

_____

_____ **5.** In the United States, Christianity has the largest number of followers.

_____

DIRECTIONS: Matching Match each item with its description.

_____ **6.** most populous ethnic group in the United States

_____ **7.** growing crops and raising livestock

_____ **8.** environmental program started to clean up hazardous waste sites

_____ **9.** nickname for the Midwest

_____ **10.** also called "manufacturing"

A. "the nation's breadbasket"

B. Caucasian

C. Superfund

D. agriculture

E. industry

DIRECTIONS: Multiple Choice Indicate the answer choice that best answers the question.

_____ **11.** What is the powerful current that flows through the Atlantic Ocean?

A. Great Stream

B. Atlantic Stream

C. Gulf Stream

D. Orlando Stream

_____ **12.** Which two rivers combine to form the Ohio River?

A. Allegheny and Monongahela

B. Kentucky and Green

C. Mississippi and Missouri

D. St. Lawrence and Allegheny

_____ **13.** What type of climate does much of the Southeast have?

    A. tropical

    B. humid temperate

    C. polar

    D. humid subtropical

_____ **14.** Why did some settlers turn back when they reached the Mississippi River?

    A. Their horses became lame.

    B. The Mississippi River was too difficult to cross.

    C. They changed their minds about settling west of the Mississippi River.

    D. They were unwilling to seek new opportunities.

_____ **15.** What are the first 10 amendments to the U.S. Constitution called?

    A. Postscript

    B. Bill of Writ

    C. Preamble

    D. Bill of Rights

"We the People of the United States, in Order to form a more perfect Union, establish Justice, insure domestic Tranquility [calm], provide for the common defence, promote the general Welfare, and secure the Blessings of Liberty . . . , do . . . establish this Constitution."

—from the United States Constitution

_____ **16.** Based on the excerpt, what is one of the purposes of the U.S. Constitution?

    A. to provide employment for U.S. citizens

    B. to provide for the protection of U.S. citizens

    C. to create new states

    D. to develop pride in the United States

_____ **17.** Based on the excerpt, what does "welfare" mean?

    A. subsidized aid

    B. food

    C. health

    D. well-being

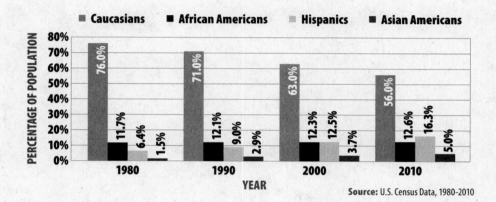

Source: U.S. Census Data, 1980–2010

_____ **18.** Based on the graph above, what generalization can be made about the percentage of population of ethnic groups in the United States?

    A. The percentage of population has increased only for Hispanics.

    B. The percentage of population of Caucasians has decreased 20 percent since 1980.

    C. The percentage of population of Asian Americans has increased 15 percent since 1980.

    D. The percentage of population of African Americans has increased the most since 1980.

_____ **19.** According to the graph, which ethnic group showed the least percentage change from 1980 to 2010?

    A. Hispanic

    B. Asian American

    C. African American

    D. Caucasian

DIRECTIONS: Essay Answer the following question on a separate piece of paper.

 20. Compare how the environment shaped the lives of Native Americans and the early colonists.

Lesson Quiz 1

networks

The United States West of the Mississippi River

DIRECTIONS: Matching Match each item with its description.

_____ 1. process by which water is supplied to dry land

_____ 2. imaginary line through the Rocky Mountains separating east- and west-flowing rivers

_____ 3. liquid fuel made from plants

_____ 4. region of parallel mountain systems

_____ 5. dry wind that blows over the Great Plains

A. cordillera

B. Continental Divide

C. irrigation

D. chinook

E. ethanol

DIRECTIONS: Multiple Choice Indicate the answer choice that best answers the question.

_____ 6. What do Alaska and Hawaii have in common?

    A. Neither state has an active volcano.

    B. Neither state borders the 48 contiguous states.

    C. Both states have tropical climates.

    D. The two states are about the same size in land mass.

_____ 7. Which state can claim to have the highest point in the United States?

    A. California   **C.** Colorado

    B. Washington   **D.** Alaska

_____ 8. What causes the Great Salt Lake to be salty?

    A. The Pacific Ocean flows directly into the lake and makes the water salty.

    B. It was formed over a huge salt lick.

    C. It has no outlet and its tributary rivers deposit salt, which is left when its water evaporates.

    D. People have long dumped their excess salt there.

_____ 9. Which landform plays a role in forming the climates in the region west of the Mississippi River?

    A. high mountains   **C.** plateaus

    B. plains   **D.** deserts

_____ 10. Which state relies on wind power to provide a quarter of its electricity?

    A. Wyoming   **C.** California

    B. South Dakota   **D.** Colorado

Lesson Quiz 2

networks

The United States West of the Mississippi River

DIRECTIONS: True/False Indicate whether the statement is true (T) or false (F).

_____ 1. The first people to live in the western states were the Spanish.

_____ 2. Missions were church-based communities for native peoples.

_____ 3. The American desire for California and other western lands led to a war with Mexico.

_____ 4. Reservations were especially suited for farming.

_____ 5. Early houses built on the Great Plains were made entirely of wood.

DIRECTIONS: Multiple Choice Indicate the answer choice that best answers the question.

_____ 6. Of what materials were teepees made?

    A. clay and sand   **C.** cotton or wool cloth

    B. animal hides and poles   **D.** bricks and glass

_____ 7. What event led to the Lewis and Clark expedition?

    A. Manifest Destiny

    B. Oregon Trail

    C. Spanish-American War

    D. Louisiana Purchase

_____ 8. What did some people who disapproved of its purchase call the area of Alaska?

    A. Seward's Folly

    B. Sherman's Folly

    C. Seward's Gold

    D. Folly Land

_____ 9. What provision of the Homestead Act encouraged people to move west of the Mississippi River?

    A. The land was cheap.

    B. Their houses had to be made of wood.

    C. The land was free.

    D. They only had to live on their farms for three years.

_____ 10. What term is used to describe a region just beyond or at the edge of a settled area?

    A. pueblo   **C.** suburb

    B. mission   **D.** frontier

Discovering World Geography

Lesson Quiz 3

networks

The United States West of the Mississippi River

DIRECTIONS: Matching Match each item with its description.

_____ **1.** name for the drought-stricken area of the 1930s and 1940s

_____ **2.** major port city

_____ **3.** oil tanker that ran aground in Alaska

_____ **4.** rapidly growing interior city

_____ **5.** tertiary economic activity

A. Los Angeles, California

B. Las Vegas, Nevada

C. Dust Bowl

D. *Exxon Valdez*

E. tourism

DIRECTIONS: Multiple Choice Indicate the answer choice that best answers the question.

_____ **6.** Because it is a major city, what is unusual about Denver's location?

    A. It is on an island in the middle of a big lake.

    B. It is not a seaport.

    C. It is on a navigable part of a river.

    D. It is on a flat plain.

_____ **7.** Which two countries are the largest markets for exports from the United States?

    A. China and Canada   **C.** Mexico and China

    B. Brazil and Canada   **D.** Mexico and Canada

_____ **8.** What is one of the biggest challenges for the western states?

    A. building more seaports

    B. attracting tourists

    C. growing businesses

    D. having an adequate water supply

_____ **9.** Which crop provides a major industry in the Great Plains states?

    A. peanuts

    B. soybeans

    C. wheat

    D. tobacco

_____ **10.** The aerospace industry is important in which city?

    A. Seattle, Washington   **C.** Anchorage, Alaska

    B. Denver, Colorado   **D.** Las Vegas, Nevada

Chapter Test, Form A

netw⊕rks

The United States West of the Mississippi River

DIRECTIONS: True/False Indicate whether the statement is true (T) or false (F). If the statement is false, rewrite it to make it true.

_____ **1.** The Great Plains are not flat but are tilted downward toward the east.

_____

_____ **2.** Of the states west of the Mississippi River, California is the largest in land area.

_____

_____ **3.** New Orleans was a Spanish settlement.

_____

_____ **4.** Drilling an oil well is an example of a primary economic activity.

_____

_____ **5.** In California, Latinos are in the minority and non-Hispanic whites constitute a large part of the population.

_____

DIRECTIONS: Matching Match each item with its description.

_____ **6.** Spanish word meaning "town" or "village"

_____ **7.** location of the Grand Canyon

_____ **8.** to take control

_____ **9.** connected to

_____ **10.** trade agreement among the United States, Canada, and Mexico

A. contiguous

B. Colorado Plateau

C. pueblo

D. annex

E. NAFTA

DIRECTIONS: Multiple Choice Indicate the answer choice that best answers the question.

_____ **11.** What is the chief body of water for the western United States?

A. Gulf of Mexico

B. Pacific Ocean

C. Colorado River

D. Columbia River

_____ **12.** What type of climate does Washington have?

A. humid temperate

B. tropical

C. cold temperate

D. marine west coast

Chapter Test, Form A *cont.*

netw◉rks

The United States West of the Mississippi River

_____ **13.** Why have many small family farms in the western states declined?

   A. There is no longer enough water to raise crops.

   B. The farmers have decided to move to the cities.

   C. They have been replaced by agribusinesses.

   D. The land is very poor and not suitable for farming.

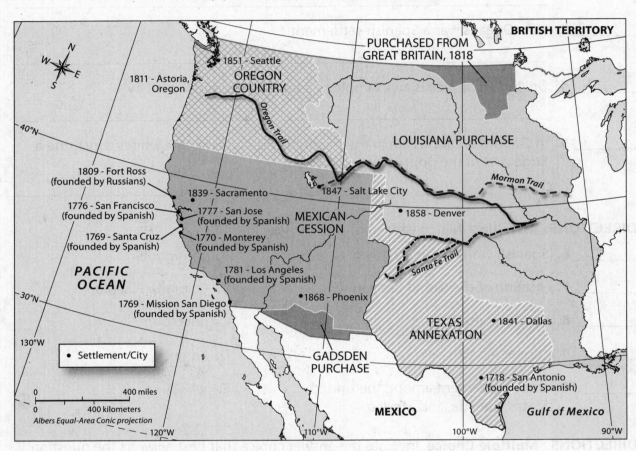

_____ **14.** Based on the map above, which city was founded in 1868?

   A. Dallas   **C.** Phoenix

   B. Denver   **D.** Sacramento

_____ **15.** Based on the map above, near which city did the Mormon Trail and the Oregon Trail split?

   A. Denver   **C.** Dallas

   B. Salt Lake City   **D.** Seattle

Chapter Test, Form A *cont.*

netw☉rks

The United States West of the Mississippi River

> Denver has an unusual location for a major city. It is not a seaport or on the navigable part of a river. Denver owes its vibrance to the mountains nearby. It originally grew as a mining town. In the late 1900s, the city attracted people who wanted to enjoy the mountains. Today, its economy is based on software, finance, and communications.
>
> —*Discovering World Geography*

_____ **16.** Based on the excerpt, what can you infer about locations of most major cities?

    A. They are usually located near a waterway or a body of water.

    B. They are usually located near mountains.

    C. They are usually located near mines.

    D. They are usually located below east-facing mountains.

_____ **17.** Based on the except, what can you infer about Denver's businesses?

    A. Its businesses have always focused on tertiary economic activities.

    B. Its businesses depend mainly on tourism.

    C. Its businesses are service-based.

    D. Its businesses are manufacturing-based.

DIRECTIONS: Short Answer Answer each of the following questions.

18. Explain why California's Central Valley is normally dry. How did this area become a major farming region?

_____

_____

_____

19. Compare the climates of Alaska and Hawaii.

_____

_____

_____

DIRECTIONS: Essay Answer the following question on a separate piece of paper.

20. How do droughts and limited water supplies impact a region's economic growth? In your essay, focus on the western states. Then explain how the region is tackling this problem. What are other ways that people can conserve water?

Chapter Test, Form B

networks

The United States West of the Mississippi River

DIRECTIONS: True/False Indicate whether the statement is true (T) or false (F). If the statement is false, rewrite it to make it true.

_____ **1.** The area east of the Mississippi is larger than the area to the west.

_____

_____ **2.** The Grand Canyon cuts deep into the Colorado Plateau.

_____

_____ **3.** Teepees were well suited to the nomadic Plains peoples.

_____

_____ **4.** To reach Oregon, settlers traveled the Salt Lake Trail.

_____

_____ **5.** Most Mormons settled in Texas.

_____

DIRECTIONS: Matching Match each item with its description.

_____ **6.** major farming region in California

_____ **7.** mountain range in Washington

_____ **8.** where the *Exxon Valdez* ran aground

_____ **9.** belief that helped promote westward expansion

_____ **10.** what some people called the area of Alaska

A. Olympic Mountains

B. Central Valley

C. Manifest Destiny

D. "Seward's Folly"

E. Prince William Sound

DIRECTIONS: Multiple Choice Indicate the answer choice that best answers the question.

_____ **11.** Which crop is Idaho famous for producing?

    A. apples   **C.** corn

    B. strawberries   **D.** potatoes

_____ **12.** Which two climate types are found in the eastern half of the Great Plains?

    A. semiarid and humid continental

    B. humid continental and humid subtropical

    C. humid subtropical and semiarid

    D. tropical rainforest and humid subtropical

Discovering World Geography

Chapter Test, Form B *cont.*

The United States West of the Mississippi River

_____ **13.** How did the spread of white settlements impact Native Americans?

    A. They lost their lands and were forced to live on reservations.

    B. They were educated in settlement schools.

    C. They moved to areas east of the Mississippi.

    D. They lived peacefully among the white settlers.

_____ **14.** Wyoming has an abundant supply of which energy resource?

    A. petroleum

    B. coal

    C. natural gas

    D. ethanol

The growth of computer technology has spawned other industries. Software and information science companies are based in the same areas that are home to computer manufacturing. Utah and Colorado have also become important in these fields. Los Angeles, San Francisco, Denver, Dallas, and Seattle have become major financial centers. Telecommunications—telephone and related services—is an important industry in Denver and Dallas.

—*Discovering World Geography*

_____ **15.** What is the best meaning of "spawned" as used in the excerpt above?

    A. done away with

    B. replaced

    C. given rise to

    D. made obsolete

_____ **16.** Based on the excerpt, what is the best reason for the software and information science companies being in the same areas as computer manufacturers?

    A. They can learn the other's trade secrets.

    B. They can quickly resolve compatibility issues between hardware and software.

    C. They can be more competitive.

    D. They can set the prices for their products.

Chapter Test, Form B *cont.*

networks

The United States West of the Mississippi River

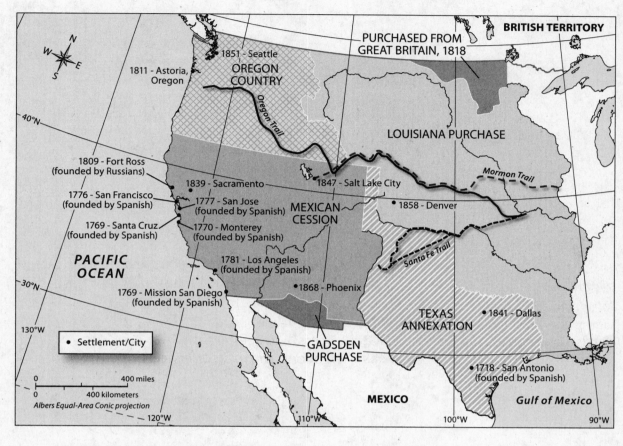

_____ **17.** What is the earliest Spanish settlement shown on the map?

   A. Monterey   **C.** San Antonio

   B. Los Angeles   **D.** San Francisco

_____ **18.** Based on the map above, what year was Salt Lake City founded?

   A. 1830   **C.** 1847

   B. 1841   **D.** 1851

_____ **19.** Based on the map above, which event or agreement led to territory that was bordered by the Mississippi River and the Rocky Mountains?

   A. Gadsen Purchase   **C.** Texas Annexation

   B. Louisiana Purchase   **D.** Mexican Cession

DIRECTIONS: Essay Answer the following question on a separate piece of paper.

20. How do droughts and limited water supplies impact a region's economic growth? In your essay, focus on the western states. Then explain how the region is tackling this problem. What are other ways that people can conserve water?

Discovering World Geography

59

Lesson Quiz 1

networks

Canada

DIRECTIONS: True/False Indicate whether the statement is true (T) or false (F).

_____ **1.** Canada has 10 provinces and three territories.

_____ **2.** Quebec is one of the Atlantic Provinces of Canada.

_____ **3.** Deciduous trees produce cones and have needles.

_____ **4.** Canada and the United States share the longest undefended border in the world.

_____ **5.** Canada has a very large population.

DIRECTIONS: Multiple Choice Indicate the answer choice that best answers the question.

_____ **6.** In which provinces do most Canadians live?
- **A.** Northern Lands
- **B.** Atlantic Provinces
- **C.** Prairie Provinces
- **D.** Quebec and Ontario

_____ **7.** Which region of Canada has areas that receive up to 100 inches of rain per year?
- **A.** Atlantic Provinces
- **B.** Quebec and Ontario
- **C.** British Columbia
- **D.** Prairie Provinces

_____ **8.** Which statement describes the landscape of British Columbia?
- **A.** It is part of the massive plateau known as the Canadian Shield.
- **B.** It is much like the northwestern United States.
- **C.** It has vast prairies and plains.
- **D.** It has no high mountains, just a few hills.

_____ **9.** How many of the Great Lakes does Canada share with the United States?
- **A.** two
- **B.** three
- **C.** four
- **D.** five

_____ **10.** What waterway connects the Gulf of St. Lawrence to Lake Ontario?
- **A.** Fraser River
- **B.** St. Lawrence River
- **C.** Ohio River
- **D.** Hudson Bay

Lesson Quiz 2

networks

Canada

DIRECTIONS: Matching Match each item with its description.

_____ 1. founded Quebec

_____ 2. first Europeans to reach Canada

_____ 3. native peoples of Canada

_____ 4. long period of intense cold

_____ 5. partly self-governing nation within the British Empire

A. Ice Age

B. Vikings

C. Samuel de Champlain

D. Dominion of Canada

E. First Nations

DIRECTIONS: Multiple Choice Indicate the answer choice that best answers the question.

_____ 6. Why did the first people who came from Asia to Canada continue moving southward?

    A. They heard rumors of vast riches in the southern lands.

    B. At that time, Canada was covered with ice.

    C. They met fierce Huron warriors and fled southward.

    D. At that time, Canada was covered with dense forests.

_____ 7. Which country did Britain compete with for power in the Americas?

    A. Germany

    B. Spain

    C. France

    D. Norway

_____ 8. What was built in the late 1800s that connected eastern and western Canada?

    A. transcontinental railroad

    B. St. Lawrence Seaway

    C. transcontinental highway

    D. transcontinental canal

_____ 9. On what chief industries was Canada's economy based in the early 1900s?

    A. manufacturing and technology

    B. retail sales and mining

    C. trading and agriculture

    D. agriculture and mining

_____ 10. What percentage of Canada's people are from the First Nations?

    A. 2 percent

    B. 10 percent

    C. 25 percent

    D. 45 percent

Discovering World Geography

Lesson Quiz 3

networks

Canada

DIRECTIONS: True/False Indicate whether the statement is true (T) or false (F).

_____ **1.** Only one out of five Canadians lives in cities or suburbs.

_____ **2.** French is the main language in Quebec.

_____ **3.** Three-quarters of all of Canada's exports go to the United States.

_____ **4.** Montreal, Quebec, is Canada's largest metropolitan area.

_____ **5.** Acid rain weakens living things.

DIRECTIONS: Multiple Choice Indicate the answer choice that best answers the question.

_____ **6.** Which city is Canada's busiest port?

    A. Alberta   **C.** Quebec

    B. Vancouver   **D.** Montreal

_____ **7.** In keeping its cultural heritage unchanged, what influence do some Canadians fear the most?

    A. They believe they should break free from all British influences.

    B. They worry that the Asians will dominate their culture.

    C. They worry that the United States will dominate their culture.

    D. They believe they should break free from all French influences.

_____ **8.** What can be said about Canada's government?

    A. It is a parliamentary system.

    B. It has no king or queen.

    C. Its legislature is called the Senate.

    D. The British king or queen carries out the laws.

_____ **9.** What might be Canada's biggest challenge?

    A. increasing trade with the United States

    B. attracting tourists

    C. staying together as a nation

    D. reviving its fishing industry

_____ **10.** What does Canada depend on to power its industries, homes, and transportation systems?

    A. electricity   **C.** water

    B. fossil fuels   **D.** solar energy

Lesson Quiz 3-...

DIRECTIONS: True/False Indicate whether the statement is true (T) or false (F).

1. Only one of five Canadians lives in cities or suburbs.

2. French is the main language in Quebec.

3. Three-quarters of all of Canada's exports go to the United States.

4. Montreal, Quebec, is Canada's largest non-Ontario area.

5. Acid rain weakens living things.

DIRECTIONS: Multiple Choice Indicate the answer choice that best answers the question.

6. Which city is Canada's busiest port?
   A. Alberta
   B. Vancouver
   C. Quebec
   D. Montreal

7. If feelings suddenly changed, what influence do some Canadians fear the most?
   A. They believe they should break free from all British influences.
   B. They worry that the nation will dominate executives.
   C. They worry that the United States will dominate how Canada...
   D. They believe they should break free from all French influences.

8. What can be said about Canada's government?
   A. It's a parliamentary system.
   B. It has a king or queen.
   C. Its legislature is called the Senate.
   D. The British king empowers nobles but the law...

9. What might be Canada's biggest challenge?
   A. increasing trade with the United States
   B. attracting tourists
   C. staying together as a nation
   D. reviving its fishing industry

10. What does Canada depend on to power its industries, homes, and transportation systems?
    A. electricity
    B. fossil fuels
    C. ...
    D. solar energy

Chapter Test, Form A

networks

Canada

DIRECTIONS: True/False Indicate whether the statement is true (T) or false (F). If the statement is false, rewrite it to make it true.

_____ **1.** In land size, Canada is the largest nation in the world.

_____

_____ **2.** Nunavut is one of Canada's three territories.

_____

_____ **3.** The Vikings settled in what is now British Columbia.

_____

_____ **4.** Canada did not become an industrial nation until the 1900s.

_____

_____ **5.** Canada's king and queen are the same as those of the United Kingdom.

_____

DIRECTIONS: Matching Match each item with its description.

_____ **6.** group of islands

_____ **7.** those who want to break away from a dominant group

_____ **8.** lands that a national government administers

_____ **9.** native

_____ **10.** building used to store harvested grain

A. territories

B. archipelago

C. aboriginal

D. granary

E. separatists

DIRECTIONS: Multiple Choice Indicate the answer choice that best answers the question.

_____ **11.** Which type of climate do Canada's territories, called the Northern Lands, have?

    A. subartic   **C.** high mountain

    B. cold temperate   **D.** tropical

_____ **12.** How did the Quebec Act of 1774 protect French settlers?

    A. It kept them from being deported to France.

    B. It allowed them to keep their language, religion, and system of laws.

    C. It built forts to protect them from the First Nations peoples.

    D. It allowed them free trade with the First Nations peoples.

Chapter Test, Form A *cont.*

networks

Canada

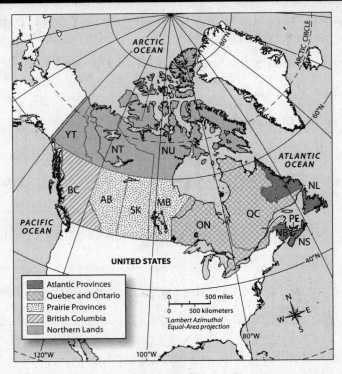

_____ **13.** Based on the map above, which region of Canada is bordered by the Arctic Ocean?

    A. Northern Lands   **C.** Atlantic Provinces

    B. Quebec and Ontario   **D.** British Columbia

_____ **14.** Based on the map above, the province of Saskatchewan is part of which region?

    A. Northern Lands   **C.** Ontario and Quebec

    B. Prairie Provinces   **D.** Atlantic Provinces

> To help increase the nation's industrial power, Canada needed more workers.
> Canada's leaders made it easier for people to enter the country. Canada's
> population began to grow, particularly after World War II, which helped Canada
> meet its need for more workers. Canada's population jumped from 12 million
> people in 1945 to nearly 35 million in 2012.
>
> —*Discovering World Geography*

_____ **15.** Based on the excerpt above, what do you think is the best reason for the increase
in Canada's population after World War II?

    A. More women entered the workforce.

    B. There was more industry in Canada than anywhere else.

    C. The workforce grew as a result of the increase in the number of immigrants.

    D. More people were moving from urban areas to rural areas.

                                                          Discovering World Geography

_____ **16.** Based on the excerpt, what did Canada do to attract more people to live there?

    A. It increased its number of farms.

    B. It made it easier for people to enter the country.

    C. It offered land grants to attract people.

    D. It made it easier for people to leave the country.

_____ **17.** In what way did the Canadian government give the First Nations more power?

    A. It guaranteed them 10 percent of the profits for their products.

    B. It gave them more rights than other citizens have.

    C. It created new parliamentary positions for them.

    D. It created a new territory, Nunavut, for them.

DIRECTIONS: Short Answer Answer each of the following questions.

18. How is the landscape of Canada's Prairie Provinces similar to that of the Great Plains in the United States?

_____

_____

_____

_____

19. Is the government of Canada more like that of the United States or the United Kingdom? Explain.

_____

_____

_____

_____

DIRECTIONS: Essay Answer the following question on a separate piece of paper.

20. A people's way of life often depends on the resources they have. How did the early First Nations people use their resources to live? Compare the lives of those who lived in the woodlands, on the Pacific coast, and in the far north.

Chapter Test, Form B

networks

Canada

DIRECTIONS: True/False Indicate whether the statement is true (T) or false (F). If the statement is false, rewrite it to make it true.

_____ **1.** The border between Canada and the United States is not defended.

_____

_____ **2.** The Grand Banks is one of the world's great hatcheries.

_____

_____ **3.** The North West Mounted Police was created to help keep order in the western territories of Canada.

_____

_____ **4.** The Yukon Territory was the last territory to join Canada as a province.

_____

_____ **5.** Canada is a member of the North Atlantic Treaty Organization (NATO).

_____

DIRECTIONS: Matching Match each item with its description.

_____ **6.** large area of relatively flat land made of ancient, hard rock

_____ **7.** flat, treeless land with frozen ground year-round

_____ **8.** when one can speak both French and English

_____ **9.** area where fish feed in huge numbers

_____ **10.** children of French and native peoples

A. tundra

B. fishery

C. métis

D. bilingual

E. shield

DIRECTIONS: Multiple Choice Indicate the answer choice that best answers the question.

_____ **11.** What percentage of Canadians live within 150 miles (241 km) of the Canada-U.S. border?

A. 45   **C.** 75

B. 50   **D.** 90

_____ **12.** Which explorer claimed the St. Lawrence River for France?

A. Robert LaSalle   **C.** Samuel de Champlain

B. Jacques Cartier   **D.** Jacques Cousteau

_____ **13.** What change is occurring in the Arctic Ocean because of climate change?

   A. There are fewer tourists because it has turned warmer.

   B. More ice is forming, preventing ship traffic in the region.

   C. Less ice is forming, and there is more ship traffic in the region.

   D. The water levels have decreased significantly.

> Canada's constitution guarantees the rights of French-speaking people in Quebec and elsewhere. Still, tension is evident. English speakers have dominated the nation. They controlled the economy of Quebec for many years. As a result, some French speakers felt they were treated as second-class citizens.
>
> In the late 1900s, some Quebec leaders launched a separatist movement. . . . Voters in Quebec have twice defeated attempts to make it independent. Still, the issue remains unsettled.
>
> —*Discovering World Geography*

_____ **14.** Based on the excerpt above, why have the French-speaking people in Quebec and elsewhere been so unhappy with their government?

   A. Their separatist movement has met opposition.

   B. They believe English speakers have led the nation astray.

   C. They believe English speakers have a bad influence on French culture.

   D. They believe the French-speaking population has been treated unfairly.

_____ **15.** Based on the excerpt above, what is the status of the separatist movement?

   A. It passed after the second vote.

   B. It is on appeal to Parliament.

   C. It has not been resolved.

   D. It is being presented for a third vote.

_____ **16.** What was the main reason the English and French communities formed the Dominion of Canada?

   A. The wanted to pool their resources.

   B. They wanted to settle their differences and become one nation.

   C. They feared a takeover from the United States.

   D. They needed to join forces against the Iroquois.

_____ **17.** Why is the Grand Banks area so important to Canada?

   A. It affects the weather in neighboring provinces.

   B. It is a popular seaside resort.

   C. It is a popular ski area, attracting skiers from all over the world.

   D. It brings in a lot of revenue from the fishing industry.

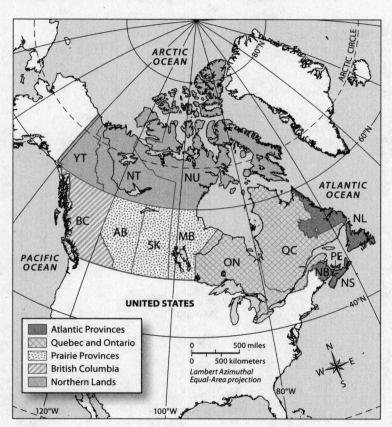

_____ **18.** Based on the map above, which region is not bordered by an ocean?

   A. Northern Lands   **C.** Atlantic Provinces

   B. British Columbia   **D.** Prairie Provinces

_____ **19.** Based on the map above, which region is the smallest in land area?

   A. Atlantic Provinces   **C.** Northern Lands

   B. Ontario and Quebec   **D.** Prairie Provinces

DIRECTIONS: Essay Answer the following question on a separate piece of paper.

20. A people's way of life often depends on the resources they have. How did the early First Nations people use their resources to live? Compare the lives of those who lived in the woodlands, on the Pacific coast, and in the far north.

Discovering World Geography

Lesson Quiz 1

netw⊙rks

Mexico, Central America, and the Caribbean Islands

DIRECTIONS: True/False Indicate whether the statement is true (T) or false (F).

_____ **1.** Mexico shares its southern border with the United States.

_____ **2.** Mexico and Central America have four distinct seasons.

_____ **3.** Mexico is an important oil-producing country.

_____ **4.** The Caribbean Sea is an arm of the Pacific Ocean.

_____ **5.** The Caribbean attracts millions of tourists to the region each year.

DIRECTIONS: Multiple Choice Indicate the answer choice that best answers the question.

_____ **6.** Which of the following are common natural occurrences in Mexico?

    A. tornadoes   **C.** earthquakes

    B. ice storms   **D.** tsunamis

_____ **7.** Which vertical climate zone in Mexico is also known as "hot land"?

    A. *tierra templada*   **C.** *tierra fria*

    B. *tierra buena*   **D.** *tierra caliente*

_____ **8.** Why has Mexico's oil production declined since 2004?

    A. There is too much conflict in Mexico.

    B. Its oil fields are old and starting to run out of oil.

    C. No one wants to buy the oil.

    D. Oil is not a good product to sell.

_____ **9.** Which Caribbean country is a commonwealth of the United States?

    A. Puerto Rico

    B. Cuba

    C. Haiti

    D. Jamaica

_____ **10.** What land, which is now a country, did Christopher Columbus first sight in 1492?

    A. Mexico

    B. Costa Rica

    C. Bahamas

    D. United States

Discovering World Geography

Lesson Quiz 2

networks

Mexico, Central America, and the Caribbean Islands

DIRECTIONS: Matching Match each item with its description.

_____ 1. led a small force of Spanish conquistadors to Mexico in 1520

_____ 2. led a revolution in Cuba in 1959

_____ 3. led a rebellion in Mexico in 1810

_____ 4. a period of violent social and political change

_____ 5. large farm where workers produce cash crops

A. Miguel Hidalgo

B. plantation

C. Hernán Cortés

D. Fidel Castro

E. revolution

DIRECTIONS: Multiple Choice Indicate the answer choice that best answers the question.

_____ 6. Which statement describes the Aztec?

    A. They made accurate calendars.

    B. No one knows why their empire collapsed.

    C. They had a complex social and religious system.

    D. They invented a complex system of writing.

_____ 7. Settlers from which country had the most wealth in colonial Mexico?

    A. United States   **C.** Sweden

    B. Britain   **D.** Spain

_____ 8. When did Panama take control of the Panama Canal?

    A. 1900   **C.** 1980

    B. 1965   **D.** 2000

_____ 9. Why do the Caribbean islands have so much diversity?

    A. The climate varies among the islands.

    B. Many people from the United States settled there.

    C. Several European countries ruled them as colonies.

    D. Their governments are democratic.

_____ 10. Why do the countries in the Caribbean islands have weak economies?

    A. Their governments are communist.

    B. They attract few tourists.

    C. They have large populations.

    D. They are small and have few resources.

Discovering World Geography

Lesson Quiz 3

networks

Mexico, Central America, and the Caribbean Islands

DIRECTIONS: Matching Match each item with its description.

_____ **1.** destructive hurricane that hit Nicaragua

A. mural

_____ **2.** large painting made on a wall

B. Mitch

_____ **3.** major service industry in Mexico

C. maquiladora

_____ **4.** type of factory in Mexico

D. communist

_____ **5.** type of government in Cuba

E. tourism

DIRECTIONS: Multiple Choice Indicate the answer choice that best answers the question.

_____ **6.** Where do nearly 20 percent of Mexico's people live?

    A. Acapulco   **C.** Mexico City

    B. Cancun   **D.** Leon

_____ **7.** What is the economic level of up to 50 percent of the population in Mexico?

    A. poor

    B. moderately wealthy

    C. wealthy

    D. extremely wealthy

_____ **8.** What is the main language in most Central American countries?

    A. English   **C.** Italian

    B. French   **D.** Spanish

_____ **9.** Which Caribbean country ranks among the world's poorest nations?

    A. Haiti

    B. Belize

    C. Jamaica

    D. Dominican Republic

_____ **10.** Which Caribbean country is known for its reggae music?

    A. Cuba

    B. Haiti

    C. Dominican Republic

    D. Jamaica

Chapter Test, Form A

netw⊙rks

Mexico, Central America, and the Caribbean Islands

DIRECTIONS: True/False Indicate whether the statement is true (T) or false (F). If the statement is false, rewrite it to make it true.

_____ **1.** The Spanish and Portuguese languages are spoken in Latin America.

_____

_____ **2.** The largest Latin American country is Belize.

_____

_____ **3.** Oil and natural gas are Mexico's most important resources.

_____

_____ **4.** The Maya made accurate calendars.

_____

_____ **5.** The biggest challenge for the Caribbean islands is to attract more tourists.

_____

DIRECTIONS: Matching Match each item with its description.

_____ **6.** trade agreement among Mexico, Canada, and the United States

_____ **7.** led Haiti's independence movement

_____ **8.** military strongmen who ruled Central American governments

_____ **9.** form of Caribbean music for which Cuba is famous

_____ **10.** one of Mexico's peninsulas

A. salsa

B. caudillos

C. Baja California

D. NAFTA

E. Toussaint L'Ouverture

DIRECTIONS: Multiple Choice Indicate the answer choice that best answers the question.

_____ **11.** What two arms of the Atlantic Ocean border Mexico and Central America on the east?

    A. Rio Bravo del Norte and the Caribbean Sea

    B. Gulf of Mexico and the Caribbean Sea

    C. Lake Nicaragua and the Rio Grande

    D. Rio Grande and the Gulf of Mexico

_____ **12.** In which climate zone does most of Mexico and Central America lie?

    A. high mountain

    B. humid temperate

    C. desert

    D. tropical

_____ **13.** Where did the Maya live?

    A. lowland plains of the Yucatán Peninsula

    B. northern area of Baja California

    C. what is now Honduras

    D. Tenochtitlán

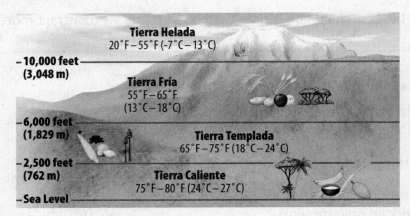

_____ **14.** Based on the diagram above, in which climate zone did the first natives of Mexico most likely grow corn?

    A. *tierra nevada*

    B. *tierra caliente*

    C. *tierra fria*

    D. *tierra templada*

_____ **15.** Based on the diagram above, which crop is best suited to a cooler, shorter growing season?

    A. bananas

    B. sugar

    C. potatoes

    D. coffee

_____ **16.** Why is English the official language of Belize?

    A. The Maya lived there.

    B. The Aztec conquered the Spanish there.

    C. The British claimed the area.

    D. The Spanish settled the area.

_____ **17.** On what resource have the countries of Central America long depended?

    A. service industries

    B. cash crops

    C. manufacturing

    D. tourism

DIRECTIONS: Short Answer Answer each of the following questions.

18. Why did so many Native Americans die during the colonial period? What effect did this have on the slave trade?

_____

_____

_____

_____

_____

19. Explain why air pollution is particularly bad in Mexico City.

_____

_____

_____

_____

DIRECTIONS: Essay Answer the following question on a separate piece of paper.

20. Discuss the Aztec's conflict with the Spanish. Why were the Aztec defeated by a small force of conquerors? How did the Spanish conquest affect life in Mexico?

Chapter Test, Form B

networks

Mexico, Central America, and the Caribbean Islands

DIRECTIONS: True/False Indicate whether the statement is true (T) or false (F). If the statement is false, rewrite it to make it true.

_____ **1.** Mexico and Central America form a peninsula between North and South America.

_____

_____ **2.** Mexico and Central America are bordered by the Pacific Ocean on the west.

_____

_____ **3.** Mexico gained its independence in 1821.

_____

_____ **4.** The Columbian Exchange resulted in the spread of disease into different parts of the world.

_____

_____ **5.** Cuba has a strong economy.

_____

DIRECTIONS: Matching Match each item with its description.

_____ **6.** former British colony

_____ **7.** group of Caribbean islands

_____ **8.** more food than is needed to survive

_____ **9.** vertical climate zone that is also known as "cold land"

_____ **10.** Caribbean country that has a successful economy

A. Belize

B. *tierra fria*

C. Trinidad and Tobago

D. Greater Antilles

E. surplus

DIRECTIONS: Multiple Choice Indicate the answer choice that best answers the question.

_____ **11.** Which of the following is one of the world's most important waterways?

    A. Rio Bravo del Norte

    B. Panama Canal

    C. Lake Nicaragua

    D. Rio Grande

Chapter Test, Form B *cont.*

networks

Mexico, Central America, and the Caribbean Islands

_____ **12.** Which of the following statements refers to Aztec farming?

    A. They forced conquered peoples to do the farming.

    B. They were not very skilled farmers.

    C. Their religion prohibited raising corn as a crop.

    D. They grew crops on small islands that they built in the lake.

_____ **13.** During the colonial period, which area did Britain claim?

    A. Haiti   **C.** Mexico

    B. Belize   **D.** Cuba

_____ **14.** Which country do economists predict will become the leading economy in Latin America in the 2010s?

    A. Mexico   **C.** Honduras

    B. Cuba   **D.** Haiti

Mexicans are proud of their blend of Spanish and native cultures. They have long celebrated the folk arts that reflect native traditions. In the early 1900s, several Mexican painters drew on these traditions to paint impressive murals celebrating Mexico's history and people. Murals are large paintings made on walls. The Ballet Folkorico performs Mexican dances.

                                         —*Discovering World Geography*

_____ **15.** Based on the excerpt above, what is "folk art"?

    A. paintings made on walls

    B. art of dancing

    C. art of the early 1900s

    D. art that reflects native traditions

_____ **16.** Based on the excerpt above, what were the subjects of murals painted in the early 1900s?

    A. Mexican dances

    B. Mexican painters

    C. Mexico's history and people

    D. Mexican walls

Chapter Test, Form B *cont.*

network

Mexico, Central America, and the Caribbean Islands

> In Haiti, a history of poor political leadership has held back economic development. Haiti ranks among the world's poorest nations. Poverty is not the country's only problem, however; widespread disease is a threat. In addition, as many as one in eight Haitians have left the country. Many of those who emigrated were among Haiti's most educated people. This loss hurts efforts to improve the economy. Finally, the country has not yet recovered from the deadly 2010 earthquake. Despite these problems, Haiti's people are determined to succeed.
>
> —*Discovering World Geography*

_____ **17.** Based on the excerpt above, what can be said about the poverty in Haiti?

   A. It is comparable to that of many small nations.

   B. It is not the only problem Haiti has to face.

   C. The spread of disease is worse than the poverty in Haiti.

   D. Every effort is being made to combat the poverty in Haiti.

_____ **18.** Based on the excerpt above, why do you believe that many of Haiti's most educated people have left the country?

   A. They felt out of place among those who were less educated.

   B. They want to go where there is more opportunity to apply their skills.

   C. They do not want to improve their skills.

   D. They want to improve the economy in Haiti.

_____ **19.** In a tropical wet/dry climate, when does the dry season occur?

   A. during the winter months

   B. during the spring months

   C. during the summer months

   D. during the fall months

DIRECTIONS: Essay Answer the following question on a separate piece of paper.

20. Discuss the Aztec's conflict with the Spanish. Why were the Aztec defeated by a small force of conquerors? How did the Spanish conquest affect life in Mexico?

Unit Test

South America

networks

DIRECTIONS: True/False Indicate whether the statement is true (T) or false (F).

_____ **1.** The area along the Equator in northern Brazil has a tropical rain forest climate.

_____ **2.** Portugal's rule of Brazil lasted only about 50 years.

_____ **3.** Ecuador, Colombia, and Venezuela have all been ruled at times by dictators.

_____ **4.** In Peru and northern Chile, the area between the Pacific Ocean and the Andes is a coastal desert.

_____ **5.** Mining is an insignificant part of the economy for most Andean countries.

DIRECTIONS: Matching Match each item with its description.

_____ **6.** first indigenous president of Bolivia

_____ **7.** climate zone with moderate rainfall and temperatures

_____ **8.** revolutionary leader who led fight against Spanish rule

_____ **9.** socialist Chilean president killed in a coup

_____ **10.** climate zone up to 10,000 feet with cold temperatures

A. *tierra templada*

B. *tierra fria*

C. Evo Morales

D. Salvador Allende

E. José de San Martin

DIRECTIONS: Multiple Choice Indicate the answer choice that best answers the question.

_____ **11.** In which country do about half of all South Americans live?

A. Brazil

B. Argentina

C. Chile

D. Peru

_____ **12.** Brazil is the world's leading supplier of which commodity?

A. coffee

B. wheat

C. oranges

D. cotton

_____ **13.** Until the late 1800s, nearly all European immigrants to Brazil were from which country?

A. Portugal

B. Spain

C. Italy

D. England

_____ **14.** What distinctive style of Brazilian music is a blend of samba and jazz?

    A. salsa   **C.** bamba

    B. jazz-funk   **D.** bossa nova

_____ **15.** What is the name of the group of islands owned by Ecuador that was the location of important studies by British naturalist Charles Darwin?

    A. Titicaca   **C.** Falklands

    B. Galápagos   **D.** Cotopaxi

_____ **16.** Which country in South America is the only one with coastlines on the Pacific Ocean and the Caribbean Sea?

    A. Venezuela   **C.** Colombia

    B. French Guiana   **D.** Ecuador

_____ **17.** The countries of the Tropical North are only about one-third the land size of which South American country?

    A. Peru   **C.** Bolivia

    B. Brazil   **D.** Argentina

_____ **18.** Which of the following South American countries is landlocked?

    A. Paraguay   **C.** Colombia

    B. Chile   **D.** Argentina

_____ **19.** By the early 1500s, what people had become the dominant indigenous group in the Andean region?

    A. the Carib   **C.** the Aztecs

    B. the Maya   **D.** the Inca

_____ **20.** In the 1980s, Argentina fought a brief war with what country over ownership of the Falkland Islands?

    A. Brazil   **C.** Great Britain

    B. Peru   **D.** Portugal

Lesson Quiz 1

Brazil

netw⊛rks

DIRECTIONS: True/False Indicate whether the statement is true (T) or false (F).

_____ **1.** The Amazon is the world's longest river.

_____ **2.** Much of the Amazon Basin is covered by the world's largest rain forest.

_____ **3.** Most of Brazil is located in the Tropics.

_____ **4.** Though Brazil has forests and rich farmland, it has few mineral resources.

_____ **5.** Coffee is Brazil's main export.

DIRECTIONS: Multiple Choice Indicate the answer choice that best answers the question.

_____ **6.** What is the largest country in South America?

    A. Argentina   **C.** Chile

    B. Brazil   **D.** Bolivia

_____ **7.** What is one reason the Amazon River carries so much water?

    A. A forest canopy shelters the soil of the Amazon Basin.

    B. Water flows freely from the highland plateaus into the lowland plains.

    C. It has more than 1,000 tributaries.

    D. It flows through a vast grassland.

_____ **8.** How are the western and eastern parts of the Brazilian highlands alike?

    A. They both contain rolling hills and plateaus.

    B. Both regions are sparsely populated.

    C. Neither area is suitable for farming.

    D. Both regions are largely grassland.

_____ **9.** Where do most Brazilians live?

    A. on the Amazon Basin

    B. on the highland plateaus

    C. on the coastal lowlands

    D. on the pampas

_____ **10.** How wide can the Amazon River get during the heavy rains of the monsoon season?

    A. 10 miles wide   **C.** 50 miles wide

    B. 25 miles wide   **D.** 100 miles wide

Discovering World Geography

Lesson Quiz 2

networks

Brazil

DIRECTIONS: True/False Indicate whether the statement is true (T) or false (F).

_____ **1.** Native peoples had lived in Brazil for more than 10,000 years before Europeans arrived.

_____ **2.** By 1820, nearly one-third of Brazil's total population was enslaved people.

_____ **3.** Brazil gained independence from Portugal after a bloody civil war.

_____ **4.** The rule of Pedro II brought great progress, including the end of slavery.

_____ **5.** In Brazil, all people aged 18 to 70 are required by law to vote.

DIRECTIONS: Multiple Choice Indicate the answer choice that best answers the question.

_____ **6.** In what way is Brazil different from every other South American country?

A. It is the only South American country where Spanish is spoken.

B. It is the only South American country where Christianity is not the main religion.

C. It is the only South American country that has a Portuguese heritage.

D. It is the only South American country with an indigenous population.

_____ **7.** Which of the following describes the native peoples known as the Tupi?

A. The Tupi were mainly farmers.

B. The Tupi lived as nomads.

C. The Tupi lived in the lowlands.

D. The Tupi did not fish.

_____ **8.** What kept the Portuguese from paying much attention to Brazil for more than 30 years after their arrival in the region?

A. The fierce native peoples of Brazil frightened the Portuguese away.

B. Brazil was thought to be a dry, barren region.

C. Portugal was at war with Spain.

D. The main focus of the Portuguese was on their colonies and trade in Asia.

_____ **9.** By the 1600s, what crop had become Brazil's main export?

A. coffee   **C.** cotton

B. sugarcane   **D.** wheat

_____ **10.** Which Portuguese commander claimed the land of Brazil for Portugal?

A. Getúlio Vargas   **C.** King John III

B. Pedro Cabral   **D.** Christopher Columbus

Discovering World Geography

Lesson Quiz 3

networks

Brazil

DIRECTIONS: True/False Indicate whether the statement is true (T) or false (F).

_____ **1.** Many Brazilians are of German or Italian ancestry.

_____ **2.** Virtually all of Brazil's Native Americans still live in the Amazon rain forest.

_____ **3.** The majority of Brazilians live in rural areas, mainly on plantations, farms, or in small towns.

_____ **4.** Roman Catholicism is the predominant religion in Brazil.

_____ **5.** Most Brazilian adults are high school graduates.

DIRECTIONS: Multiple Choice Indicate the answer choice that best answers the question.

_____ **6.** Which statement about Brazil's population is correct?

    A. Mixed-race marriages are more acceptable in Brazil than in many other countries.

    B. Very few Brazilians have European ancestry.

    C. Almost 80 percent of Brazilians have mixed racial ancestry.

    D. The largest mixed-race group in Brazil is of African and Native American descent.

_____ **7.** What would you most likely encounter a *favela*, or shantytown?

    A. in a small, rural town   **C.** on a plantation

    B. on the edge of a city   **D.** in the rain forest

_____ **8.** Which set of attitudes would Brazilians call the "Brazilian Way"?

    A. controlling, scheming, calculating

    B. rude, distant, impolite

    C. efficient, fast, energetic

    D. friendly, easygoing, laid back

_____ **9.** How are rural life and urban life in Brazil similar?

    A. Most rural and urban dwellers live middle-class lives.

    B. Poor people in rural and urban areas usually own their own homes.

    C. The rural and urban poor eat similar foods.

    D. Nearly all rural and urban dwellers own automobiles.

_____ **10.** What was one major consequence of the construction of the Transamazonica Highway?

    A. increased destruction of the Amazon rain forest

    B. widespread emigration out of Brazil

    C. de-emphasis on agriculture and mining

    D. the collapse of Brazil's logging industry

Discovering World Geography

DIRECTIONS: True/False Indicate whether the statement is true (T) or false (F).

_____ 1. Most Brazilians are both men of Italian ancestry.

_____ 2. Today, millions of Brazil's Native Americans still live in the Amazon rain forest.

_____ 3. The majority of Brazilians live in mansions, many on plantations, farms, or in small towns.

_____ 4. Roman Catholicism is the predominant religion in Brazil.

_____ 5. Most Brazilians are high school graduates.

DIRECTIONS: Multiple Choice Indicate the answer choice that best answers the question.

_____ 6. Which statement about Brazil's population is correct?
A. Mixed-race marriages are more acceptable in Brazil than in many other countries.
B. Very few Brazilians have European ancestry.
C. Almost 50 percent of Brazilians have mixed racial ancestry.
D. The largest single race group in Brazil is of African and Native American descent.

_____ 7. Where would you most likely encounter a favela, or shantytown?
A. in a small, rural town   C. on a plantation
B. on the edge of a city   D. in the rain forest

_____ 8. What sort of attitude would Brazilians call the "Brazilian Way"?
A. controlling, scheming, calculating
B. rude, distant, moody
C. efficient, tasteful, chic
D. open, lively, easygoing and lavish

_____ 9. How are rural life and urban life in Brazil similar?
A. Poor rural and urban dwellers live middle-class lives.
B. Poor people in rural and urban areas usually own their own homes.
C. The rural and urban poor eat similar foods.
D. Wealthy rural and urban group dwellers own automobiles.

_____ 10. What was the major consequence of the construction of the Trans-Amazonian Highway?
A. increased destruction of the Amazon rain forest
B. widespread emigration out of Brazil
C. an emphasis on agriculture and farming
D. the collapse of Brazil's logging industry

Chapter Test, Form A

netw♁rks

Brazil

DIRECTIONS: True/False Indicate whether the statement is true (T) or false (F). If the statement is false, rewrite it to make it true.

_____ **1.** Because Brazil has a high number of well-supported political parties, coalition governments are common.

_____

_____ **2.** Slavery was legalized in Brazil in 1888.

_____

_____ **3.** The largest group of multiethnic Brazilians shares European and Native American ancestry.

_____

_____ **4.** Spanish is Brazil's official language.

_____

_____ **5.** About 10 percent of Brazilians live on less than $2 a day.

_____

DIRECTIONS: Matching Match each item with its description.

_____ **6.** grassy, treeless plains in southern Brazil

_____ **7.** a smaller river that feeds into a larger one

_____ **8.** steep slopes rising from the Atlantic coast to the Brazilian highlands

_____ **9.** areas of high, flat land

_____ **10.** the area that a river and its tributaries drain

A. tributary

B. basin

C. plateaus

D. escarpments

E. pampas

DIRECTIONS: Multiple Choice Indicate the answer choice that best answers the question.

_____ **11.** In what way are the western highlands of Brazil similar to the Atlantic lowlands?

    A. both areas are populated mainly by Native Americans

    B. both areas are dominated by rain forests

    C. both areas are good for farming

    D. neither area contains any large cities

Chapter Test, Form A *cont.*

net w rks

Brazil

_____ **12.** What type of climate exists in areas along the Amazon River?

    A. semiarid

    B. temperate

    C. tropical wet/dry

    D. tropical rain forest

_____ **13.** In the 1500s, King John III of Portugal gave large tracts of land in Brazil to his supporters, who agreed to develop the land. Which of the following was a direct consequence of the land-grant system?

    A. Colonists forced the native population into slavery.

    B. Portugal went bankrupt from giving away so much valuable land.

    C. Colonists became wealthy by selling the land to the native population.

    D. Spain sent troops into the region to prevent the colonization of Brazil.

> Each February, Brazilians celebrate a four-day holiday called Carnival. Millions of working-class and middle-class Brazilians spend much of the year preparing for it by making costumes and building parade floats. Nearly all city neighborhoods are strung with lights. Rio de Janeiro's Carnival is the largest and is world famous. Elaborately costumed Brazilians ride equally elaborate floats in dazzling parades. They are accompanied by thousands of costumed samba dancers moving to the lively music.
>
>   —*Discovering World Geography*

_____ **14.** Based on the excerpt, how would you compare the way middle-class and working-class Brazilians participate in Carnival?

    A. Middle-class Brazilians look down on the holiday as beneath them.

    B. The responsibility for building parade floats falls mostly to middle-class Brazilians.

    C. Both groups enjoy Carnival and take large roles in it.

    D. Working-class Brazilians decorate with lights during Carnival, but middle-class Brazilians do not.

_____ **15.** Based on the excerpt, if Carmen wants to attend the largest Carnival of all, to which Brazilian city should she travel?

    A. Salvador   **C.** Brasília

    B. Rio de Janeiro   **D.** São Paulo

Discovering World Geography

_____ **16.** Which event helped draw European immigrants to Brazil in the 1720s?

   A. the king's desire to convert native peoples to Christianity

   B. the discovery of diamonds in Brazil's interior

   C. widespread famine throughout Europe

   D. the discovery of oil off Brazil's Atlantic coast

_____ **17.** Why did Brazilian plantation owners support the overthrow of Pedro II?

   A. Pedro II had offered land to attract European immigrants to Brazil.

   B. Pedro II had taken plantation owners' land and given it to landless Brazilians.

   C. Pedro II had imposed high taxes on plantation owners.

   D. Pedro II had pushed through an end to slavery.

DIRECTIONS: Short Answer Answer each of the following questions.

18. What role did Napoleon Bonaparte play in the history of Brazilian independence?

_____

_____

_____

_____

19. Why is the Portuguese spoken in Brazil so different from the language spoken in Portugal?

_____

_____

_____

_____

DIRECTIONS: Essay Answer the following question on a separate piece of paper.

20. Describe the terms of the Treaty of Tordesillas and explain why the treaty was necessary. Then tell which country benefited most from the treaty—Spain or Portugal—and explain why.

Chapter Test, Form B

networks

Brazil

DIRECTIONS: True/False Indicate whether the statement is true (T) or false (F). If the statement is false, rewrite it to make it true.

_____ **1.** The Amazon is the largest river in terms of the amount of salt water it carries.

_____

_____ **2.** Brazil has one of the longest strips of coastal plains in South America.

_____

_____ **3.** Logging in the Amazon Basin has become a major environmental issue.

_____

_____ **4.** Brazil got its name from the Brazil nuts that grow in the region.

_____

_____ **5.** Wealthy coffee growers in the southeast dominated the early Brazilian republic.

_____

_____ **6.** Today, Brazil is ruled by the military; generals hold most of the important government positions.

_____

DIRECTIONS: Matching Match each item with its description.

_____ **7.** a remote inland region

_____ **8.** a makeshift community on the edge of a city

_____ **9.** the largest or most important city in a metropolitan area

_____ **10.** a city and the built-up areas around it

A. hinterland

B. metropolitan area

C. central city

D. favela

DIRECTIONS: Multiple Choice Indicate the answer choice that best answers the question.

_____ **11.** Which statement best describes the Brazilian climate?

    A. Brazil has just two seasons—a wet summer and a dry winter.

    B. Almost all of Brazil consists of a tropical rain forest climate.

    C. The climate of Brazil is very much like the climate of the U.S. Gulf Coast.

    D. Brazil's climate varies greatly from region to region.

_____ **12.** Brazil's sugarcane is used to make which fuel for cars and trucks?

    A. natural gas   **C.** ethanol

    B. gasoline   **D.** benzene

_____ **13.** How did the Jesuits affect life in sixteenth-century Brazil?

    A. They angered many colonists because they protected native peoples from slavery.

    B. They gained control over vast tracts of land and became wealthy.

    C. They discouraged immigration into Brazil and thereby damaged the economy.

    D. They helped plantations grow by finding native peoples to work in the fields.

_____ **14.** After the end of slavery, what immigrant group did Brazil's coffee growers depend on to pick their crops?

    A. Portuguese   **C.** Lebanese

    B. Japanese   **D.** Italians

_____ **15.** To relieve poverty and overcrowding, poor rural Brazilians have been offered free land in the Amazon Basin if they will develop it. Why might this pose a problem?

    A. Factories located in the cities might not have enough available workers.

    B. Development in the region threatens the existence of the rain forest.

    C. Wealthy Brazilians will easily drive out the poor and claim the land for themselves.

    D. Rural Brazilians lack the skills needed to develop the land.

The northeastern part of the Brazilian Highlands has a semiarid climate. This region is the hottest and driest part of the country. The daily high temperature during the summer often reaches 100°F (38°C). Frequent and severe droughts have caused many of the region's farms to fail. Even so, the desertlike plant life supports some light ranching.

—Discovering World Geography

_____ **16.** From the context of the excerpt, which phrase best describes a semiarid climate?

    A. a fertile or green spot in a desert or wasteland

    B. having no rainfall and unable to support any plant life

    C. characterized by moderate temperatures; neither hot nor cold

    D. having low precipitation but able to support grassland and scrubby vegetation

Chapter Test, Form B *cont.*

Brazil

_____ **17.** Based on the excerpt, which of the following is a valid conclusion?

  A. Crop growing is not a major part of the economy of the northeastern highlands.

  B. The climate of the northeastern Brazilian Highlands is similar to the climate in the Pacific northwest of the United States.

  C. The northeastern Brazilian Highlands is the most densely populated part of Brazil.

  D. Most Brazilians who live in the northeastern highlands are very poor.

European Slave Trade by Destination

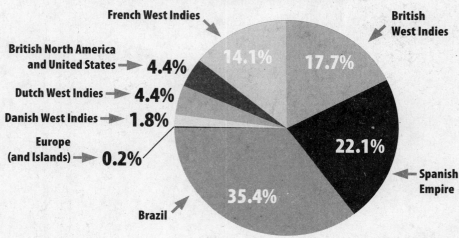

Source: THE SLAVE TRADE, by Hugh Thomas. Copyright ©1997.

_____ **18.** Based on the graph, what was the destination of more than half of the Africans transported to the New World by Europeans?

  A. the Spanish Empire and the British West Indies

  B. British North America and Brazil

  C. Brazil and the Spanish Empire

  D. the French West Indies and Brazil

_____ **19.** Based on the graph, which of the following is a valid conclusion?

  A. The practice of slavery had little effect on Brazilian culture.

  B. A large number of present-day Brazilians have an African ancestry.

  C. The practice of slavery was more brutal in Brazil than in the United States.

  D. Most enslaved Brazilians were freed by the mid-1800s.

DIRECTIONS: Essay Answer the following question on a separate piece of paper.

20. Describe the terms of the Treaty of Tordesillas and explain why the treaty was necessary. Then tell which country benefited most from the treaty—Spain or Portugal—and explain why.

Discovering World Geography

Lesson Quiz 1

netwrks

The Tropical North

DIRECTIONS: True/False Indicate whether the statement is true (T) or false (F).

_____ **1.** Venezuela is larger than Colombia in land area.

_____ **2.** The Orinoco River has more than 400 tributaries.

_____ **3.** A tropical climate means that an area remains cool all year long.

_____ **4.** Colombia is the world's leading producer of emeralds.

_____ **5.** Fishing is a major activity in the Tropical North's economy.

DIRECTIONS: Multiple Choice Indicate the answer choice that best answers the question.

_____ **6.** In what country is Angel Falls, the world's highest waterfall, located?

A. Colombia   **C.** United States

B. Venezuela   **D.** Ecuador

_____ **7.** What feature of the Galápagos Islands makes them an ideal home to many unusual animals?

A. They are heavily populated with humans.

B. They attract many tourists who feed the animals regularly.

C. They are isolated and many have no human population.

D. They are similar to a huge zoo that puts the animals on exhibit.

_____ **8.** Which feature is most typical of a tropical monsoon climate?

A. long dry season

B. very hot days

C. very cool evenings

D. long wet season with heavy rainfall

_____ **9.** Which country is South America's top producer of oil?

A. Venezuela   **C.** Colombia

B. Ecuador   **D.** Suriname

_____ **10.** What physical features in Ecuador and Colombia allow them to grow both bananas and coffee?

A. high arid plains

B. differing elevations and climates

C. acidic soils

D. rich river valleys

Lesson Quiz 2

networks

The Tropical North

DIRECTIONS: Matching Match each item with its description.

_____ **1.** colony that became the country of Suriname

_____ **2.** first president of Gran Colombia

_____ **3.** rebel groups in Suriname who are descendants of escaped slaves

_____ **4.** an early people of the Tropical North

_____ **5.** large estate

A. Cara

B. hacienda

C. Simón Bolívar

D. Dutch Guiana

E. Maroons

DIRECTIONS: Multiple Choice Indicate the answer choice that best answers the question.

_____ **6.** Which one of the following early peoples lived in the Tropical North?

    A. Maya   **C.** Aztec

    B. Carib   **D.** Huron

_____ **7.** In what locations did the Spanish like to place their colonial capital cities?

    A. on hills above the Native American villages

    B. on the coastlines

    C. on flatlands

    D. where the Native Americans already had settlements

_____ **8.** What event did Spanish colonists use to their advantage in order to gain independence?

    A. Spanish-American War   **C.** Napoleon's conquest of Spain

    B. U.S. Revolutionary War   **D.** U.S. Civil War

_____ **9.** What event led to the breaking apart of Gran Colombia?

    A. Simón Bolívar died.

    B. The natives rioted.

    C. The French conquered the country.

    D. The Inca reclaimed their lands.

_____ **10.** What is the chief cause of conflict among the Tropical North's countries?

    A. They cover a vast area and are hard to govern.

    B. Their governments are unstable.

    C. They fight to control the resources.

    D. They have never determined fixed borders.

Discovering World Geography

Lesson Quiz 3

networks

The Tropical North

DIRECTIONS: Matching Match each item with its description.

_____ 1. capital of Venezuela

_____ 2. a dance popular in parts of Colombia and Venezuela

_____ 3. capital of Colombia

_____ 4. group of languages developed by enslaved Africans

_____ 5. someone of white and Native American blood

A. mestizo

B. Bogotá

C. Caracas

D. Creole

E. *cumbia*

DIRECTIONS: Multiple Choice Indicate the answer choice that best answers the question.

_____ 6. Which country in the Tropical North has the highest proportion of indigenous people in its population?

    A. Ecuador   **C.** Colombia

    B. Venezuela   **D.** Suriname

_____ 7. In what area of the country do most Venezuelans live?

    A. near oil fields   **C.** along the coast

    B. in the hills   **D.** in the flatlands

_____ 8. Which of the following statements about the culture of South America's Tropical North is most accurate?

    A. People speak only Spanish in all countries.

    B. No one culture unifies the Tropical North.

    C. Venezuelans have carefully preserved the purity of the Spanish language.

    D. Roman Catholicism is the only religion practiced in the region.

_____ 9. Besides ending tariffs between member nations, what is another goal of the Union of South American Nations?

    A. banning trade with the United States

    B. importing more foreign goods

    C. exporting less oil

    D. adopting a uniform currency

_____ 10. Which class of Venezuela's population supports President Hugo Chávez's policies?

    A. middle class   **C.** business owners

    B. working class   **D.** professionals

Discovering World Geography

101

Chapter Test, Form A

networks

The Tropical North

DIRECTIONS: True/False Indicate whether the statement is true (T) or false (F). If the statement is false, rewrite it to make it true.

_____ 1. The Tropical North is composed entirely of independent nations.

_____

_____ 2. Niagara Falls is more than 20 times higher than Angel Falls.

_____

_____ 3. The Tropical North has coastlines on both the Atlantic and Pacific Oceans.

_____

_____ 4. Some Tropical North countries have been ruled by dictators.

_____

_____ 5. Colombia's Pacific coast region is heavily populated.

_____

DIRECTIONS: Matching Match each item with its description.

_____ 6. where France sent some of its worst convicts

_____ 7. world's highest active volcano

_____ 8. president of Ecuador

_____ 9. led resistance to Spanish rule in the north

_____ 10. cold zone that begins at an elevation of about 10,000 feet

A. Cotopaxi

B. *páramo*

C. Devil's Island

D. Simón Bolívar

E. Rafael Correa

DIRECTIONS: Multiple Choice Indicate the answer choice that best answers the question.

_____ 11. Why is there little farming in French Guiana?

   A. The government places high taxes on farms.

   B. There is not enough water for irrigation.

   C. Much of the land is covered in rain forests.

   D. The people prefer not to farm.

_____ **12.** What were the first Spanish adventurers seeking along the northern coasts of South America?

    A. gold

    B. a fabled silver mine

    C. farmland to settle

    D. a passage to the Pacific Ocean

_____ **13.** In which country was African slavery most common?

    A. Colombia

    B. Venezuela

    C. French Guiana

    D. Suriname

> After his election, Chávez promised to use Venezuela's oil income to improve conditions for the country's poor. Among other actions that angered U.S. leaders, in 2009 he seized control of U.S. companies that were developing oil resources in Venezuela. His strong rule has split Venezuela into opposing groups. Working-class people support Chávez, but middle-class and wealthy Venezuelans oppose his policies.
>
> —*Discovering World Geography*

_____ **14.** Based on the excerpt, how has Chávez's rule affected Venezuela?

    A. He has made good on all of his promises to the people.

    B. He has banned the import of all U.S. products.

    C. He has favored the working class while angering other Venezuelans.

    D. He has won the support of all parts of Venezuelan society.

_____ **15.** Based on the excerpt, which of the following are Chávez's supporters?

    A. wealthy

    B. working class

    C. middle class

    D. U.S. leaders

Chapter Test, Form A *cont.*

The Tropical North

_____ **16.** What event caused tension between Ecuador and Colombia in 2008?

    A. Ecuadorian rebel groups took control of a Colombian waterway.

    B. Colombian rebel groups attacked the Ecuadorian embassy.

    C. Colombian forces attacked a Colombian rebel camp in Ecuador.

    D. Ecuadorian forces attacked an Ecuadorian rebel camp in Colombia.

_____ **17.** What language is spoken by most residents of Guyana?

    A. Spanish

    B. Hindi

    C. Portuguese

    D. English

DIRECTIONS: Short Answer Answer each of the following questions.

18. How did the Spanish *encomienda* affect Native Americans?

_____

_____

_____

_____

_____

19. The countries of the Tropical North exhibit great extremes of climate. Explain why some parts of the region are very cold and others are very hot.

_____

_____

_____

_____

_____

DIRECTIONS: Essay Answer the following question on a separate piece of paper.

20. Relations between the United States and countries of the Tropical North have sometimes been strained. Do you think relations are better now than in the past? Provide specific examples in your response.

Chapter Test, Form B

networks

The Tropical North

DIRECTIONS: True/False Indicate whether the statement is true (T) or false (F). If the statement is false, rewrite it to make it true.

_____ **1.** In the Tropical North, Suriname has the least amount of land.

_____

_____ **2.** Ecuador owns the Galápagos Islands.

_____

_____ **3.** Colombia is South America's top producer of coal.

_____

_____ **4.** Laborers from India and China worked on British and Dutch plantations in the Tropical North.

_____

_____ **5.** The official language of Ecuador is Portuguese.

_____

DIRECTIONS: Matching Match each item with its description.

_____ **6.** group of early Native Americans

_____ **7.** mineral used to make aluminum

_____ **8.** capital of Ecuador

_____ **9.** forest-covered mesas

_____ **10.** group of languages widely spoken by enslaved people

A. *tepuis*

B. bauxite

C. Chibcha

D. creole

E. Quito

DIRECTIONS: Multiple Choice Indicate the answer choice that best answers the question.

_____ **11.** On which three bodies of water does the Tropical North region have coastlines?

A. Gulf of Mexico, Pacific Ocean, Atlantic Ocean

B. Pacific Ocean, Caribbean Sea, Atlantic Ocean

C. Black Sea, Pacific Ocean, Caribbean Sea

D. Gulf of Mexico, Atlantic Ocean, Caribbean Sea

_____ **12.** Which product is Venezuela's main cash crop?

A. corn

B. bananas

C. wheat

D. coffee

_____ **13.** Which of the following statements describes the goal of the first Spaniards who came to Tropical North?

　　A. They came seeking the rich coffees of the area.

　　B. They came to quickly conquer the Native American peoples.

　　C. They wanted gold but found none at first.

　　D. They wanted to convert the Native American peoples to the Christian faith.

_____ **14.** Why were some Tropical North countries torn by conflict after independence?

　　A. Businesspeople and wealthy landholders competed for power.

　　B. Roman Catholic priests revolted against injustice.

　　C. Spain stirred up landless workers against the upper classes.

　　D. Native American peoples formed armies and fought for self-rule.

_____ **15.** How did Venezuela's population change in the mid-1900s?

　　A. Wave after wave of immigrants flocked to the country.

　　B. Large numbers of people moved from rural areas to cities.

　　C. Large numbers of people moved from cities to rural areas.

　　D. More and more people fell into poverty.

The differing elevations and climates in Ecuador and Colombia allow farmers to grow a variety of crops. Both countries export bananas from their tropical lowlands and coffee from the *tierra templada*. Ecuador's agriculture, however, is not well developed. The amount of farmland is limited, and most rural Ecuadorans grow only enough to feed their families. Corn, potatoes, beans, and cassava are common crops in both countries. Colombia produces rice, wheat, sugarcane, and cattle for sale, as well as cotton for the country's large textile industry.

—*Discovering World Geography*

_____ **16.** Based on the excerpt, what can be said about agriculture in Ecuador and Colombia?

　　A. Ecuador's agriculture is well developed.

　　B. Colombia focuses on raising cotton.

　　C. The farmers in Ecuador have surplus crops.

　　D. Colombia's agriculture is more developed than Ecuador's.

_____ **17.** Based on the excerpt, what is the most likely reason that farmers in Ecuador raise only enough to feed their families?

    A. Ecuador has too few people to supply workers for farms.

    B. Most farmers have small-acreage farms.

    C. Seeds for commercial crops are too expensive.

    D. Most farmers have very small families.

Colombia's Caribbean lowlands are home to about 20 percent of its people, mainly in Cartagena and other port cities along the coast. The country's Pacific coast is sparsely settled. Most of the people there are descendants of enslaved Africans who worked on plantations near the Caribbean Sea. As they were freed or escaped, they migrated into remote areas in western Colombia. The Llanos, where cattle ranching is the main activity, is another area with few people.

—*Discovering World Geography*

_____ **18.** Based on the excerpt, which two areas in Colombia are not well populated?

    A. along the Caribbean coast and around Cartagena

    B. around Cartagena and on the Llanos

    C. along the Pacific coast and on the Llanos

    D. along the Pacific and Caribbean coasts

_____ **19.** Based on the excerpt, what do you think is the most likely reason that the freed or escaped Africans chose to live in western Colombia?

    A. They were less likely to be noticed or caught.

    B. They went there to find work.

    C. They liked living in coastal areas.

    D. They wanted to work on cattle ranches.

DIRECTIONS: Essay Answer the following question on a separate piece of paper.

20. Relations between the United States and countries of the Tropical North have sometimes been strained. Do you think relations are better now than in the past? Provide specific examples in your response.

Lesson Quiz 1

networks

Andes and Midlatitude Countries

DIRECTIONS: True/False Indicate whether the statement is true (T) or false (F).

_____ **1.** The Andes are the longest continuous group of mountain ranges in the world.

_____ **2.** South America has few large lakes, but the largest lake in the Andean region is Lake Titicaca.

_____ **3.** The most densely populated area of the Andes is the *tierra helada*.

_____ **4.** Paraguay gets almost all of its electricity from its extensive coal reserves.

_____ **5.** Llamas serve as pack animals in the Andes and are important sources of food, wool, and hides.

DIRECTIONS: Multiple Choice Indicate the answer choice that best answers the question.

_____ **6.** What is the correct order, from north to south, of the countries that make up the bulk of the Andean region in South America?

    A. Chile, Bolivia, Peru   **C.** Peru, Bolivia, Chile

    B. Bolivia, Peru, Chile   **D.** Chile, Peru, Bolivia

_____ **7.** Which term describes the area of Peru between the Andes and the Pacific?

    A. high plateau   **C.** tundra

    B. desert   **D.** fertile plain

_____ **8.** Which statement describes the climate of the midlatitude countries of eastern South America?

    A. Rainfall occurs mostly in the spring.

    B. The temperature is relatively stable throughout the year.

    C. Winters are warmer than summers.

    D. The climate is generally temperate, or moderate.

_____ **9.** What causes the weather disturbances called El Niño and La Niña?

    A. changes in wind patterns and ocean currents in the Pacific Ocean

    B. movements of the tectonic plates under the Pacific Ocean

    C. variations in monsoon winds originating in the mid-Atlantic

    D. cold winds blowing north from Antarctica

_____ **10.** Which of the following statements about the mineral resources of the Andean and midlatitude countries of South America is accurate?

    A. Mining is almost unheard of in the rugged Andean region.

    B. The region has very few mineral resources.

    C. Copper mining is an important industry in the Andean region.

    D. Precious metals are scarce in the region, though there is some petroleum.

Lesson Quiz 2

networks

Andes and Midlatitude Countries

DIRECTIONS: True/False Indicate whether the statement is true (T) or false (F).

_____ **1.** Early Native American societies in the Andes were based primarily on agriculture.

_____ **2.** The Inca were peace loving and cooperated with neighboring groups.

_____ **3.** The Spaniards conquered the Inca because they greatly outnumbered the Inca.

_____ **4.** Uneven distribution of wealth led to social and political instability in many South American nations after independence.

_____ **5.** Both Chile and Argentina have had women as presidents.

DIRECTIONS: Multiple Choice Indicate the answer choice that best answers the question.

_____ **6.** Which statement accurately describes an aspect of Inca civilization?

    A. The Inca were largely hunter-gatherers.

    B. The Inca built a complex road system for travel.

    C. The Inca carefully preserved their history on handwritten parchments.

    D. The Inca practiced an advanced form of democracy.

_____ **7.** Who held the highest positions in the Inca's highly structured society?

    A. engineers and builders   **C.** emperor and high priest

    B. artisans and physicians   **D.** farmers and laborers

_____ **8.** Which Spanish conquistador conquered the empire of the Inca?

    A. Vasco Núñez de Balboa   **C.** Francisco Pizarro

    B. Capac Yupanqui   **D.** Christopher Columbus

_____ **9.** For what purpose did the Inca use the device known as the quipu?

    A. counting   **C.** cooking

    B. farming   **D.** writing

_____ **10.** Which generalization about South American governments is most valid?

    A. After gaining independence, most South American countries strongly supported democracy.

    B. A strong middle class has helped most South American nations maintain stable governments over the past century.

    C. By the mid-1900s, Native Americans held leadership positions in most South American nations.

    D. In the first half of the twentieth century, many South American governments were dictatorships.

Discovering World Geography

Lesson Quiz 3

networks

Andes and Midlatitude Countries

DIRECTIONS: True/False Indicate whether the statement is true (T) or false (F).

_____ **1.** Buenos Aires is the capital of Chile.

_____ **2.** Wealthy South Americans would be unlikely to live in pueblos jóvenes.

_____ **3.** Because of the relatively harsh living conditions, people of the Andean and midlatitude countries have not developed arts, music, and literature.

_____ **4.** In the Andean and midlatitude countries, family ties are very important.

_____ **5.** Potatoes and grains are grown on highland terraces in Peru.

DIRECTIONS: Multiple Choice Indicate the answer choice that best answers the question.

_____ **6.** How does the population of Peru differ from other countries in the region?

    A. the Native American population is very small

    B. few inhabitants are of European ancestry

    C. large numbers of Middle Easterners live there

    D. more of the population is of African descent

_____ **7.** Why do coastal portions of the region have the highest population density?

    A. The moderate climate there is healthy and pleasant.

    B. The dense vegetation offers an abundance of plant and animal resources.

    C. The mineral resources there provide many good-paying jobs.

    D. The coastal areas offer fertile land and easy transportation.

_____ **8.** Which phrase accurately describes Isabel Allende?

    A. hero of South America's fight for independence

    B. former president of Chile

    C. contemporary South American writer

    D. leader of Bolivia's environmental movement

_____ **9.** Guarani customs and folk art are an important part of the culture in which South American nation?

    A. Peru   **C.** Paraguay

    B. Argentina   **D.** Chile

_____ **10.** Why did four South American countries form Mercosur in 1991?

    A. to encourage free trade within the region

    B. to develop a highway system within the four countries

    C. to promote human rights in nations emerging from dictatorship

    D. to compete in international soccer, or football, leagues

Discovering World Geography

Chapter Test, Form A

network

Andes and Midlatitude Countries

DIRECTIONS: True/False Indicate whether the statement is true (T) or false (F). If the statement is false, rewrite it to make it true.

_____ **1.** Today, Bolivia and Peru have large Native American populations.

_____

_____ **2.** During the centuries of Spanish colonization, the Lutheran Church was one of the most important institutions in the Andean region.

_____

_____ **3.** Baseball is the most popular sport in the Andean and midlatitude regions of South America.

_____

DIRECTIONS: Matching Match each item with its description.

_____ **4.** South American independence leader

_____ **5.** series of parallel mountain ranges

_____ **6.** Argentina's first elected woman president

_____ **7.** Spanish conquistador who conquered the Inca

_____ **8.** high plain in Peru and Bolivia

_____ **9.** popular wife of overthrown Argentinian president

_____ **10.** an area where the ocean tide meets a river current

A. cordillera

B. estuary

C. altiplano

D. Cristina Fernández de Kirchner

E. Francisco Pizarro

F. Eva Perón

G. Simón Bolivar

DIRECTIONS: Multiple Choice Indicate the answer choice that best answers the question.

_____ **11.** The Paraná, Paraguay, and Uruguay rivers form the second-largest river system in South America. Why is this system especially important to Paraguay?

    A. Paraguay is landlocked, so the rivers form an important transportation route.

    B. The river system is the only source of drinking water for the country.

    C. The people of Paraguay rely on fish for much of their diet.

    D. The river system provides access to the Pacific Ocean.

_____ **12.** Why is the population in the *tierra helada* region of the Andes sparse?

    A. Fierce Native American tribes keep out potential settlers.

    B. The area is covered almost entirely by water, preventing settlement.

    C. The region is protected as a sanctuary for native wildlife species.

    D. The cold, harsh climate discourages widespread settlement.

_____ **13.** What is the main factor that determines climate in the Andes?

    A. temperature

    B. humidity

    C. altitude

    D. precipitation

Management of natural resources presents many important issues and challenges. An example is conflict between countries over gas reserves. Bolivia has the second-largest reserve of natural gas in Latin America. Bolivia is landlocked. So, to export the gas, it must move through Peru or Chile.

In 2003 the Bolivian government proposed that natural gas be exported through Chile, because it would be cheaper than an alternate plan to go through Peru. The Bolivian people turned out in huge numbers to protest. In Bolivia, suspicion and anger against Chile are widespread. These feelings date back to the Pacific War of the early 1880s, when Chile took over Bolivia's only access to the sea.

—*Discovering World Geography*

_____ **14.** Based on the excerpt, what is the main problem Bolivia faces in exporting its natural gas reserves?

    A. The country lacks enough qualified workers to access the gas.

    B. Drilling for natural gas is too expensive for a poor nation.

    C. The country has no outlet to the sea.

    D. The price of natural gas is too low.

_____ **15.** Based on the excerpt, what would likely have happened if Bolivia's government had proposed to export the natural gas through Peru rather than Chile?

    A. Bolivia's government would probably have been turned out of office.

    B. The Bolivian public would have been more accepting of the plan.

    C. Bolivians would have demanded the cheaper route through Chile.

    D. Chile would have declared war on Bolivia for backing out of a deal.

_____ **16.** How did the American and French Revolutions affect South Americans?

    A. Many South Americans moved to the United States and France to find freedom.

    B. South Americans were encouraged to fight for their own independence.

    C. South Americans hired U.S. mercenaries to fight against the Spanish.

    D. South Americans decided that wars for independence were too risky.

_____ **17.** How are the practices of the Kallawaya healers of Bolivia different from those of most U.S. doctors?

    A. Kallawaya healers do not charge for their services.

    B. Kallawaya healers rely solely on manipulation of the spine.

    C. Kallawaya healers perform surgery without using anesthetics.

    D. Kallawaya healers use herbs and rituals in their cures.

DIRECTIONS: Short Answer Answer each of the following questions.

18. Explain how the Andes were formed.

_____

_____

_____

_____

_____

19. Explain how the actions of U.S. and European multinational companies affected the people of the Andes and midlatitude countries in the first part of the twentieth century.

_____

_____

_____

_____

DIRECTIONS: Essay Answer the following question on a separate piece of paper.

20. Describe the causes and effects of the extreme weather event known as El Niño.

Chapter Test, Form B

net w⊕rks

Andes and Midlatitude Countries

DIRECTIONS: True/False Indicate whether the statement is true (T) or false (F). If the statement is false, rewrite it to make it true.

_____ **1.** A series of knotted cords used by the Inca for record keeping was called an abacus.

_____

_____ **2.** The introduction of epidemic diseases from Europe drastically reduced the Native American population of South America.

_____

_____ **3.** The Perón government in Argentina enacted reforms that helped working people but also limited free speech and censored the press.

_____

_____ **4.** The population of the Andean region is not evenly distributed.

_____

_____ **5.** Pachamanca is a traditional Andean bread still enjoyed throughout the region.

_____

_____ **6.** Disputed borders have presented challenges in the Andean and midlatitude countries for years.

_____

DIRECTIONS: Matching Match each item with its description.

_____ **7.** Andean zone containing forests and grassy areas

_____ **8.** most densely populated Andean zone

_____ **9.** Andean zone with the highest altitude

_____ **10.** the "hot land" of the Andean zones

A. *tierra caliente*

B. *tierra templada*

C. *tierra fría*

D. *tierra helada*

DIRECTIONS: Multiple Choice Indicate the answer choice that best answers the question.

_____ **11.** How does the lack of mountain ranges affect the climate in Paraguay?

    A. It helps make Paraguay the hottest country in South America.

    B. It causes deserts to cover much of Paraguay.

    C. It contributes to Paraguay's strong winds.

    D. It helps give Paraguay warm summers and warm winters.

_____ **12.** Why did Argentina and Great Britain go to war in the 1980s?

    A. Great Britain tried to establish a new colony in Argentina.

    B. Argentina's president had insulted the British royal family.

    C. Both countries claimed ownership of the Falkland Islands.

    D. Great Britain attempted to overthrow a corrupt Argentinian government.

_____ **13.** Which style of literature is especially popular in Latin America?

    A. graphic novel   **C.** science fiction

    B. magic realism   **D.** medieval romance

_____ **14.** What is one difference between crops grown in Peru's highlands and crops grown in Peru's coastal valleys?

    A. Coffee is grown in the highlands, while sugarcane is grown in the coastal valleys.

    B. Only highland crops are exported to other countries.

    C. The crops of the coastal valleys are much more profitable.

    D. Cotton is grown in both regions, but the highlands produce three times as much.

_____ **15.** Which countries are building the Transoceanic Highway?

    A. Bolivia and Paraguay   **C.** Argentina and Panama

    B. Chile and Argentina   **D.** Peru and Brazil

> The largest city in the region is Buenos Aires, the capital of Argentina. This is a bustling port and cultural center. It resembles a European city with its parks, buildings, outdoor cafes, and wide streets. About 2.8 million people live in the central city of Buenos Aires, but the metropolitan area includes 11.5 million people. This is more than one-fourth of Argentina's entire population. So, although Argentina as a whole is not densely populated, the area in and around Buenos Aires is.
>
> —*Discovering World Geography*

_____ **16.** Based on the excerpt, which of the following statements about Buenos Aires is correct?

    A. It is a large port city and cultural center.

    B. The city is not as densely populated as the rest of Argentina.

    C. It is the capital of Peru.

    D. A majority of the people live in the central part of the city.

_____ **17.** Based on the excerpt, about what percentage of the entire population of Argentina lives in Buenos Aires?

    A. 10 percent

    B. 25 percent

    C. 50 percent

    D. 80 percent

> Significant changes were also taking place in the country of Chile. In the presidential election of 1970, Chileans elected a socialist candidate named Salvador Allende. Allende took action to redistribute wealth and land. The government took over Chile's copper industry and banking system. Allende's economic reforms were popular with workers but angered the upper classes. In 1973 Chilean military officers staged a coup, an illegal seizure of power, and killed Allende. A military dictatorship, headed by General Augusto Pinochet, ruled Chile for the next 16 years.
>
> —*Discovering World Geography*

_____ **18.** Based on the excerpt, how did wealthy Chileans respond to Salvador Allende's election?

    A. They chose an opposition candidate to run against Allende in the next election.

    B. They gave him their overwhelming support.

    C. They worked closely with Allende to redistribute wealth and land.

    D. They strongly opposed his economic reforms.

_____ **19.** Based on the excerpt, which of the following is a valid conclusion?

    A. Allende was a dictator who was ultimately overthrown by the people.

    B. Pinochet was a legitimately elected leader of Chile.

    C. The military coup did not find wide support among Chile's workers.

    D. Allende's policies would have bankrupted Chile.

DIRECTIONS: Essay Answer the following question on a separate piece of paper.

20. Describe the causes and effects of the extreme weather event known as El Niño.

Unit Test

networks

Europe

DIRECTIONS: True/False Indicate whether the statement is true (T) or false (F).

_____ **1.** Moscow is the cultural, educational, and scientific capital of Russia.

_____ **2.** The Roman Empire never included any of the British Isles.

_____ **3.** Northern Europe includes the countries of Greece and Spain.

_____ **4.** Athens was the most developed city-state in ancient Greece after the Persian Wars.

_____ **5.** Russia is the largest country by area in the world.

DIRECTIONS: Matching Match each item with its description.

_____ **6.** peninsula that includes most of Denmark

_____ **7.** mass murder of members of an ethnic or cultural group

_____ **8.** busy sea route connecting the North Sea with the Atlantic Ocean

_____ **9.** period of slow economic growth or decline

_____ **10.** England's lawmaking body

A. English Channel

B. Parliament

C. Jutland

D. recession

E. genocide

DIRECTIONS: Multiple Choice Indicate the answer choice that best answers the question.

_____ **11.** Why does Western Europe have a milder climate than other areas at the same latitude?

A. Cool winds off the North Sea make the climate milder.

B. Hot winds from southern France blow northeast and make the climate milder.

C. Warm winds off the Atlantic Ocean make the climate milder.

D. A hot air mass rests above Western Europe and makes the climate milder.

_____ **12.** What is feudalism?

A. the period of transition between ancient and modern times

B. the period after the Renaissance

C. the tithe given to the church

D. the system of order that developed during the Middle Ages

_____ **13.** Which Western European country was the birthplace of the Protestant Reformation?

A. Austria

B. Ireland

C. Germany

D. France

Discovering World Geography

_____ **14.** Which two events nearly wiped out Europe's Jewish population?

    A. Feudalism and Black Death   **C.** World War I and the Industrial Revolution

    B. Holocaust and World War II   **D.** World War II and the Enlightenment

_____ **15.** Which body of water is most important in Southern Europe?

    A. Mediterranean Sea   **C.** North Sea

    B. Norwegian Sea   **D.** Black Sea

_____ **16.** Who were the Vikings?

    A. servants to the Normans   **C.** pirates from northern France

    B. warriors from Scandinavia   **D.** people conquered by the Romans

_____ **17.** Which is the most accurate description of the population of Northern and Southern Europe?

    A. The population is becoming more rural and is getting younger.

    B. The population has few people who are 65 or older.

    C. The population is mostly Protestant.

    D. The population is becoming more urban and is getting older.

_____ **18.** How did the collapse of the USSR affect Russia's economy?

    A. Russia's transition to a free market economy went smoothly and quickly.

    B. A sizable drop in the prices of goods and services helped boost the economy.

    C. Russia's transition to a free market economy was slow and difficult.

    D. The production of goods increased almost immediately after the collapse.

_____ **19.** Which of the following statements most accurately describes communism?

    A. All property should belong to the state, not to private individuals.

    B. A small group of people should control all the property for their own goals.

    C. The people who own property should share part of it with the state.

    D. One person alone should own all property and decide how it is to be shared.

_____ **20.** Why did international popular culture have less influence in Eastern Europe and Western Russia before the 1990s?

    A. Social apps, such as Facebook, had not been developed before the 1990s.

    B. Most people in the region were under Soviet control before the 1990s.

    C. Most people in the region lived in rural areas and lacked access to media.

    D. Most people in the region had little interest in popular entertainers.

Discovering World Geography

Lesson Quiz 1

networks

Western Europe

DIRECTIONS: Matching Match each item with its description.

_____ **1.** land reclaimed from the sea

_____ **2.** decomposed plant and animal material that makes fertile soil

_____ **3.** Belgium, the Netherlands, and Luxembourg

_____ **4.** strong winds that travel from west to east

_____ **5.** tallest mountain in the Alps

A. Benelux Countries

B. Mont Blanc

C. polders

D. Westerlies

E. humus

DIRECTIONS: Multiple Choice Indicate the answer choice that best answers the question.

_____ **6.** What forces formed the Alps?

    A. tsunamis and glaciers

    B. volcanoes and the Westerlies

    C. glaciers and the Westerlies

    D. plate tectonics and glaciers

_____ **7.** What underwater structure connects Britain to mainland Europe?

    A. London Bridge   **C.** Northern European Plain

    B. the Chunnel   **D.** Main-Danube Canal

_____ **8.** Which features are most typical of a marine west coast climate?

    A. hot summers and cold winters

    B. very hot days and very cool evenings

    C. cool summers and mild winters

    D. warm days and warm evenings

_____ **9.** Which country is Western Europe's leading agricultural producer?

    A. United Kingdom   **C.** Ireland

    B. the Netherlands   **D.** France

_____ **10.** Why does mainland Europe have a wider variety of plant life than the British Isles?

    A. Mainland Europe has a more diverse climate than the British Isles.

    B. Mainland Europe receives more rain than the British Isles.

    C. The British Isles have a more diverse climate than mainland Europe.

    D. The British Isles have a warmer climate than mainland Europe.

Lesson Quiz 2

networks

Western Europe

DIRECTIONS: True/False Indicate whether the statement is true (T) or false (F).

_____ **1.** Christianity began in the western Roman Empire.

_____ **2.** A plague, called the Black Death, spread during the Hundred Years' War.

_____ **3.** Nicolaus Copernicus confirmed that the sun orbits Earth.

_____ **4.** During the Industrial Revolution, many people moved from rural to urban areas.

_____ **5.** More civilians than military forces died during World War II.

DIRECTIONS: Multiple Choice Indicate the answer choice that best answers the question.

_____ **6.** When did Rome's western empire fall?

    A. when Emperor Constantine adopted Christianity

    B. when Christian subjects rose up against Roman rule

    C. when Germanic groups invaded Western Europe from the northeast

    D. when invaders from North Africa conquered Rome

_____ **7.** Which of the following statements accurately describes feudalism?

    A. Feudalism served to spread Christianity throughout Western Europe.

    B. Feudalism began as a way to protect those on pilgrimages to Jerusalem.

    C. The rise of feudalism marked the end of the Medieval Age.

    D. Under feudalism, kings gave land to nobles in exchange for their military service.

_____ **8.** Which of the following statements explains Martin Luther's conflict with the Roman Catholic Church?

    A. Luther believed that pilgrimages to the Holy Land were too costly.

    B. Luther believed that Church officials should not sell pardons for people's sins.

    C. Luther believed that Church leaders were paid too much.

    D. Luther believed that women should be able to become priests.

_____ **9.** In what year did World War I begin?

    A. 1914   **C.** 1920

    B. 1916   **D.** 1925

_____ **10.** What conflict ended when the government of the Soviet Union fell apart?

    A. World War II   **C.** Cold War

    B. Vietnam War   **D.** Korean War

Lesson Quiz 3

networks

Western Europe

DIRECTIONS: True/False Indicate whether the statement is true (T) or false (F).

_____ **1.** The European Union (EU) has 12 member nations.

_____ **2.** English is a Germanic language.

_____ **3.** The rise of high-speed rail travel in Europe helped limit air pollution.

_____ **4.** More Western Europeans work in service industries than in agriculture.

_____ **5.** Migration is the main cause of population growth in Western Europe.

DIRECTIONS: Multiple Choice Indicate the answer choice that best answers the question.

_____ **6.** When did the two halves of Germany reunite?

    A. immediately after World War II

    B. at the start of the Cold War

    C. when the European Union was formed

    D. after the Soviet Union lost control of Eastern Europe

_____ **7.** What is the most common Romance language in Western Europe?

    A. Spanish   **C.** French

    B. German   **D.** English

_____ **8.** Which of the following is one of the world's most famous playwrights?

    A. Johann Sebastian Bach   **C.** John Locke

    B. William Shakespeare   **D.** Nicolaus Copernicus

_____ **9.** Why is Western Europe's economy called postindustrial?

    A. More people work in service jobs than in manufacturing.

    B. Most workers are employed by small businesses.

    C. Agriculture is more important than manufacturing.

    D. Most industrial products are exported to other countries.

_____ **10.** Which statement describes a way in which the European Union has benefited its member nations?

    A. The EU has shielded member nations from trade with other parts of the world.

    B. The EU has converted European currencies to U.S. dollars.

    C. The EU has helped members compete more successfully with larger economies.

    D. The EU has promoted agriculture as a substitute for manufacturing.

Chapter Test, Form A

netw⊙rks

Western Europe

DIRECTIONS: True/False Indicate whether the statement is true (T) or false (F). If the statement is false, rewrite it to make it true.

_____ **1.** Sand dunes along the North Sea coastline are from deposits left during the last ice age.

_____

_____ **2.** The English Channel separates southern England from Spain.

_____

_____ **3.** The North Sea has become an important source for oil and natural gas.

_____

_____ **4.** The Middle Ages are also known as the Medieval Age.

_____

_____ **5.** The high-speed rail lines in Western Europe serve only French cities.

_____

DIRECTIONS: Matching Match each item with its description.

_____ **6.** German priest responsible for the Protestant Reformation

_____ **7.** river that flows through Germany into the North Sea

_____ **8.** unique language spoken in the Pyrenees region of France and Spain

_____ **9.** French general who conquered much of Europe

_____ **10.** where part of the sea connects to the lower end of a river

A. Basque

B. estuary

C. Martin Luther

D. Napoleon Bonaparte

E. Elbe

DIRECTIONS: Multiple Choice Indicate the answer choice that best answers the question.

_____ **11.** Which body of water lies along Britain's east coast?

    A. North Sea

    B. English Channel

    C. Baltic Sea

    D. Atlantic Ocean

_____ **12.** What causes the summers in southern France to be hot and dry?

    A. the Westerlies, which take all the moisture northward

    B. the Mediterranean Sea, which moderates the climate

    C. the Azores High, which pushes moist air northward

    D. the Alps, which put southern France in a rain shadow

_____ **13.** What makes the soils of the Northern European Plain so good for farming?

    A. They are acidic.   **C.** They are marshy.

    B. They contain sand.   **D.** They contain humus.

_____ **14.** What did the Romans build to transport water to cities and towns?

    A. bridges   **C.** the Chunnel

    B. aqueducts   **D.** concrete roads

_____ **15.** Which of the following statements about the Hundred Years' War is accurate?

    A. It was a war between Spain and England.

    B. It lasted less than 100 years.

    C. It contributed to the spread of the Black Death.

    D. It resulted from differences between Catholics and Protestants.

Two major divisions of Indo-European languages spoken in Western Europe are Romance and Germanic. Romance languages are based on Latin, the language of the Roman Empire. The most common Romance language in Western Europe is French. The Germanic languages spoken in Western Europe include German, Dutch, and English, although about half of the English vocabulary comes from the Romance languages. Not all European languages are Indo-European, however. For example, Basque, a language spoken in the Pyrenees region of France and Spain, is unrelated to any other language spoken today. It is common for Western Europeans to speak more than one language—their native language plus English, French, or German.

—*Discovering World Geography*

_____ **16.** Based on the excerpt, what can be said about the languages spoken in Western Europe?

    A. English is a combination of Germanic and Romance languages.

    B. All European languages are Indo-European.

    C. Latin is the most common Romance language in Western Europe.

    D. Basque is related to the Germanic languages.

Discovering World Geography

_____ **17.** Based on the excerpt, what is one trait that is common among Western Europeans?

    A. They always speak English in public.

    B. They are bilingual.

    C. They speak Latin as their primary language.

    D. They speak only their native language.

DIRECTIONS: Short Answer Answer each of the following questions.

18. Explain how the Gulf Stream affects the climate of the Western European nations.

_____

_____

_____

_____

_____

_____

19. Explain what the Cold War was and how it ended.

_____

_____

_____

_____

_____

_____

DIRECTIONS: Essay Answer the following question on a separate piece of paper.

20. Explain how the outcome of World War I helped lead to another world war.

Chapter Test, Form B

Western Europe

netw⊙rks

DIRECTIONS: True/False Indicate whether the statement is true (T) or false (F). If the statement is false, rewrite it to make it true.

_____ **1.** The island of Britain contains England, Wales, and Northern Ireland.

_____

_____ **2.** Peat, or decaying vegetable matter, can be used as a source of heat.

_____

_____ **3.** The Roman Empire controlled most of the island of Britain.

_____

_____ **4.** Following World War I, the victorious countries demanded that Great Britain pay for damages.

_____

_____ **5.** The European Union was formed in 1993.

_____

DIRECTIONS: Matching Match each item with its description.

_____ **6.** refers to a tree that loses its leaves in autumn

_____ **7.** period when machines began taking over work once done by hand

_____ **8.** refers to a tree that keeps its needle-shaped leaves all winter

_____ **9.** mountain range that separates Western Europe and Southern Europe

_____ **10.** a trip to visit the holy places of one's religion

A. Alps

B. deciduous

C. pilgrimage

D. Industrial Revolution

E. coniferous

DIRECTIONS: Multiple Choice Indicate the answer choice that best answers the question.

_____ **11.** What is one reason that France is Western Europe's leading agricultural producer?

    A. France imports more grain than any other nation in the region.

    B. France has a drier climate than any other nation in the region.

    C. France receives more rain than any other nation in the region.

    D. France devotes more land to agriculture than any other nation in the region.

Chapter Test, Form B *cont.*

Western Europe

_____ **12.** Which of the following is a well-known English river?

  A. Elbe

  B. Thames

  C. Rhine

  D. Loire

_____ **13.** Why were the Middle Ages given their name?

  A. They were a transition period between ancient and modern times.

  B. They refer to the midpoint of civilization's history.

  C. They are neither young nor old.

  D. They came just before the Dark Ages.

_____ **14.** Which factor contributed most to Napoleon Bonaparte's defeat?

  A. wrath of Spain

  B. violent upheaval in France

  C. combined might of France's enemies in conquered lands

  D. bickering among his troops

_____ **15.** Which is an accurate statement about World War I?

  A. It involved only the countries of Western Europe.

  B. It grew out of political changes and rivalries among European powers.

  C. It led to Germany's division into two countries.

  D. In the end, Germany was pardoned for starting the war.

The arts are an important part of Western European culture. Museums and cultural institutions celebrate each nation's art and history, and national governments support the arts. The German government, for example, funds hundreds of theaters, and concerts and plays attract large audiences. Most important is the influence Western European culture has had on the rest of the world. German architects from the Bauhaus School influenced buildings in cities throughout the 1900s. British popular music and television have had an impact, especially on American culture.

—*Discovering World Geography*

_____ **16.** Based on the excerpt, in which cultural area have the Germans had worldwide influence?

  A. popular music

  B. television

  C. painting

  D. architecture

Discovering World Geography

_____ **17.** Based on the excerpt, what do Americans particularly like about British culture?

  A. popular music and television

  B. architecture and concerts

  C. buildings and food

  D. television and architecture

In the past few decades, the number of industrial workers has also declined. Only about 25 percent of Western Europeans work in the industrial, or secondary, sector of the economy. Many more people work in the tertiary sector—service industries, such as government, education, health care, banking and financial services, retail, computing, and repair of mechanical equipment. The United Kingdom was the birthplace of modern industry. Yet today, only 18.2 percent of the workforce in the United Kingdom works in industry.

—*Discovering World Geography*

_____ **18.** Based on the excerpt, how does the United Kingdom compare to Western Europe as a whole?

  A. Fewer of its workers are employed in agriculture.

  B. More than 25 percent of its workers are employed in industry.

  C. Fewer of its workers are employed in the industrial sector.

  D. More of its workers are unemployed.

_____ **19.** Based on the excerpt, which one of the following positions would be part of the tertiary sector?

  A. wheat farmer

  B. computer repair person

  C. cattle rancher

  D. worker on an auto-assembly line

DIRECTIONS: Essay Answer the following question on a separate piece of paper.

 20. Explain how the outcome of World War I helped lead to another world war.

Lesson Quiz 1

networks

Northern and Southern Europe

DIRECTIONS: Matching Match each item with its description.

_____ 1. region of frozen subsoil and few plants

_____ 2. fishing ship that tows a large net behind it

_____ 3. weathering and erosion caused by moving glaciers

_____ 4. area where mostly short grasses and shrubs grow

_____ 5. deep, narrow, water-filled valley

A. glaciation

B. fjord

C. tundra

D. scrubland

E. trawler

DIRECTIONS: Multiple Choice Indicate the answer choice that best answers the question.

_____ 6. Which sea dominates the coast of much of southern Europe?

    A. Arctic Sea

    B. Norwegian Sea

    C. Mediterranean Sea

    D. North Sea

_____ 7. In which country is the Po River found?

    A. Spain

    B. Greece

    C. Portugal

    D. Italy

_____ 8. Which climate is found in Finland, where the influence of seas is limited?

    A. continental climate

    B. Mediterranean climate

    C. tundra climate

    D. monsoon climate

_____ 9. What tree crop grows well in the scrublands near the Mediterranean?

    A. apples

    B. olives

    C. pears

    D. elderberries

_____ 10. Why has whaling declined as an industry in Northern Europe?

    A. Whaling was not as profitable as shrimping.

    B. Whaling was far too costly to maintain.

    C. The seas have become so icy that ships cannot navigate them.

    D. Many of the larger whale species are considered endangered.

Lesson Quiz 2

networks

Northern and Southern Europe

DIRECTIONS: Matching Match each item with its description.

_____ 1. period of artistic and intellectual activity

_____ 2. period between A.D. 500 and 1500

_____ 3. religion with many gods and myths, such as that of the Vikings

_____ 4. independent country located within the city of Rome

_____ 5. powerful Greek city-state and first known democracy

A. Middle Ages

B. Athens

C. pagan

D. Renaissance

E. Vatican City

DIRECTIONS: Multiple Choice Indicate the answer choice that best answers the question.

_____ 6. What kingdom, led by Alexander, conquered the Greek city-states?

    A. Persia   **C.** Macedon

    B. Rome   **D.** Cyprus

_____ 7. Which of the following statements about the rule of the Roman Empire is accurate?

    A. The Roman Empire was situated entirely on the Italian peninsula.

    B. Emperor Constantine ruled from the city of Rome.

    C. The Roman Empire had few provinces.

    D. The eastern empire lasted almost 1,000 years after the western empire fell.

_____ 8. Which city was one of the earliest centers of the Renaissance?

    A. Constantinople   **C.** Athens

    B. Florence   **D.** Sparta

_____ 9. What was the religion of the Moors who invaded Spain from Northern Africa?

    A. Islam   **C.** Greek Orthodoxy

    B. Roman Catholicism   **D.** Judaism

_____ 10. Since World War II, which of the following changes has taken place in many nations of Southern Europe?

    A. They adopted communism.

    B. They converted to Christianity.

    C. They withdrew from international trade.

    D. They became democracies.

Discovering World Geography

Lesson Quiz 3

networks

Northern and Southern Europe

DIRECTIONS: True/False Indicate whether the statement is true (T) or false (F).

_____ **1.** Most of Spain's population lives in the rugged rural Meseta Central region.

_____ **2.** The Sami, or Lapps, were the original settlers of the countries of Northern Europe.

_____ **3.** The Protestant Reformation had a lasting impact on Northern Europe.

_____ **4.** The literacy rate is very high in Sweden, Denmark, and Norway.

_____ **5.** Taxes are relatively low in the countries of Northern Europe.

DIRECTIONS: Multiple Choice Indicate the answer choice that best answers the question.

_____ **6.** Which is a correct statement about the population of Northern and Southern Europe?

    A. The population is growing more quickly than in the past.

    B. The infant mortality rate is increasing.

    C. Birthrates have declined, and the population is aging.

    D. Most people live in rural areas.

_____ **7.** Which of the following statements about the languages of Northern Europe is accurate?

    A. Finnish is not related to the other languages of Northern Europe.

    B. People from one country can rarely understand those from another country.

    C. All of the languages came from different language bases.

    D. All of the languages came from a common French base.

_____ **8.** Which country in Southern Europe is known for using the guitar as a serious musical instrument?

    A. Greece   **C.** France

    B. Spain   **D.** Italy

_____ **9.** What is the main intent of welfare capitalism?

    A. to ensure that all people have jobs

    B. to ensure that all people have easy access to public buildings

    C. to ensure that all people graduate from college

    D. to ensure that all people have access to the essential aspects of life

_____ **10.** What is a cause of cultural conflict in Northern and Southern Europe?

    A. low levels of education in urban areas

    B. a widening gap between rich and poor

    C. immigration from non-European nations

    D. migration from urban to rural areas

Chapter Test, Form A

netw⊙rks

Northern and Southern Europe

DIRECTIONS: True/False Indicate whether the statement is true (T) or false (F). If the statement is false, rewrite it to make it true.

_____ **1.** The countries of Northern Europe are known as the Nordic countries.

_____

_____ **2.** The Adriatic Sea is the most important body of water in Southern Europe.

_____

_____ **3.** When they conquered the Byzantine Empire, the Ottoman Turks brought Islam with them.

_____

_____ **4.** After fighting a civil war in the 1930s, Italy did not fight in World War II.

_____

_____ **5.** Denmark is noted as the place where the LEGO, a children's toy, originated.

_____

DIRECTIONS: Matching Match each item with its description.

_____ **6.** opening to the Mediterranean that separates the southern tip of Spain from Africa

_____ **7.** birthplace of the Renaissance

_____ **8.** mountain range separating the Italian peninsula from the rest of Europe

_____ **9.** capital of the eastern Roman Empire

_____ **10.** powerful city-state in ancient Greece

A. Alps

B. Strait of Gibraltar

C. Sparta

D. Constantinople

E. Italy

DIRECTIONS: Multiple Choice Indicate the answer choice that best answers the question.

_____ **11.** Why is the climate in eastern Norway colder than the climate in the western part of the country?

    A. Eastern Norway has a higher elevation.

    B. Western Norway has more snow.

    C. Winds carry warmer air west.

    D. Mountains reduce the flow of warmer air from the Norwegian Current.

_____ **12.** What type of landmass is Iceland?

    A. peninsula   **C.** island

    B. continent   **D.** isthmus

_____ **13.** Which country in Northern Europe uses geothermal energy to heat its capital city?

    A. Denmark   **C.** Finland

    B. Iceland   **D.** Sweden

_____ **14.** Which of the following statements about the ancient Greek city-states is accurate?

    A. The eastern Roman Empire ruled them.

    B. Sparta was the most developed city-state.

    C. They had a common enemy, the Persians.

    D. They had one central government.

_____ **15.** How were Greek Christians treated under Ottoman rule?

    A. Greek Christians had limited rights but could practice their religion.

    B. Greek Christians had to practice their religion in secret.

    C. Greek Christians had to convert to Islam.

    D. Greek Christians had the same rights as Muslims.

> The populations of the Northern European countries are relatively homogeneous, or alike, although they have some ethnic diversity due to immigration from Asia and Africa. However, the population of Norway is more than 90 percent Norwegian, and the population of Finland is more than 90 percent Finnish. Denmark and Sweden are similar. The original settlers of these lands were the Sami people, or Lapps. Many of the Sami live by fishing and hunting, as they have for thousands of years. Most live in the northern parts of Sweden, Norway, and Finland. Iceland was first settled by Celts and later conquered by Norway. The bulk of the population in Iceland is a blend of the two ethnic groups.
>
> —*Discovering World Geography*

_____ **16.** Based on the excerpt, which of the following statements about the population of Norway is most accurate?

    A. The population is a blend of two ethnic groups.

    B. The population is very homogeneous.

    C. The population is descended from the Celts.

    D. The population has significant ethnic diversity.

_____ **17.** Based on the excerpt, which are the dominant ethnic groups in Iceland?

    A. Sami and Norwegian

    B. Asian and Celtic

    C. African and Norwegian

    D. Celtic and Norwegian

DIRECTIONS: Short Answer Answer each of the following questions.

18. Explain how a country could have an aging population even when its infant mortality rate decreases.

_____

_____

_____

_____

_____

19. Compare how the Protestant Reformation affected the Roman Catholic religion in Northern and Southern Europe.

_____

_____

_____

_____

_____

DIRECTIONS: Essay Answer the following question on a separate piece of paper.

20. Explain how the system of welfare capitalism works. What benefits has it provided for the people of Northern Europe?

Chapter Test, Form B

networks

Northern and Southern Europe

DIRECTIONS: True/False Indicate whether the statement is true (T) or false (F). If the statement is false, rewrite it to make it true.

_____ **1.** Iceland's terrain was formed by volcanic activity.

_____

_____ **2.** Sweden is Europe's biggest exporter of oil.

_____

_____ **3.** The Vikings had no seafaring experience.

_____

_____ **4.** During World War II, Italy sided with Nazi Germany.

_____

_____ **5.** There are more Protestants in Southern Europe than there are Roman Catholics.

_____

DIRECTIONS: Matching Match each item with its description.

_____ **6.** early commerce between Europe and the Americas

_____ **7.** landform made up of Norway and Sweden

_____ **8.** capital city of Finland

_____ **9.** plateau on which most of Spain lies

_____ **10.** first of a series of Roman emperors

A. Scandinavian Peninsula

B. Meseta Central

C. Augustus

D. Columbian Exchange

E. Helsinki

DIRECTIONS: Multiple Choice Indicate the answer choice that best answers the question.

_____ **11.** Which two countries form the Iberian Peninsula?

A. Spain and Italy   **C.** Norway and Sweden

B. Spain and Portugal   **D.** Denmark and Finland

_____ **12.** Why is the Baltic Sea more likely to freeze than other bodies of salt water?

A. It is isolated from other bodies of salt water.

B. It lies directly in the path of the Gulf Stream.

C. It is shallow and has a fairly low concentration of salt.

D. Mountains funnel cold winds across its waters.

Chapter Test, Form B *cont.*

netw✺rks

_____ **13.** Which of the following is one of the most important crops in Southern Europe?

    A. barley   **C.** rye

    B. bananas   **D.** olives

_____ **14.** Why did Emperor Constantine move the capital of the Roman Empire from Rome to Constantinople?

    A. He preferred Constantinople's climate and food.

    B. He wanted a site that would be less threatened by barbarian invaders than Rome.

    C. He wanted to live in the city bearing his name.

    D. He wanted a location on a sea route to China.

_____ **15.** Which country in Northern Europe had three of its biggest banks fail in the financial crisis that swept the world in 2008?

    A. Iceland   **C.** Sweden

    B. Denmark   **D.** Finland

The northern part of Norway is located as far north as Alaska, but it is not nearly as cold. The Norwegian Current, part of the Gulf Stream, flows past Norway carrying warm water from the tropics. As a result, western Norway has a marine climate, with mild winters and cool summers. The relatively mild climate does not extend far to the east. Mountains reduce the eastward flow of milder air. Eastern Norway thus has colder and snowier winters. Even so, the climate in eastern Norway and in Sweden is milder than in other parts of the world at the same latitude.

—Discovering World Geography

_____ **16.** Based on the excerpt, which of the following statements is true?

    A. Western Norway has colder and snowier winters than Eastern Norway.

    B. Eastern Norway has a more severe climate than other parts of the world at the same latitude.

    C. Eastern Norway has colder and snowier winters than Western Norway.

    D. Western Norway has very hot summers.

_____ **17.** Based on the excerpt, where do the warm waters of the Norwegian Current originate?

    A. in the warmer air above   **C.** in the English Channel

    B. in the North Sea   **D.** in the tropics

Discovering World Geography

Chapter Test, Form B *cont.*

Northern and Southern Europe

netw⊛rks

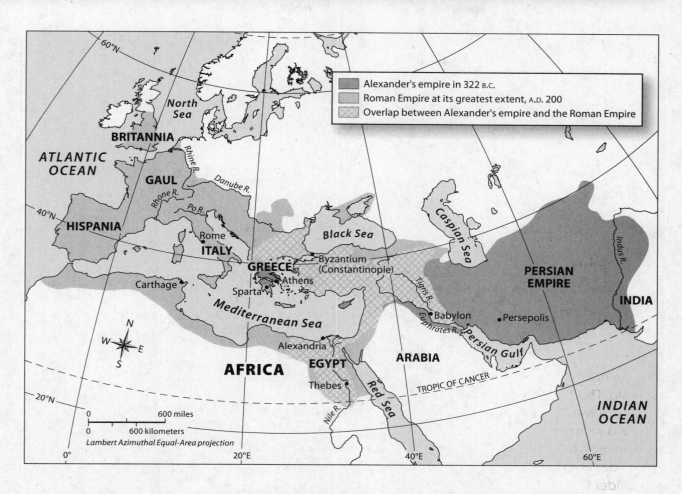

_____ **18.** Based on the map, which of the following is a true statement about Alexander's empire?

    A. It extended west as far as Hispania.

    B. It included the Persian Empire and part of India.

    C. It reached its greatest extent in A.D. 200.

    D. It extended north as far as Britannia.

_____ **19.** Based on the map, which two cities are within the boundaries of both Alexander's empire and the Roman Empire at its greatest extent?

    A. Babylon and Thebes   **C.** Sparta and Persepolis

    B. Byzantium and Rome   **D.** Carthage and Persepolis

DIRECTIONS: Essay Answer the following question on a separate piece of paper.

20. Explain how the system of welfare capitalism works. What benefits has it provided for the people of Northern Europe?

Discovering World Geography

Lesson Quiz 1

networks

Eastern Europe and Western Russia

DIRECTIONS: True/False Indicate whether the statement is true (T) or false (F).

_____ **1.** Western Russia is the portion of Russia that lies within Europe.

_____ **2.** The Northern European Plain is confined entirely to Eastern Europe.

_____ **3.** A humid continental climate is found in much of Eastern Europe and Western Russia.

_____ **4.** More than one-half of the world's forests are in Russia.

_____ **5.** Fishing plays only a minor role in Russia's economy.

DIRECTIONS: Multiple Choice Indicate the answer choice that best answers the question.

_____ **6.** Which of the following lie north of Eastern Europe and Western Russia?

    A. the Caucasus Mountains   **C.** the Baltic and Barents seas

    B. the Adriatic and Black seas   **D.** the Ural Mountains

_____ **7.** Which statement best describes the physical geography of Eastern Europe and Western Russia?

    A. The area consists mostly of vast plains.

    B. The region is covered almost entirely by glaciers.

    C. Most of the region is rugged and mountainous.

    D. The area is dominated by flat, arid deserts.

_____ **8.** What is one way the Carpathian Mountains differ from the Ural Mountains?

    A. The Carpathian Mountains form a boundary between Europe and Asia.

    B. Unlike the Urals, the Carpathian Mountains are situated entirely within Russia.

    C. The Carpathian Mountains are covered in glaciers, while the Urals are not.

    D. The Carpathian Mountains are much younger than the Ural Mountains.

_____ **9.** The Baltic Sea consists of seawater mixed with river water. Which of the following statements is a reasonable conclusion from this fact?

    A. The Baltic Sea is not used for transportation.

    B. The Baltic Sea is somewhat salty.

    C. The Baltic Sea cannot support aquatic life.

    D. The Baltic Sea is heavily polluted.

_____ **10.** Poland is one of the world's richest sources of which mineral?

    A. tin   **C.** silver

    B. sulfur   **D.** bauxite

Lesson Quiz 2

networks

Eastern Europe and Western Russia

DIRECTIONS: True/False Indicate whether the statement is true (T) or false (F).

_____ **1.** World War I was triggered by the assassination of the heir to Austria-Hungary's throne.

_____ **2.** Beginning in the 1600s, the Romanov family ruled Russia for 300 years.

_____ **3.** Joseph Stalin was known for bringing democratic reforms to the Soviet Union once he took power in 1924.

_____ **4.** After the end of World War II, the Soviet Union installed communist governments in most Eastern European countries.

_____ **5.** Solidarity was an organization that emerged in Czechoslovakia in the late 1960s to reform the communist government there.

DIRECTIONS: Multiple Choice Indicate the answer choice that best answers the question.

_____ **6.** Which group has dominated Russia's politics and culture throughout most of its history?

    A. Slavs   **C.** Ukrainians

    B. Magyars   **D.** Mongols

_____ **7.** What was the name for farm laborers who could be bought and sold with the land in czarist Russia?

    A. communists   **C.** serfs

    B. Slavs   **D.** collectivists

_____ **8.** Which of the following best summarizes the impact of World War I on Russia?

    A. Russia's victory reinforced the Romanovs' control over the country.

    B. The war weakened Russia, setting the stage for the rise of communism.

    C. The war led to increased economic ties between Russia and its western allies.

    D. Russia was defeated by the Allies and lost half of its empire as a result.

_____ **9.** What organization did the USSR create in 1955?

    A. NATO   **C.** *Glasnost*

    B. Warsaw Pact   **D.** Solidarity

_____ **10.** Why did some Soviet leaders stage a coup against Mikhail Gorbachev?

    A. They claimed he wanted to limit industrialization.

    B. They objected to policies that undermined private property rights.

    C. They feared he would brutally crack down on dissent.

    D. They thought his lenient policies threatened the existence of the Soviet Union.

Lesson Quiz 3

netw⚙️rks

Eastern Europe and Western Russia

DIRECTIONS: True/False Indicate whether the statement is true (T) or false (F).

_____ **1.** After the end of the Soviet Union, inflation was a problem in Russia.

_____ **2.** President Vladimir Putin tried but failed to stabilize the Russian economy.

_____ **3.** East Slavs live mainly in Poland and the Czech Republic.

_____ **4.** Pop music from the United States has many fans in Russia and Eastern Europe.

_____ **5.** A majority of people in Russia and Eastern Europe work in factories.

DIRECTIONS: Multiple Choice Indicate the answer choice that best answers the question.

_____ **6.** In the Soviet Union, most industry centered on what products?

    A. wines and spirits

    B. consumer goods

    C. automobiles for export

    D. military hardware and industrial machinery

_____ **7.** Which of the following statements about population distribution in Eastern Europe is most accurate?

    A. Virtually all residents of Eastern Europe are urban dwellers.

    B. The urban population is larger in Eastern Europe than in Western Europe.

    C. The biggest population centers in Eastern Europe are the capital cities.

    D. Most of the people in Eastern Europe live on farms.

_____ **8.** In the past century, why have many emigrants from Eastern Europe come to the United States?

    A. to seek political freedom and economic opportunity

    B. to be reunited with their American friends and families

    C. to settle in a country with a climate better suited to agriculture

    D. to spread European values and culture to America

_____ **9.** In which country are Muslims a majority?

    A. Albania   **C.** Croatia

    B. Serbia   **D.** Poland

_____ **10.** Of what commodity is Russia one of the world's leading suppliers?

    A. citrus fruit   **C.** peanut oil

    B. natural gas   **D.** coffee

networks

PARTS AND THE WEST — RUSSIA

DIRECTIONS: True/False Indicate whether the sentence is true (T) or false (F)

_____ 1. Leader Lenin of the Soviet Union, Ihor Livation was a moderate in Russia.

_____ 2. President Vladimir Putin tried but failed to stabilize the Russian economy.

_____ 3. Slavs live mainly in Poland and the Czech Republic.

_____ 4. Pop music from the United States has many fans in Russia and Eastern Europe.

_____ 5. A majority of people in Russia and Eastern Europe work in factories.

DIRECTIONS: Multiple Choice Indicate the answer choice that best answers the question.

_____ 6. In the Soviet Union, most industry centered on which products?
   A. cars, vans, and ships
   B. consumer goods
   C. appliances for fashion
   D. military hardware and industrial machinery

_____ 7. Which of the following statements about population distribution in Eastern Europe is most accurate?
   A. Virtually all residents of Eastern Europe are urban dwellers.
   B. The urban proportion is larger in Eastern Europe than in Western Europe.
   C. The biggest population centers in Eastern Europe are the capital cities.
   D. Most of the people in Eastern Europe live on farms.

_____ 8. In the past century, why have many emigrants from Eastern Europe come to the United States?
   A. to seek political freedom and economic opportunity
   B. to be reunited with their American friends and families
   C. to never return anywhere with areas that are better suited to agriculture
   D. to spread European values and culture to America

_____ 9. In which country are Muslims a majority?
   A. Albania   C. Croatia
   B. Serbia   D. Poland

_____ 10. What commodity is Russia one of the world's leading suppliers?
   A. citrus fruit   C. peanut oil
   B. natural gas   D. coffee

Networks Reproducible

Chapter Test, Form A

networks

Eastern Europe and Western Russia

DIRECTIONS: True/False Indicate whether the statement is true (T) or false (F). If the statement is false, rewrite it to make it true.

_____ **1.** The northern Ural Mountains are covered with grassy plains.

_____

_____ **2.** Early Slavs migrated from Southern Europe and settled in the area that now includes Ukraine and Poland.

_____

_____ **3.** The transfer of industry to private ownership in Russia did not improve the living conditions for most Russians.

_____

_____ **4.** The dominant religion in Russia and most Eastern European countries is the Roman Catholic Church.

_____

_____ **5.** Russia still has boundary disputes with former Soviet republics like Estonia and Ukraine.

_____

DIRECTIONS: Matching Match each item with its description.

_____ **6.** vast, level area of grassy land

_____ **7.** Russian farm laborer who could be bought and sold in czarist times

_____ **8.** area of land that slopes gently downward from the surrounding land

_____ **9.** ruler of Russia before 1917

_____ **10.** area of high elevation

A. upland

B. steppe

C. basin

D. serf

E. czar

DIRECTIONS: Multiple Choice Indicate the answer choice that best answers the question.

_____ **11.** What is the longest river in Europe and Russia's most important waterway?

    A. Dnieper

    B. Danube

    C. Volga

    D. Dniester

_____ **12.** What part of Russia is covered with ice year-round?

    A. west Siberian plain   **C.** Russian plain

    B. Black Sea coast   **D.** Novaya Zemlya

_____ **13.** Which of the following statements accurately summarizes the effects of the fall of communism on Yugoslavia?

    A. The country disintegrated into several smaller countries based on ethnic groups.

    B. Yugoslavia was invaded by Serbia and ceased to exist as an independent country.

    C. Of all Soviet satellites, Yugoslavia faced the fewest challenges.

    D. The country became a major power in Eastern Europe due to its many resources.

> The most powerful of these princes [of Muscovy], Ivan IV, defeated the Mongols and declared himself the czar of Russia. *Czar* is Russian for Caesar, or powerful ruler. The Russian nobility, dissatisfied with the czars who ruled after Ivan, looked for a young noble to lead the country. In 1613 they elected 16-year-old Michael Romanov as czar. The Romanovs ruled for the next 300 years.
>
> Later, a czar now known as Peter the Great attempted to turn Russia into a major power. After Peter's death in 1725, Russia endured a string of weak czars. During the late 1700s, Empress Catherine the Great came to power. Catherine encouraged the development of Russian education, journalism, architecture, and theater. During her reign, Russia expanded its empire and took possession of the entire northern coast of the Black Sea.
>
> —*Discovering World Geography*

_____ **14.** Based on the excerpt, which Russian czar drove the Mongols out of Russia?

    A. Michael Romanov   **C.** Peter the Great

    B. Catherine the Great   **D.** Ivan IV

_____ **15.** Based on the excerpt, which of the following statements is the most accurate?

    A. Catherine the Great was not concerned with the education of the Russian people.

    B. Russian nobility had a significant influence on the leadership of Russia.

    C. The Romanovs marked the end of the Russian czars.

    D. Peter the Great was not a strong leader.

_____ **16.** Which of the following statements about Albanians is accurate?

    A. Albanians are descended from the West Slavs.

    B. Albanians speak a dialect of the Greek language.

    C. Albanians speak a non-Slavic language.

    D. Most Albanians practice the Eastern Orthodox religion.

_____ **17.** Which of the following is a direct effect of the collapse of communism in Eastern Europe and Russia?

    A. The region has stepped up its production of military hardware.

    B. National traditions and identity have grown stronger in the region.

    C. The practice of religion has gone into decline in the region.

    D. The region has been cut off from international popular culture.

DIRECTIONS: Short Answer Answer each of the following questions.

18. How has the physical geography of the Balkan Peninsula affected migration and population patterns in the region?

_____

_____

_____

_____

_____

19. Briefly explain how most Eastern European countries became satellites of the Soviet Union after the end of World War II.

_____

_____

_____

_____

_____

DIRECTIONS: Essay Answer the following question on a separate piece of paper.

20. What conclusions can you draw about the relation between the physical location of Russia and the impact of European and Asian ideas on Russian culture?

Chapter Test, Form B

net**w**o**rks**

Eastern Europe and Western Russia

DIRECTIONS: True/False Indicate whether the statement is true (T) or false (F). If the statement is false, rewrite it to make it true.

_____ **1.** The Russian Plain stretches east from Belarus and Ukraine.

_____

_____ **2.** The southern coast of Ukraine is bordered by the Caspian Sea.

_____

_____ **3.** The Danube River has long been a major trade route.

_____

_____ **4.** Most of Russia's vast coal, oil, and natural gas reserves are in Chechnya.

_____

_____ **5.** The rivalry and conflict between the USSR and the United States following World War II was called the Cold War.

_____

DIRECTIONS: Matching Match each item with its description.

_____ **6.** political capital of Russia

_____ **7.** Soviet leader who allowed more social and political freedoms

_____ **8.** conflict among ethnic groups within a state, country, or region

_____ **9.** Soviet premier during the Cuban Missile Crisis

_____ **10.** one of a small group of people who control the government

A. Mikhail Gorbachev

B. oligarch

C. Nikita Khrushchev

D. balkanization

E. Moscow

DIRECTIONS: Multiple Choice Indicate the answer choice that best answers the question.

_____ **11.** What are summers like in Albania and Macedonia?

    A. short and cool   **C.** mild and rainy

    B. hot and dry   **D.** hot and humid

_____ **12.** What empire formed in the A.D. 800s covered much of central Europe?

    A. Ottoman Empire   **C.** Great Moravia

    B. Kievan Rus   **D.** Austro-Hungarian Empire

_____ **13.** Which of the following statements about Russia's forestry industry is accurate?

    A. Deforestation has caused the industry to become almost nonexistent.

    B. Environmental groups have succeeded in largely shutting down the industry.

    C. Russia's forests are so vast that there is no danger of the industry ever dying out.

    D. The industry is challenged by the slow rates of forest growth.

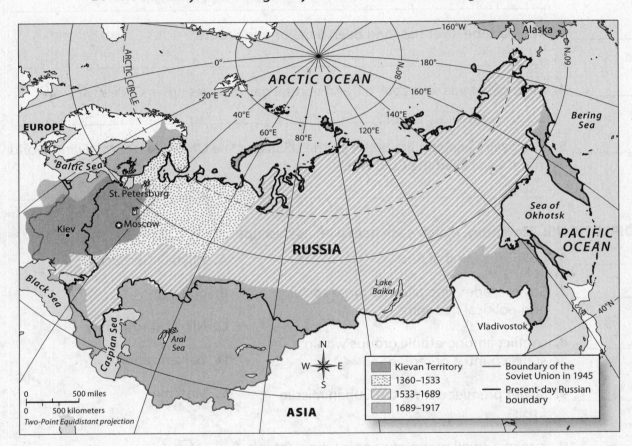

_____ **14.** Based on the map, which city is located outside the boundary of present-day Russia?

    A. Kiev   **C.** Moscow

    B. St. Petersburg   **D.** Vladivostok

_____ **15.** Based on the map, which statement about the present-day Russian boundary is most accurate?

    A. The boundary includes all of the Kievan Territory.

    B. The boundary is larger than the boundary of the Soviet Union in 1945.

    C. The boundary is smaller than the boundary of the Soviet Union in 1945.

    D. The boundary does not include any of the Kievan Territory.

Discovering World Geography

_____ **16.** Which of the following statements about current daily life in Russia is the most accurate?

    A. The generation gap is narrowing between those who grew up under communism and the post-Soviet generation.

    B. Young Russians are having the same cultural experiences as young Americans.

    C. There is a growing loss of national traditions and identity.

    D. Western culture has had little impact on the arts.

_____ **17.** Why were some Russians unhappy with President Vladimir Putin?

    A. He was unwilling to modernize the Russian economy.

    B. He was unable to put down the Chechen rebellion.

    C. He discouraged the practice of Russian folk and religious traditions.

    D. He limited freedoms of speech and the press in Russia.

When the Soviet Union existed, the central government kept tight control over its many ethnic groups. Some groups wanted to form their own countries. Among them are the Chechens, who live in Chechnya near the Caspian Sea and Caucasus Mountains in southern Russia. The region has many oil reserves, and its many oil pipelines transport fuel to major Russian cities. Russian troops fought Chechen rebels to keep Chechnya a part of Russia. When Russia finally pulled out in 1996, the Chechen rebellion was still not over. President Boris Yeltsin was widely blamed for being unable to solve these problems.

—Discovering World Geography

_____ **18.** Based on the excerpt, who was president of Russia during the Chechen rebellion?

    A. Joseph Stalin   **C.** Mikhail Gorbachev

    B. Boris Yeltsin   **D.** Dimitry Medvedev

_____ **19.** Based on the passage, which of the following is a reasonable conclusion?

    A. Russia wanted to hold Chechnya because of its oil wealth.

    B. Yeltsin was unpopular with Russians because he sympathized with the Chechens.

    C. One day Chechnya will become an independent nation.

    D. The region surrounding the Caucasus Mountains contains few natural resources.

DIRECTIONS: Essay Answer the following question on a separate piece of paper.

 20. What conclusions can you draw about the relation between the physical location of Russia and the impact of European and Asian ideas on Russian culture?

Unit Test

networks

Asia

DIRECTIONS: True/False Indicate whether the statement is true (T) or false (F).

_____ **1.** East Asia contains some of the most densely populated places on Earth.

_____ **2.** Some of the world's busiest shipping lanes pass through Southeast Asia's seas and their waterways.

_____ **3.** More and more Indians are moving from crowded cities to rural areas.

_____ **4.** Virtually no oil or gas reserves are found in Central Asia.

_____ **5.** The dominant climate in Southwest Asia is a Mediterranean climate.

DIRECTIONS: Matching Match each item with its description.

_____ **6.** occurs when a country imports more than it exports

_____ **7.** geographically or politically unique part of a larger continent

_____ **8.** large farm on which a single crop is grown for export

_____ **9.** to supply water to land or crops

_____ **10.** area in a desert where underground water permits plant life

A. plantation

B. oasis

C. irrigate

D. subcontinent

E. trade deficit

DIRECTIONS: Multiple Choice Indicate the answer choice that best answers the question.

_____ **11.** Which of the following forms the eastern boundary of East Asia?

   A. the Atlantic Ocean
   B. the Pacific Ocean
   C. Siberia
   D. the Himalaya

_____ **12.** Which of the following countries is located on a peninsula?

   A. North Korea
   B. Japan
   C. Taiwan
   D. Mongolia

_____ **13.** Which country comprises the northernmost islands in the Malay Archipelago?

   A. Indonesia
   B. the Philippines
   C. Malaysia
   D. East Timor

_____ **14.** What do the Javanese and the Tagalog have in common?

    A. These ethnic groups dominate the Southeast Asian mainland.

    B. These ethnic groups both speak the same language.

    C. These ethnic groups live predominately on Southeast Asia's islands.

    D. These ethnic groups have largely been driven out of Southeast Asia.

_____ **15.** Which of the following lists the castes of ancient South Asia in the correct order, from top class to bottom class?

    A. warriors, Brahmans, laborers, merchants

    B. Brahmans, merchants, warriors, laborers

    C. merchants, Brahmans, laborers, warriors

    D. Brahmans, warriors, merchants, laborers

_____ **16.** Which of the following religions has no founder, no holy book, and no central core of beliefs?

    A. Hinduism   **C.** Jainism

    B. Buddhism   **D.** Islam

_____ **17.** The mountain areas of Central Asia have which type of climate?

    A. arctic   **C.** humid subtropical

    B. humid continental   **D.** semiarid

_____ **18.** How have events in Tajikistan and Georgia been similar since the end of Soviet rule?

    A. Both countries have endured civil war and government corruption.

    B. Islam has become the majority religion in both countries.

    C. Both countries have fought brief but bloody wars with Russia.

    D. Ethnic Russians have migrated to both countries in large numbers.

_____ **19.** What is one way Turkey and Iran differ?

    A. Turkey does not border the Persian Gulf, but Iran does.

    B. Turkey does not contain significant deposits of coal, but Iran does.

    C. Turkey consists largely of desert, while Iran has no desert areas.

    D. Turkey is a mountainous country, while Iran sits mostly below sea level.

_____ **20.** Which country has a majority Jewish population?

    A. Jordan   **C.** Turkey

    B. Saudi Arabia   **D.** Israel

Lesson Quiz 1

networks

East Asia

DIRECTIONS: True/False Indicate whether the statement is true (T) or false (F).

_____ 1. China is the largest country in the region of East Asia.

_____ 2. The Kunlun Shan range is higher than the Himalaya.

_____ 3. The North China Plain is an important farming area.

_____ 4. Japan's climate is very dry and hot compared to areas in mainland China at the same latitude.

_____ 5. Japan and Taiwan are among the world's leading industrial nations.

DIRECTIONS: Multiple Choice Indicate the answer choice that best answers the question.

_____ 6. What is the subregion of mainland East Asia that is often called "the roof of the world"?

    A. Mount Fuji   **C.** Himalaya range

    B. Mount Everest   **D.** Plateau of Tibet

_____ 7. Which of the following statements about Japan is accurate?

    A. Japan lacks forest resources.

    B. Japan has hundreds of small earthquakes each year.

    C. Glaciation formed the islands of Japan.

    D. Japan has extensive plains on all its main islands.

_____ 8. Which river flows through Seoul, the capital of South Korea?

    A. Huang He (Yellow River)   **C.** Han River

    B. Yalu River   **D.** Chang Jiang (Yangtze River)

_____ 9. Which of the following statements about the natural resources in East Asia is accurate?

    A. The resources are not evenly distributed.

    B. China has fewer resources than any other country in East Asia.

    C. Japan and Taiwan have an abundant supply of minerals.

    D. China relies entirely on its own resources to meet its energy needs.

_____ 10. What is the chief reason that forestland has declined in eastern China?

    A. Large numbers of trees died as the result of a fungus.

    B. People cut down the trees for heating and building and to create farmland.

    C. Most of eastern China's timber has been exported to other countries.

    D. Climate change made the area too dry for trees to survive.

Lesson Quiz 2

networks

East Asia

DIRECTIONS: Matching Match each item with its description.

_____ 1. 4,000-mile-long caravan trade route

_____ 2. landowning warriors in early Japan

_____ 3. line of rulers from a single family

_____ 4. area of country where a single foreign power has exclusive trading rights

_____ 5. military leader in early Japan

A. dynasty

B. shogun

C. samurai

D. Silk Road

E. sphere of influence

DIRECTIONS: Multiple Choice Indicate the answer choice that best answers the question.

_____ 6. What kept most foreign invaders from China's lands?

    A. fearsome samurai

    B. natural barriers such as seas, mountains, and deserts

    C. soldiers placed along the Silk Road

    D. Mongol warriors hired by China's emperors

_____ 7. Which Chinese thinker based his teachings on the idea that people should live in harmony with nature?

    A. Confucius   **C.** Chiang Kai-shek

    B. Zheng He   **D.** Laozi

_____ 8. What was the main reason the rulers of Japan decided to isolate their country from all foreigners in the 1600s?

    A. They wanted to weed out rebels from foreign countries.

    B. They thought the Europeans sided with China.

    C. They feared that European powers planned a military conquest of Japan.

    D. They did not want to share any profits from trade with foreigners.

_____ 9. What was the main purpose of Mao Zedong's Great Leap Forward?

    A. to increase industrial output

    B. to create state-owned farms

    C. to increase the number of teachers

    D. to slow the growth of China's population

_____ 10. Which East Asian nation became a global economic power by the 1990s?

    A. North Korea   **C.** Mongolia

    B. South Korea   **D.** Japan

Lesson Quiz 3

networks

East Asia

DIRECTIONS: True/False Indicate whether the statement is true (T) or false (F).

_____ 1. China's population underwent a sharp decline in the mid-1900s.

_____ 2. Japan has a higher level of urbanization than China.

_____ 3. Ceramics and pottery have long been an important part of East Asian art.

_____ 4. The United States and Europe import many manufactured goods from East Asia.

_____ 5. To meet a worker shortage, China encourages families to have three or more children.

DIRECTIONS: Multiple Choice Indicate the answer choice that best answers the question.

_____ 6. Why is Hong Kong called "one of the most vertical places on earth"?

    A. It is perched on the side of a mountain.

    B. Its limited territory is dominated by tall buildings.

    C. It sprawls across a broad, level plain.

    D. Its economy has experienced sudden ups and downs.

_____ 7. Which statement about ethnic groups in East Asian countries is accurate?

    A. Most people in East Asia are of mixed ethnic background.

    B. All East Asian ethnic groups speak Mandarin Chinese.

    C. People within each country tend to be ethnically similar.

    D. All East Asians are either ethnic Chinese or ethnic Japanese.

_____ 8. What is calligraphy?

    A. written words turned into expressive images

    B. hand-painted decorations on vases

    C. baskets woven from multicolored strands

    D. a traditional form of Japanese verse

_____ 9. What is the main reason that the percentage of elderly people has increased in China and Japan's populations?

    A. Fewer children are born as resources are used up.

    B. More children are born as living standards decline.

    C. More children are born as resources are used up.

    D. Fewer children are born as living standards rise.

_____ 10. Which country in East Asia has a dispute with Russia over the Kuril Islands?

    A. North Korea   **C.** Japan

    B. South Korea   **D.** China

DIRECTIONS: True/False Indicate whether the statement is true (T) or false (F).

_____ 1. China's population under Mao Zedong grew to fifty million people.

_____ 2. Japan has a higher level of urbanization than China.

_____ 3. Factories and pollution have long been an important part of East Asian life.

_____ 4. The United States and European countries manufacture most goods from East Asia.

_____ 5. Farmer's worker shortages have encouraged families to have more children.

DIRECTIONS: Multiple Choice Indicate the answer choice that best completes the statement or answers the question.

_____ 6. Why is Hong Kong's population so high? Circle the letter of each correct answer on each line.
        A. It is perched on the side of a mountain.
        B. It is limited in area; is dominated by tall buildings.
        C. It sprawls across a broad, level plain.
        D. Its economy has experienced sudden ups and downs.

_____ 7. Which statement about ethnic groups in East Asia or language is accurate?
        A. Most people in East Asia are of mixed ethnic background.
        B. All East Asian ethnic groups speak Mandarin Chinese.
        C. People within each country tend to be ethnically similar.
        D. All East Asians are either ethnic Chinese or ethnic Japanese.

_____ 8. What is calligraphy?
        A. written words turned into expressive images
        B. hand-painted designs on glass vases
        C. baskets woven from multicolored strands
        D. a traditional form of Japanese verse

_____ 9. What is the main reason that the percentage of elderly people has increased in China and Japan's population?
        A. Fewer children are born; healthcare is used up.
        B. More children are born as immigrants are deported.
        C. More children are born as foreigners are used up.
        D. Fewer children are born; healthcare was used up.

_____ 10. Which country in East Asia has a dispute with Russia over the Kuril Islands?
        A. North Korea   C. Japan
        B. South Korea   D. China

Chapter Test, Form A

networks

East Asia

DIRECTIONS: True/False Indicate whether the statement is true (T) or false (F). If the statement is false, rewrite it to make it true.

_____ **1.** The country of Taiwan is not legally recognized as a separate country.

_____

_____ **2.** The climates in the countries of East Asia are very similar.

_____

_____ **3.** The Chinese built the Great Wall of China to prevent lowland flooding.

_____

_____ **4.** Confucius was an important Chinese thinker.

_____

_____ **5.** Air pollution in Japan has produced acid rain and other problems.

_____

DIRECTIONS: Matching Match each item with its description.

_____ **6.** belief system founded by the great thinker Laozi

_____ **7.** world's tallest mountain range

_____ **8.** what occurs when a country exports more than it imports

_____ **9.** program to rid China of anticommunism among intellectuals

_____ **10.** huge ocean wave triggered by an earthquake

A. Himalaya

B. tsunami

C. Daoism

D. Cultural Revolution

E. trade surplus

DIRECTIONS: Multiple Choice Indicate the answer choice that best answers the question.

_____ **11.** Which river is the longest in China and the third longest in the world?

A. Chang Jiang (Yangtze River)

B. Han River

C. Huang He (Yellow River)

D. Shinano River

_____ **12.** How did the Huang He (Yellow River) get its name?

    A. The river is heavily polluted with industrial chemicals.

    B. The river originates far to the west in a mountain range rich in copper.

    C. Large amounts of silt give the river a yellow-brown hue.

    D. The river flows through a region called the Yellow Plain.

U.S. Trade Deficit with China, 2001-2011

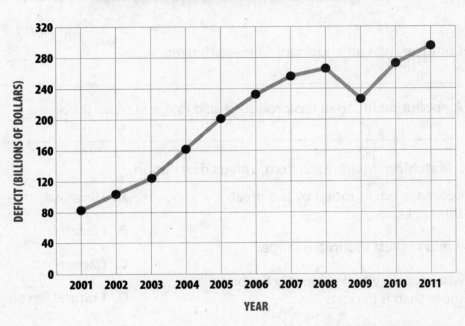

Source: U.S. Department of Commerce; U.S. International Trade Commission (ITC)

_____ **13.** Based on the graph above, what can be said in general about the U.S. trade deficit with China?

    A. The trade deficit rose steadily from 2001 through 2011.

    B. The trade deficit rose steadily each year, except in 2009.

    C. The trade deficit was $120 billion in 2004.

    D. The trade deficit has decreased since 2009.

_____ **14.** Based on the graph above, during which of the following periods did the trade deficit decrease?

    A. 2001–2002   **C.** 2006–2007

    B. 2003–2004   **D.** 2008–2009

Discovering World Geography

_____ **15.** What is the main reason that Japan limits logging in some areas of the country?

    A. The trees are too young to harvest.

    B. There is less demand for wood products in those areas.

    C. The trees are too diseased to harvest.

    D. The people think many forest areas are sacred.

_____ **16.** From which country was Buddhism introduced into China?

    A. Mongolia   **C.** Japan

    B. India   **D.** Taiwan

_____ **17.** In which system does the government control all economic goods and services?

    A. socialism   **C.** capitalism

    B. anarchism   **D.** communism

DIRECTIONS: Short Answer Answer each of the following questions.

18. Explain why East Asia has a great range of climates. What factors affect the region's climates?

_____

_____

_____

_____

_____

19. What is woodblock printing, and what was its impact on Chinese culture?

_____

_____

_____

_____

_____

DIRECTIONS: Essay Answer the following question on a separate piece of paper.

20. Explain how rapid economic growth can lead to problems for a country's environment. Use China and Japan as examples in your answer.

Chapter Test, Form B

networks

East Asia

DIRECTIONS: True/False Indicate whether the statement is true (T) or false (F). If the statement is false, rewrite it to make it true.

_____ **1.** Russia lies to the south of East Asia.

_____

_____ **2.** Mount Everest is the highest mountain in the world.

_____

_____ **3.** The samurai were great warriors as well as landowners.

_____

_____ **4.** Japan has a higher gross national product than China.

_____

_____ **5.** East Asian cultures place a high value on education.

_____

DIRECTIONS: Matching Match each item with its description.

_____ **6.** Greater Tokyo, for example

_____ **7.** a leader of the People's Republic of China

_____ **8.** group or chain of islands

_____ **9.** a popular type of music in East Asia

_____ **10.** de facto country in East Asia

A. Taiwan

B. archipelago

C. Mao Zedong

D. megalopolis

E. "K-pop"

DIRECTIONS: Multiple Choice Indicate the answer choice that best answers the question.

_____ **11.** Which East Asian country has the largest deposits of fossil fuels?

    A. Mongolia

    B. China

    C. Japan

    D. North Korea

_____ **12.** Why do trees not grow in western and northwestern China?

    A. Those areas are frozen tundra.

    B. Trees in those areas died as a result of a fungus.

    C. Those areas are too dry.

    D. The soil in those areas is too poor.

_____ **13.** Which of the following was the last dynasty in China?

    A. Qing   **C.** Shang

    B. Zhou   **D.** Han

_____ **14.** In the early 1900s, how did many Chinese respond to the growth of Western influence in their country?

    A. They welcomed Westerners and their technology.

    B. They adopted many Western manners.

    C. They allowed Western control of the government.

    D. They were angry, and that anger fueled a revolution.

_____ **15.** Which of the following statements about Japan's population policy is accurate?

    A. Japan has adopted a hands-off policy toward population growth.

    B. Japan provides programs such as child care to encourage more births.

    C. Japan has a "one-child" policy to slow uncontrolled population growth.

    D. Japan welcomes foreign immigrants to help build up the population.

> Southeastern China stays hot and rainy through much of the year. Vegetation is lush, and conditions are ideal for growing grain, especially rice. Farther north in eastern China, more seasonal variation occurs. Summers are hot and rainy, but winters are cold and fairly dry. China's capital, Beijing, lies in this part of the country. In the summer, temperatures in Beijing often soar above 90°F (32°C). In the winter, icy winds from the northwest whip through the city, and temperatures can drop below 0°F (−18°C).
>
>   —*Discovering World Geography*

_____ **16.** Based on the excerpt, what is an important crop in southeastern China?

    A. wheat   **C.** rice

    B. rye   **D.** corn

_____ **17.** Based on the excerpt, which of the following describes the climate in China's capital, Beijing?

    A. hot summers and cold winters

    B. mild summers and cold winters

    C. hot summers and mild winters

    D. mild summers and mild winters

Discovering World Geography

> Japan was ruled by emperors, but over time, they began to lose power, and
> eventually landowning families set up a feudal system. Under the system, high
> nobles gave land to lesser nobles in return for their loyalty and military service. At
> the bottom of the social ladder, peasants farmed nobles' estates in exchange for
> protection. By the 1100s, armies of local nobles had begun fighting for control of
> Japan. Minamoto Yoritomo (mee·nah·moh·toh yho·ree·toh·moh) became Japan's
> first shogun, or military leader. Landowning warriors called samurai (SA·muh·RY)
> supported the shogun. Although the emperor kept his title, the shoguns held the
> real power.
>
> —*Discovering World Geography*

_____ **18.** Based on the excerpt, what person had the most power in feudal Japan?

    A. samurai

    B. emperor

    C. noble

    D. shogun

_____ **19.** Based on the excerpt, who created Japan's feudal system?

    A. emperors

    B. landowning families

    C. shoguns

    D. peasants

DIRECTIONS: Essay Answer the following question on a separate piece of paper.

20. Explain how rapid economic growth can lead to problems for a country's environment. Use China and Japan as examples in your answer.

Lesson Quiz 1

networks

Southeast Asia

DIRECTIONS: True/False Indicate whether the statement is true (T) or false (F).

_____ **1.** The Malay Archipelago is larger in area than any other island group.

_____ **2.** Earthquakes and volcanic eruptions are very rare in Southeast Asia.

_____ **3.** The region's largest seas are the South China and Andaman Seas.

_____ **4.** Climates in Southeast Asia are generally hot and humid.

_____ **5.** Many of Southeast Asia's animal species are found nowhere else in the world.

DIRECTIONS: Multiple Choice Indicate the answer choice that best answers the question.

_____ **6.** What is one way the physical geography of the Philippines differs from that of Cambodia?

    A. The Philippines occupies islands, while Cambodia lies on the mainland.

    B. The Philippines is part of Indochina, while Cambodia is not.

    C. Cambodia is part of the Malay Archipelago, while the Philippines is not.

    D. Cambodia has no mountains, while the Philippines is mountainous.

_____ **7.** What is Krakatoa?

    A. a mountain range that stretches through Laos and Vietnam

    B. a small island country just off the southern tip of the Malay Peninsula

    C. an Indonesian volcano that erupted in 1883 and caused great loss of life

    D. the largest island in the Malay Archipelago

_____ **8.** In what way are the natural resources of Indonesia and Malaysia similar?

    A. Both countries have large reserves of oil and natural gas.

    B. Both countries are the top producers of granite and limestone.

    C. The countries are the two top coal producers in the world.

    D. Both countries are leading exporters of iron ore.

_____ **9.** The Mekong River is most important to which of the following countries?

    A. Indonesia   **C.** Brunei

    B. the Philippines   **D.** Vietnam

_____ **10.** Which part of Southeast Asia has a tropical rain forest climate?

    A. inland areas north of Thailand

    B. the southern Malay Peninsula and parts of the Philippines and Indonesia

    C. the coastal mainland along the South China Sea

    D. the northern Indochinese peninsula

Lesson Quiz 2

networks

Southeast Asia

DIRECTIONS: True/False Indicate whether the statement is true (T) or false (F).

_____ **1.** The ancient Dong Son metalworking culture was located in northern Vietnam.

_____ **2.** By the 1600s, Buddhism was the chief religion in the Malay Archipelago.

_____ **3.** Burma and Malaysia had become British colonies by the early 1900s.

_____ **4.** The first Southeast Asian colony to gain independence from Europe was East Timor.

_____ **5.** Some Southeast Asian countries have had communist governments.

DIRECTIONS: Multiple Choice Indicate the answer choice that best answers the question.

_____ **6.** How was the physical geography of Southeast Asia different 40,000 years ago as compared to today?

    A. Myanmar was separated from the mainland by water.

    B. There were more islands.

    C. The mainland was connected to Sumatra, Java, and Borneo.

    D. All of the Sunda Shelf lay below water.

_____ **7.** Which two cultures have had the greatest impact on Southeast Asia?

    A. India and Japan   **C.** Japan and China

    B. China and India   **D.** China and Tibet

_____ **8.** How was the kingdom of Srivijaya able to dominate Southeast Asia for hundreds of years?

    A. Its vast reserves of gold made it the wealthiest empire in Southeast Asia.

    B. Its capital city became an important center of Buddhism.

    C. The warriors of Srivijaya were well trained and widely feared.

    D. Its location on the Strait of Malacca allowed it to control trade through the region.

_____ **9.** What product first attracted European traders to the region of Southeast Asia?

    A. spices   **C.** exotic hardwoods

    B. gold   **D.** oil

_____ **10.** Which Southeast Asian country is a constitutional monarchy?

    A. Malaysia   **C.** Thailand

    B. Indonesia   **D.** Myanmar

Discovering World Geography

Lesson Quiz 3

networks

Southeast Asia

DIRECTIONS: True/False Indicate whether the statement is true (T) or false (F).

_____ **1.** Southeast Asia is the most populous region on Earth.

_____ **2.** The city of Manila is the capital of Indonesia.

_____ **3.** *Sepaktakraw* is a traditional food eaten in Southeast Asia.

_____ **4.** Farming is the most common livelihood in most of Southeast Asia.

_____ **5.** Copper and gold are mined on the Indonesian portion of New Guinea.

DIRECTIONS: Multiple Choice Indicate the answer choice that best answers the question.

_____ **6.** In which Southeast Asian country do 40 percent of the region's people live?

    A. Vietnam   **C.** Singapore

    B. Thailand   **D.** Indonesia

_____ **7.** Which Southeast Asian country has a large ethnic Tagalog minority?

    A. Malaysia   **C.** Laos

    B. the Philippines   **D.** Myanmar

_____ **8.** What is the most common religion in most of mainland Southeast Asia?

    A. Buddhism   **C.** Hinduism

    B. Islam   **D.** Roman Catholicism

_____ **9.** What is one reason for the low literacy rate in East Timor?

    A. The government discourages education in order to control the people.

    B. Most schools were destroyed during the country's fight for independence.

    C. A strict form of religion practiced in East Timor prohibits teaching girls to read.

    D. The tuition fees for schools are set so high that only the rich can afford them.

_____ **10.** What has been a problem caused by the creation of dams for hydroelectric power along the Mekong River?

    A. Conflict among countries for control of the Mekong has increased.

    B. The dams have made it more difficult for farmers to obtain water for their fields.

    C. The fishing industry has been affected along the Mekong.

    D. Ecotourism in the region has dropped dramatically.

Chapter Test, Form A

netw⊚rks

Southeast Asia

DIRECTIONS: True/False Indicate whether the statement is true (T) or false (F). If the statement is false, rewrite it to make it true.

_____ **1.** Southeast Asia's major agricultural societies developed where rice could be grown.

_____

_____ **2.** Funan, one of the first important trade-based states in Southeast Asia, covered parts of present-day Indonesia.

_____

_____ **3.** Textiles and tourism are important parts of Cambodia's economy.

_____

_____ **4.** Three-quarters of the people in Southeast Asia live in rural areas.

_____

_____ **5.** The Association of Southeast Asian Nations (ASEAN) includes all countries in the region except Indonesia.

_____

DIRECTIONS: Matching Match each item with its description.

_____ **6.** plant life

_____ **7.** name given to the area bordering the Pacific Ocean

_____ **8.** an area comprised of islands

_____ **9.** name given to a seismically active zone around much of the Pacific Ocean

_____ **10.** animal life

A. Pacific Rim

B. Ring of Fire

C. flora

D. fauna

E. insular area

DIRECTIONS: Multiple Choice Indicate the answer choice that best answers the question.

_____ **11.** What is the largest country in Southeast Asia?

    A. Singapore

    B. Cambodia

    C. Indonesia

    D. Malaysia

_____ **12.** The Khmer empire was centered in what modern-day Southeast Asian nation?

    A. Laos   **C.** Myanmar

    B. Malaysia   **D.** Cambodia

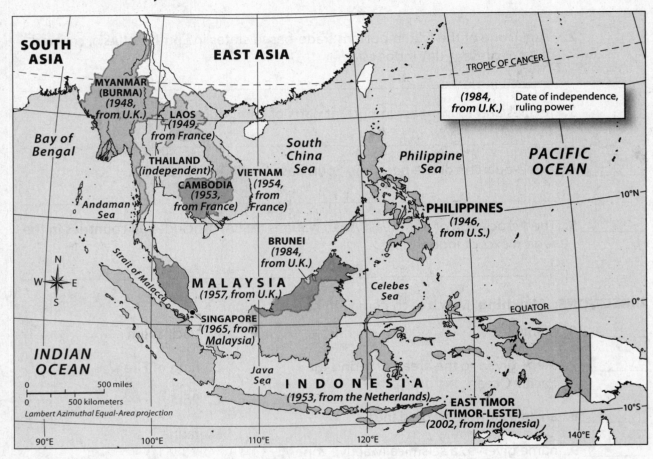

_____ **13.** Based on the map, which country in the region was once ruled by the United States?

    A. the Philippines   **C.** Burma

    B. Thailand   **D.** Singapore

_____ **14.** Based on the map, which three countries most likely made up the area that was once called French Indochina?

    A. East Timor, Malaysia, Indonesia

    B. Laos, Cambodia, Vietnam

    C. Myanmar, Thailand, Philippines

    D. Philippines, Singapore, Malaysia

Discovering World Geography

_____ **15.** About a quarter of the world's trade goes through which waterway in Southeast Asia?

    A. Mekong River

    B. Strait of Malacca

    C. Irrawaddy River

    D. Philippine Sea

_____ **16.** Which of the following groups is most likely to practice animism?

    A. farmers in Vietnam's delta regions

    B. miners in the Philippines

    C. indigenous peoples in remote Malaysia

    D. city dwellers in Singapore

_____ **17.** What is one difference between the rivers on Southeast Asia's mainland and the rivers on the region's islands?

    A. The rivers on the islands are shorter.

    B. The rivers on the mainland contain no aquatic life.

    C. The rivers on the mainland do not form deltas.

    D. The rivers on the mainland are not navigable.

DIRECTIONS: Short Answer Answer each of the following questions.

18. Southeast Asia is located along important maritime trade routes. Name one way this has enriched the region and one way it has harmed the region.

_____

_____

_____

19. Explain how the many islands and volcanoes of Southeast Asia were created.

_____

_____

_____

DIRECTIONS: Essay Answer the following question on a separate piece of paper.

20. Describe some ways that growth and development are negatively affecting the environment of Southeast Asia. Why might some governments in the region be reluctant to place strong environmental controls on industry? What is more important: a strong economy or a healthy environment?

Chapter Test, Form B

Southeast Asia

netw⊗rks

DIRECTIONS: True/False Indicate whether the statement is true (T) or false (F). If the statement is false, rewrite it to make it true.

_____ **1.** Much of the land in Southeast Asia is rugged and mountainous.

_____

_____ **2.** Indonesia, Malaysia, and Thailand rank among the world's top gold producers.

_____

_____ **3.** The seas that surround Southeast Asia have a moderating effect on air temperatures in the region.

_____

_____ **4.** The port of Malacca was the center of an important Buddhist kingdom.

_____

_____ **5.** In the 1970s, a rural communist movement called the Khmer Rouge terrorized the people of Singapore.

_____

_____ **6.** Jakarta, Indonesia, is the center of a major metropolitan area.

_____

DIRECTIONS: Matching Match each item with its description.

_____ **7.** a business that draws visitors to rain forests and coral reefs

_____ **8.** government in which a ruler has ultimate governing power over a country

_____ **9.** practice of growing just enough food to feed one's family

_____ **10.** government in which a ruler's powers are limited by laws

A. absolute monarchy

B. constitutional monarchy

C. subsistence farming

D. ecotourism

DIRECTIONS: Multiple Choice Indicate the answer choice that best answers the question.

_____ **11.** What river flows south through a valley in Myanmar's center?

    A. Mekong

    B. Irrawaddy

    C. Salween

    D. Chao Phraya

Discovering World Geography

_____ **12.** Which type of natural disaster occurred in Indonesia in 2004, causing the deaths of more than 230,000 people?

A. typhoon

B. volcanic eruption

C. tsunami

D. hurricane

_____ **13.** How did Thailand differ from other Southeast Asian nations during the colonial era?

A. Thailand was the only nation in the region that itself owned colonies.

B. Thailand was the only nation that was a constitutional monarchy.

C. Thailand was the only U.S. colony in the region.

D. Thailand was the only Southeast Asian nation that was not colonized.

_____ **14.** What is *likay*?

A. a form of folk theater popular in Thailand

B. a type of volleyball game played with the feet, knees, head, and chest

C. a traditional Vietnamese food made of fermented fish

D. a religious festival celebrated in the Philippines

_____ **15.** What is the most widely grown crop in Southeast Asia?

A. coffee

B. wheat

C. rice

D. olives

Latitude and air currents play major roles in shaping Southeast Asia's climates. Nearly the entire region lies within the Tropics—the zone that receives the hottest, most direct rays of the sun. From November to March, the direct rays of the sun are south of the Equator in the Southern Hemisphere. This produces areas of low pressure that draw monsoon winds that blow across the region from the northeast to the southwest. These winds bring cooler, drier air to much of the mainland but deliver heavy rains to the southern Malay Peninsula and to the islands. From May to September, the pattern reverses. The direct rays of the sun and the associated low pressure are north of the Equator. This causes monsoon winds to blow from the southwest to the northeast, bringing warm air and rain to the islands and the mainland.

—*Discovering World Geography*

_____ **16.** Based on the excerpt, a monsoon is most likely to bring rain to which country in January?

A. Laos

B. Indonesia

C. Myanmar

D. Cambodia

_____ **17.** Based on the excerpt, it is reasonable to conclude that monsoons occur under what conditions?

    A. when indirect sun creates an area of low pressure that draws winds and moisture

    B. when direct sun creates an area of high pressure that draws winds and moisture

    C. when indirect sun creates an area of high pressure that draws winds and moisture

    D. when direct sun creates an area of low pressure that draws winds and moisture

---

In the early 1500s, Portuguese navigators discovered they could reach India and Southeast Asia by sailing around the southern tip of Africa. In 1511 the Portuguese conquered Malacca. That same year, they discovered the sources of cloves, nutmeg, and mace: the Moluccas and the Banda Islands, which became known as the Spice Islands. . . .

At the start of the 1600s, Holland (known today as the Netherlands) jumped into the spice trade. Because the Portuguese controlled the Strait of Malacca, the Dutch charted a new route to the Spice Islands. By the middle of the century, they replaced the Portuguese as the dominant trading power.

—*Discovering World Geography*

_____ **18.** Based on the excerpt, the Spice Islands were once controlled by which European nation?

    A. Spain   **C.** England

    B. Portugal   **D.** France

_____ **19.** Based on the excerpt, why did the Dutch need to find an alternate route to the Spice Islands?

    A. because their ships could not withstand the longer voyage to the region

    B. because their navigators were not as skilled as the Spanish sailors

    C. because the Portuguese controlled the Strait of Malacca

    D. because their ships were unarmed and vulnerable to attack

DIRECTIONS: Essay Answer the following question on a separate piece of paper.

20. Describe some ways that growth and development are negatively affecting the environment of Southeast Asia. Why might some governments in the region be reluctant to place strong environmental controls on industry? What is more important: a strong economy or a healthy environment?

Lesson Quiz 1

networks

South Asia

DIRECTIONS: Matching Match each item with its description.

_____ **1.** small, ring-shaped island

_____ **2.** resource found in Sri Lanka that is used as "lead" in pencils

_____ **3.** area of fertile soil deposited by floodwaters

_____ **4.** large, swirling storm that can cause devastation

_____ **5.** seasonal wind pattern that affects rainfall

A. alluvial plain

B. atoll

C. monsoon

D. cyclone

E. graphite

DIRECTIONS: Multiple Choice Indicate the answer choice that best answers the question.

_____ **6.** What part of South Asia is one of the world's most fertile farming regions?

    A. Deccan Plateau   **C.** Brahmaputra/Ganges delta

    B. Hindu Kush   **D.** Khyber Pass

_____ **7.** What is the main reason that the climate in South Asia is so diverse?

    A. Most lands are inland with no seacoasts.

    B. The mountains in the north keep some lands wet and some lands dry.

    C. Cold winds come in from Central Asia; warm winds, from the Indian Ocean.

    D. Physical features vary greatly across the region.

_____ **8.** Which of the following features is typical of a tropical wet/dry climate?

    A. hot, dry days and cold, wet nights

    B. three seasons—hot, wet, and cool

    C. hot, wet days and cool, dry nights

    D. two seasons—hot and hotter

_____ **9.** What is the main reason that some South Asians oppose projects like the Narmada River dam?

    A. Flooding will displace people and destroy ecosystems.

    B. Boating and shipping will be greatly restricted.

    C. Those living below the dam will be in harm's way should the dam break.

    D. Building the dam will cost too much.

_____ **10.** Which South Asian wood is especially valued for its sweet scent?

    A. mahogany   **C.** sandalwood

    B. sal   **D.** teak

Lesson Quiz 2

networks

South Asia

DIRECTIONS: True/False Indicate whether the statement is true (T) or false (F).

_____ **1.** One of the oldest known civilizations originated near the Indus River.

_____ **2.** Merchants were the top class in the caste system of the ancient Aryans.

_____ **3.** Hinduism is the main religion of India.

_____ **4.** Mughal rulers were Muslim rather than Hindu.

_____ **5.** Mohandas Gandhi organized violent resistance to British rule.

DIRECTIONS: Multiple Choice Indicate the answer choice that best answers the question.

_____ **6.** What sign of advanced civilization did the Indus Valley people leave?

    A. brick houses with drains and bathrooms

    B. long poetic texts known as the Vedas

    C. an extensive system of aqueducts between cities

    D. a system of social classes, or castes

_____ **7.** What is "karma"?

    A. the belief that life is full of suffering

    B. the belief that a disciplined child makes a better adult

    C. the belief that actions in this life can affect one's next life

    D. the belief that selfish desire will be punished

_____ **8.** Which is a true statement about Akbar the Great?

    A. He was a pious Hindu.

    B. He ignored religious scholars.

    C. He punished Hindus who converted to Islam.

    D. He encouraged freedom of religion.

_____ **9.** What was the British imperialist rule of India called?

    A. the Vedas   **C.** the Sanskrit

    B. the Raj   **D.** the Varnas

_____ **10.** Which two new religions arose in South Asia around 500 B.C.?

    A. Hinduism and Jainism   **C.** Jainism and Buddhism

    B. Hinduism and Buddhism   **D.** Jainism and Islam

Lesson Quiz 3

networks

South Asia

DIRECTIONS: Matching Match each item with its description.

_____ **1.** agricultural advances using irrigation, fertilizers, and high-yielding crops

_____ **2.** group of people also called the "untouchables"

_____ **3.** the hiring of an outside company or individual to do work

_____ **4.** stringed instrument popular in India

_____ **5.** small businesses that employ people in their homes

A. sitar

B. green revolution

C. cottage industries

D. outsourcing

E. _dalits_

DIRECTIONS: Multiple Choice Indicate the answer choice that best answers the question.

_____ **6.** What is the most populous country in South Asia?

A. Pakistan   **C.** Sri Lanka

B. India   **D.** Bangladesh

_____ **7.** Which religion is followed by most Pakistanis?

A. Christianity   **C.** Islam

B. Judaism   **D.** Hinduism

_____ **8.** After India won independence, how were its state boundaries set up?

A. Boundaries were based mainly on natural borders such as rivers.

B. Boundaries were set by a special committee.

C. Boundaries were arranged so that states had equal populations.

D. Boundaries were based mainly on ethnic groups and languages.

_____ **9.** What is the main reason that U.S. companies outsource work?

A. U.S. companies want to save money.

B. U.S. companies want to impress their customers.

C. U.S. companies want to build a positive image in other countries.

D. U.S. companies have problems keeping full-time staffs.

_____ **10.** What is the main cause of enduring trouble between India and Pakistan?

A. Both countries want exclusive trading rights with Central Asia.

B. Neither country wants to trade with the other.

C. Both countries want to control the largely Muslim territory of Kashmir.

D. Both countries claim fishing rights along the coastlines.

Chapter Test, Form A

networks

South Asia

DIRECTIONS: True/False Indicate whether the statement is true (T) or false (F). If the statement is false, rewrite it to make it true.

_____ **1.** South Asia forms a continent.

_____

_____ **2.** Most of South Asia's mineral resources are found in India.

_____

_____ **3.** Hindus believe in reincarnation, or the rebirth of a soul in another body.

_____

_____ **4.** India is the world's most populous country today.

_____

_____ **5.** New South Asian cities have grown up around the high-tech field.

_____

DIRECTIONS: Matching Match each item with its description.

_____ **6.** opening in mountain range between Afghanistan and Pakistan

_____ **7.** social classes in which people are assigned strict roles and tasks

_____ **8.** recreational travel based on environmental awareness

_____ **9.** highest mountain in the world

_____ **10.** site of early civilization in what is now Pakistan

A. Mount Everest

B. Indus Valley

C. castes

D. Khyber Pass

E. ecotourism

DIRECTIONS: Multiple Choice Indicate the answer choice that best answers the question.

_____ **11.** Which of the following are the two island countries of South Asia?

A. Nepal and Hindu Kush

B. Himalaya and Bhutan

C. Sri Lanka and Maldives

D. Pakistan and Bangladesh

_____ **12.** In what language were the Vedas, ancient Aryan poetic texts, written?

A. Aryan

B. Hindi

C. Urdu

D. Sanskrit

Chapter Test, Form A *cont.*

networks

South Asia

South Asia: Seasonal Rains

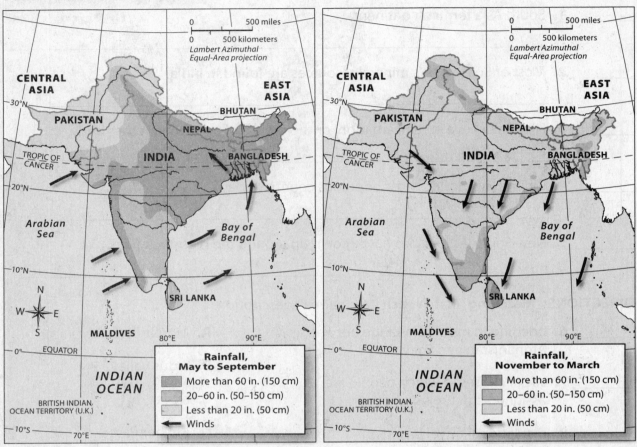

13. Based on the maps, what can be said in general about the amount of rainfall in South Asia?

   A. Pakistan has more rain from November to March.

   B. Sri Lanka never has less than 20 inches (50 cm) of rain.

   C. Most of South Asia has less rain from November to March.

   D. No part of India ever has more than 60 inches (150 cm) of rain.

14. Based on the maps, how does the wind direction from May to September compare to the wind direction from November to March?

   A. The wind blows constantly from the southeast all year long.

   B. From May to September, most winds come from the southwest; from November to March, winds come from the northeast and northwest.

   C. The wind blows constantly from the northeast all year long.

   D. From May to September, most winds come from the northeast; from November to March, they come from the southeast.

Discovering World Geography

_____ **15.** Which was a title of respect for Indian independence leader Mohandas Gandhi?

    A. Gautama   **C.** Gupta

    B. Mahatma   **D.** Sikh

_____ **16.** Which city in India is considered the country's business center?

    A. Mumbai   **C.** Bengaluru

    B. New Delhi   **D.** Kolkata

_____ **17.** Which of the following situations is an example of outsourcing?

    A. U.S. customer using the Internet to compare the pricing of a product

    B. U.S. auto service center hiring an immigrant from Poland as a full-time mechanic

    C. U.S. firm hiring a temporary worker to fill in for an employee who is on leave for six weeks

    D. U.S. manufacturer engaging a company in India to provide customer service

DIRECTIONS: Short Answer Answer each of the following questions.

18. Why are forests an important habitat in South Asia? How are South Asians protecting this habitat? Explain.

_____

_____

_____

_____

19. In what ways are population trends changing in India? Provide specific examples in your answer.

_____

_____

_____

_____

DIRECTIONS: Essay Answer the following question on a separate piece of paper.

20. What are the two legacies of the ancient Aryan civilization? What impact did each of those legacies have on South Asians? Provide specific examples in your answer.

Chapter Test, Form B

networks

South Asia

DIRECTIONS: True/False Indicate whether the statement is true (T) or false (F). If the statement is false, rewrite it to make it true.

_____ **1.** Plate tectonics created the Himalaya range.

_____

_____ **2.** The *Rig Veda* was part of a literary legacy left by the Mauryas.

_____

_____ **3.** The Four Noble Truths are central to Buddhist beliefs.

_____

_____ **4.** The famous Taj Mahal was built by an emperor in memory of his wife.

_____

_____ **5.** Arranged marriages are now banned in South Asia.

_____

DIRECTIONS: Matching Match each item with its description.

_____ **6.** ruler of the Mauryas who converted to Buddhism

_____ **7.** religion that developed nearly 2,000 years after Buddhism

_____ **8.** area that straddles the border between Pakistan and India

_____ **9.** a leader of India's independence movement

_____ **10.** high flat area that makes up most of southern India

A. Deccan Plateau

B. Thar Desert

C. Ashoka

D. Jawaharlal Nehru

E. Sikhism

DIRECTIONS: Multiple Choice Indicate the answer choice that best answers the question.

_____ **11.** Which language is spoken by a majority of Sri Lankans?

A. Sinhalese

B. Sanskrit

C. Tamil

D. Hindi

_____ **12.** From what part of the world are the Aryans believed to have come?

A. East Asia

B. Northern Europe

C. southern Russia and Central Asia

D. Southern Europe

Chapter Test, Form B *cont.*

netw⊙rks

South Asia

South Asia: Seasonal Rains

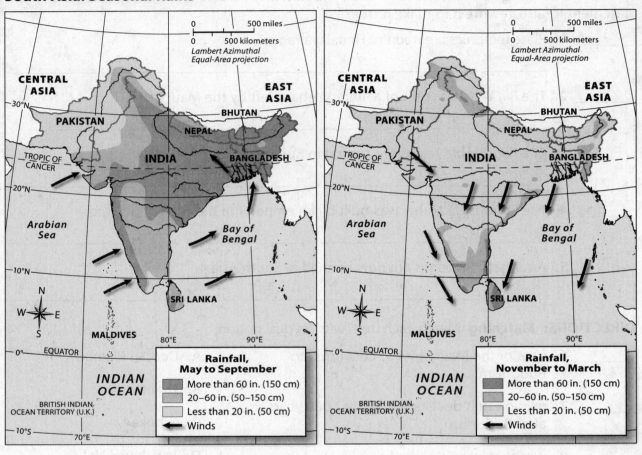

13. Based on the maps, which area in southern India has more rain all year long?

    A. eastern coast   **C.** tip of southern coast

    B. western coast   **D.** northern coast

14. Based on the maps, what can be said about the rainfall in Pakistan?

    A. Pakistan has a rainy season from May to December.

    B. Pakistan is rather dry all year long.

    C. Pakistan has far more rain than India from May to December.

    D. Pakistan has just about as much rain as Bhutan all year long.

15. In what significant way has the rapid growth of South Asia affected its cities?

    A. Hinduism has become the only religion practiced in the cities.

    B. Resources are strained and air and water pollution have increased.

    C. Many people have left the cities and returned to rural areas.

    D. The population density in Mumbai is only slightly more than the world's average.

Discovering World Geography

Chapter Test, Form B *cont.*

South Asia

> Artistic expression is rich in South Asia. Two great epic poems of ancient India, the *Ramayana* and the *Mahabharata,* embody Hindu social and religious values. Their impact extends far beyond the Hindu community, though. South Asian children of all religions can tell you about the plots and characters of these epics. They are part of the region's heritage.
>
> South Asia also is a center for classical dance. Music is a thriving art, and many of the region's musicians, singers, and composers are popular. Ravi Shankar, born in 1920, is probably the best-known Indian musician. He performs on the sitar, a stringed instrument. Motion pictures first arrived in India in 1896. The country now has the largest film industry in the world. The Hindi film industry, nicknamed "Bollywood," is based in Mumbai. Kolkata is also a filmmaking center.
>
> —*Discovering World Geography*

_____ **16.** Based on the excerpt, what is the *Mahabharata*?

    A. a song by Ravi Shankar   **C.** a stringed instrument

    B. a Bollywood movie   **D.** an epic poem of ancient India

_____ **17.** Based on the excerpt, which of the following statements is most accurate?

    A. Movies only recently became a part of the Indian culture.

    B. South Asian culture is not concerned with developing the arts.

    C. The film industry in India is larger than the film industry in the United States.

    D. The epic poems of ancient India are only taught to Hindu children.

_____ **18.** For which political tactic is Mohandas Gandhi famous?

    A. protesting with signs   **C.** door-to-door campaigning

    B. taunting police   **D.** civil disobedience

_____ **19.** Which of the following statements is most accurate about the crop yields in South Asia since they began using the advances of the green revolution?

    A. There has been no change to the crop yields.

    B. The crop yields have decreased.

    C. Crop yields have increased but productivity has failed to keep up with growing needs.

    D. Crop yields have increased and productivity continues to keep up with growing needs.

DIRECTIONS: Essay Answer the following question on a separate piece of paper.

20. What are the two legacies of the ancient Aryan civilization? What impact did each of those legacies have on South Asians? Provide specific examples in your answer.

Lesson Quiz 1

networks

Central Asia, the Caucasus, and Siberian Russia

DIRECTIONS: True/False Indicate whether the statement is true (T) or false (F).

_____ **1.** The eastern part of Russia is known as the Caucasus.

_____ **2.** Central Asia is made up of lowland mountains and dune-covered deserts.

_____ **3.** Eastern and central Siberia have some of the coldest winters on Earth.

_____ **4.** The Aral Sea separates the Caucasus and Central Asia.

_____ **5.** Because Siberia's taiga contains about 20 percent of all the world's trees, logging is an important part of the regional economy.

DIRECTIONS: Multiple Choice Indicate the answer choice that best answers the question.

_____ **6.** Which is the most sparsely populated country in Central Asia?

    A. Kazakhstan   **C.** Pakistan

    B. Uzbekistan   **D.** Turkmenistan

_____ **7.** Which of the following statements about the Caucasus Mountains is accurate?

    A. The range generally marks the western border of Siberia.

    B. The range generally marks a border between the Caucasus and Central Asia.

    C. The range supports little plant life.

    D. The range generally marks a border between Europe and Asia.

_____ **8.** What do the Kyzyl Kum and Kara-Kum areas have in common?

    A. Both are mountainous areas that border China.

    B. Both are desert areas of Central Asia.

    C. Both have very high rainfall in most years.

    D. Both are covered by permafrost.

_____ **9.** How can the climate of most of Central Asia be characterized?

    A. arid   **C.** temperate

    B. humid subtropical   **D.** humid continental

_____ **10.** Where is Lake Baikal located?

    A. Uzbekistan

    B. the Urals

    C. Siberia

    D. Azerbaijan

Lesson Quiz 2

netw⊙rks

Central Asia, the Caucasus, and Siberian Russia

DIRECTIONS: True/False Indicate whether the statement is true (T) or false (F).

_____ **1.** Invaders from Manchuria were the first of several peoples to conquer parts of Siberia and add it to their empire.

_____ **2.** Soviet leaders moved some factories to Siberia during World War II.

_____ **3.** The Russian czars' main interest in Central Asia was mining gold.

_____ **4.** The Caucasus has a complex ethnic history.

_____ **5.** During World War I, Ottoman troops killed hundreds of thousands of ethnic Georgians.

DIRECTIONS: Multiple Choice Indicate the answer choice that best answers the question.

_____ **6.** By which century did Russian control of Siberia extend to the Pacific Ocean?

    A. 1900   **C.** 1700

    B. 1800   **D.** 1600

_____ **7.** Which religion was brought to Central Asia after it was conquered by the Arabs in the early A.D. 700s?

    A. Judaism   **C.** Christianity

    B. Islam   **D.** Buddhism

_____ **8.** When were Central Asia's present-day countries formed?

    A. after the collapse of the Soviet Union in the 1990s

    B. at the end of World War II following the defeat of Germany

    C. at the beginning of the Russian Revolution in 1917

    D. shortly after Timur conquered the region in the mid-1300s

_____ **9.** What is one way the histories of Georgia and Armenia are similar?

    A. Both successfully resisted coming under Persian control.

    B. Neither had ever existed as an independent nation before the 1990s.

    C. They were two of the earliest countries to convert to Christianity.

    D. They were two of the earliest countries to convert to Islam.

_____ **10.** How did Soviet rule change the Caucasus?

    A. The Soviets encouraged the people to show pride in their ethnic identities.

    B. The region changed from an agricultural area to an urban and industrial area.

    C. Islam slowly became the dominant religion throughout the region.

    D. The nations in the region finally gained their independence under Soviet rule.

                  Discovering World Geography

Lesson Quiz 3

net works

Central Asia, the Caucasus, and Siberian Russia

DIRECTIONS: True/False Indicate whether the statement is true (T) or false (F).

_____ **1.** Turkmenistan is the only Central Asian country that is mostly urban.

_____ **2.** Two-thirds of Kyrgyzstan's people are ethnic Russians.

_____ **3.** Russian is widely spoken throughout Central Asia.

_____ **4.** The countries of the Caucasus made a smooth transition to democracy.

_____ **5.** Russia and Japan both claim ownership of parts of the Kuril Islands.

DIRECTIONS: Multiple Choice Indicate the answer choice that best answers the question.

_____ **6.** How do settlement patterns in the Caucasus differ from those in Siberia and most of Central Asia?

    A. The Caucasus is a more urban region than Siberia or Central Asia.

    B. Unlike in Siberia and Central Asia, most people in the Caucasus live on farms.

    C. The rural areas of Siberia and Central Asia are more densely populated than those of the Caucasus.

    D. Unlike Siberia and Central Asia, the Caucasus has no large cities.

_____ **7.** Most cities and towns in Siberia are located along or near which feature?

    A. Siberia's eastern coast   **C.** the route of the Trans-Siberian Railroad

    B. the Yenisey River   **D.** the Ob' and Lena rivers

_____ **8.** Where is Azerbaijan's most densely populated area?

    A. in the extreme southeast, between the Caspian Sea and the Iranian border

    B. on the Ararat plain, near the Turkish border

    C. around its capital city, Baku

    D. in the area along the Black Sea coast

_____ **9.** Which of the following has been a source of unrest in Georgia?

    A. Christians in Georgia have demanded the right to practice their religion freely.

    B. Ethnic minority groups in Georgia have sought independence and self-rule.

    C. Income inequality between rural Muslims and urban Christians has led to rioting.

    D. Georgian Communists, backed by Russian troops, have fought Islamic groups.

_____ **10.** Which of the following activities is important in most Central Asian cultures?

    A. raising and racing horses   **C.** growing flowers

    B. breakdancing   **D.** sculpting statues from ice

Discovering World Geography   **201**

Chapter Test, Form A

networks

Central Asia, the Caucasus, and Siberian Russia

DIRECTIONS: True/False Indicate whether the statement is true (T) or false (F). If the statement is false, rewrite it to make it true.

_____ **1.** Central Asia depends on the Syr Dar'ya and the Amu Dar'ya rivers for irrigation.

_____

_____ **2.** Central Asia has many trees because of the region's wet climate.

_____

_____ **3.** The Central Siberian Plateau supplies most of Central Asia's coal.

_____

_____ **4.** Most of Siberia's people are ethnic Russians.

_____

DIRECTIONS: Matching Match each item with its description.

_____ **5.** related to the keeping or herding of animals

_____ **6.** Soviet labor camps

_____ **7.** alike; of the same kind

_____ **8.** green area by a water source in a dry region

_____ **9.** large government-run farms in the Soviet Union

_____ **10.** round tent with a domed roof used by rural people in Central Asia

A. oasis

B. yurt

C. gulags

D. collectives

E. homogenous

F. pastoral

DIRECTIONS: Multiple Choice Indicate the answer choice that best answers the question.

_____ **11.** In what way are Turkmenistan and Uzbekistan different?

A. Turkmenistan covers a much larger area than Uzbekistan.

B. Turkmenistan has a much smaller population than Uzbekistan.

C. Turkmenistan is in Central Asia while Uzbekistan is in the Caucasus.

D. Turkmenistan is mostly a grassy plain, while Uzbekistan is almost entirely desert.

Discovering World Geography

_____ **12.** Which of the following countries is part of the Caucasus region?

    A. Kyrgyzstan   **C.** Kazakhstan

    B. Tajikistan   **D.** Azerbaijan

Population Density of the Regions

_____ **13.** Based on the map, which city has the greatest population?

    A. Tbilisi, Georgia   **C.** Ashkhabad, Turkmenistan

    B. Tashkent, Uzbekistan   **D.** Yerevan, Armenia

_____ **14.** Based on the map, which of the following is a valid conclusion?

    A. Azerbaijan is more densely populated than Kazakhstan.

    B. Kazakhstan is a more urban country than Azerbaijan.

    C. More people live in Azerbaijan than in Kazakhstan.

    D. Azerbaijan is less densely populated than Kazakhstan.

_____ **15.** Why is Siberia's taiga swampy?

    A. The region's numerous rivers flood during the long winters.

    B. Too many canals and irrigation ditches have been constructed in the region.

    C. The region is covered in permafrost.

    D. Siberia receives over 200 inches of rainfall annually.

_____ **16.** Which of the following events began in 1891?

    A. construction of the Trans-Siberian Railroad

    B. ascension of Peter the Great as czar of Russia

    C. creation of gulags to house political prisoners

    D. collapse of the Soviet Union

_____ **17.** What was the greatest prize for many early conquerors of Central Asia?

    A. access to the region's mineral resources

    B. control of the region's oases

    C. access to the Caspian Sea

    D. control of the Silk Road

DIRECTIONS: Short Answer Answer each of the following questions.

18. How do the Caspian and Black Seas affect the climate in the Caucasus?

_____

_____

_____

_____

19. Describe Timur's contributions to the arts and sciences in Central Asia in the mid-1300s.

_____

_____

_____

_____

DIRECTIONS: Essay Answer the following question on a separate piece of paper.

20. Describe the causes and effects of the changes that have taken place to the Aral Sea in the past 60 years.

Chapter Test, Form B

netw✺rks

Central Asia, the Caucasus, and Siberian Russia

DIRECTIONS: True/False Indicate whether the statement is true (T) or false (F). If the statement is false, rewrite it to make it true.

_____ **1.** The first humans in Siberia came from North America.

_____

_____ **2.** For most of their history, Central Asian countries were part of outside empires.

_____

_____ **3.** From the late 1400s, Ottomans and Persians competed for the Caucasus.

_____

_____ **4.** Tajikistan is mainly rural, and its settled areas are sparsely populated.

_____

_____ **5.** Most Azerbaijanis are Christians, and most Armenians and Georgians are Muslims.

_____

DIRECTIONS: Matching Match each item with its description.

_____ **6.** a treeless zone found near the Arctic Circle

_____ **7.** Uzbekistan's capital city and Central Asia's largest city

_____ **8.** brutal Soviet dictator

_____ **9.** an area of dry grasslands

_____ **10.** Central Asian conqueror in the mid-1300s

A. tundra

B. Joseph Stalin

C. Tashkent

D. steppe

E. Timur

DIRECTIONS: Multiple Choice Indicate the answer choice that best answers the question.

_____ **11.** How does the Amur River differ from other main Siberian rivers?

    A. It drains to the east rather than to the north.

    B. It forms the border between Russia and Kazakhstan.

    C. It is the only Siberian river that drains into the Arctic Ocean.

    D. Its valley is the coldest region in Siberia.

_____ **12.** Which of the following was a change brought about by Soviet rule in Central Asia?

    A. Russian Orthodox missionaries converted most Central Asians to Christianity.

    B. Soviet-built dams generated hydroelectric power on Central Asian rivers.

    C. Soviet leaders encouraged local ethnic cultures to flourish.

    D. Local farmers and herders were given free land.

_____ **13.** What is one way the natural resources of the Caucasus differ from those of Siberia and Central Asia?

    A. The Caucasus is completely lacking in forests.

    B. The Caucasus is the only country in the region with large deposits of gold.

    C. The Caucasus has fewer energy resources than the other two regions.

    D. Unlike the other two regions, the Caucasus gets little rainfall.

When the czar was overthrown and the Communists took control [of Russia] in 1917, some Siberian leaders resisted the new government. In 1922 the Communists brought Siberia under control. Siberia became part of the Union of Soviet Socialist Republics (also called the Soviet Union and USSR)—the country they formed from the Russian Empire.

Soviet leaders increased mining and industry in the region, especially along the Trans-Siberian Railroad. Much of this expansion came through the use of forced labor. Labor camps called gulags spread across Siberia in the 1930s. Millions of people who disagreed with Communist government policies were imprisoned in gulags. The Communists also combined the lands of small farmers into large, government-run farms called collectives. Farmers who resisted giving up their land were sent to the gulags.

—Discovering World Geography

_____ **14.** Based on the excerpt, when did Siberia become part of the Soviet Union?

    A. 1917   **C.** in the 1930s

    B. 1922   **D.** after World War II

_____ **15.** Based on the excerpt, what do you think the phrase "being sent to Siberia" means?

    A. being exiled, imprisoned, or disgraced

    B. being rewarded for hard work

    C. being given new tasks

    D. being assigned to a job in a company's home office

_____ **16.** How did the Communist victory in Russia's civil war affect the Caucasus?

    A. Soviet rule brought very little change to the largely agricultural area of the Caucasus.

    B. Soviet power introduced decades of invasion and instability into the region.

    C. The Soviet Union created three Soviet socialist republics in the region.

    D. The Soviet Union slowed the development of industries in the Caucasus.

_____ **17.** How did the emigration of ethnic Russians following the end of Soviet rule affect Central Asia?

    A. The literacy rate in Central Asia dropped dramatically.

    B. Most Central Asian nations moved quickly to set up democratic governments.

    C. The Aral Sea became filled with salt and farm chemicals.

    D. Some Central Asian countries did not have enough skilled workers.

Compared to the rest of the Caucasus, Armenians are homogenous, or of the same kind. The Turks and Azeris, who live in the countries bordering Armenia, historically have been the Armenians' enemies. In the 1890s and again during World War I, the Turks massacred millions of Armenians who were living under Turkish rule. Meanwhile, Christian Armenians were fighting the influence of Islam being spread by Azeris living in the Caucasus and Iran.

More recently, Armenians and Azeris have been fighting over Nagorno-Karabakh, a region with an Armenian majority that is part of Azerbaijan. In 1988 Armenia seized Nagorno-Karabakh and the territory that connected it to Azerbaijan. As tensions and violence increased, many Azeris fled the region. The dispute remains unsettled.

—Discovering World Geography

_____ **18.** Based on the excerpt, why do many Armenians consider Turks to be their enemies?

    A. The Armenians resent the Turks' attempts to spread Islam into their country.

    B. Being homogeneous, Armenians consider themselves to be superior to Turks.

    C. The Turks have twice committed atrocities against the Armenian people.

    D. Turkey considers Armenia a Turkish province and repeatedly tries to conquer it.

_____ **19.** Based on the excerpt, which is a true statement about Nagorno-Karabakh?

    A. Nagorno-Karabakh has recently become an independent nation.

    B. Armenia currently governs the Nagorno-Karabakh region.

    C. Most residents of the Nagorno-Karabakh region are ethnic Azeris.

    D. The territory of Armenia surrounds the Nagorno-Karabakh region.

DIRECTIONS: Essay Answer the following question on a separate piece of paper.

20. Describe the causes and effects of the changes that have taken place to the Aral Sea in the past 60 years.

Lesson Quiz 1

networks

Southwest Asia

DIRECTIONS: Matching Match each item with its description.

_____ **1.** world's largest sand sea

_____ **2.** an opening in the Hindu Kush range that has served as a trade route

_____ **3.** waterway that connects the Persian Gulf to the Indian Ocean

_____ **4.** nomadic people who keep herds of camels, horses, and sheep

_____ **5.** landlocked body of water between Israel and Jordan

A. Khyber Pass

B. Dead Sea

C. Strait of Hormuz

D. Rub' al-Khali, or Empty Quarter

E. Bedouin

DIRECTIONS: Multiple Choice Indicate the answer choice that best answers the question.

_____ **6.** In what Southwest Asian country is Mount Ararat the highest peak?

    A. Afghanistan   **C.** Iran

    B. Turkey   **D.** Israel

_____ **7.** What does "Mesopotamia" mean in Greek?

    A. great beginning   **C.** fertile land

    B. alluvial plain   **D.** land between the rivers

_____ **8.** Which of the following statements best describes the climate of Southwest Asia?

    A. Most of the region falls within a semiarid climate zone.

    B. The northern part of the region falls within a subarctic climate zone.

    C. Most of the region falls within an arid climate zone.

    D. The southern part of the region falls within a tropical climate zone.

_____ **9.** Which of the following natural resources are found in abundance in Southwest Asia?

    A. oil and natural gas   **C.** gold and gemstones

    B. forests and wildlife   **D.** forests and freshwater

_____ **10.** Which of the following statements about the location of Yemen is accurate?

    A. Yemen's western border lies along the Red Sea.

    B. Yemen is located at the northern end of the Arabian Peninsula.

    C. Yemen is a landlocked country that borders on Israel.

    D. Yemen lies along the western shore of the Persian Gulf.

Discovering World Geography

Lesson Quiz 2

networks

Southwest Asia

DIRECTIONS: Matching Match each item with its description.

_____ 1. Islamist organization that carried out 2001 attacks on U.S. soil

_____ 2. belief in many gods

_____ 3. belief in just one God

_____ 4. ancient writing system used by Mesopotamians

_____ 5. period of a thousand years

A. cuneiform

B. polytheism

C. millennium

D. monotheism

E. al-Qaeda

DIRECTIONS: Multiple Choice Indicate the answer choice that best answers the question.

_____ 6. How did the shift from hunting and gathering to agriculture affect the way of life of early peoples?

    A. Their way of life became nomadic.

    B. Their way of life focused more on hunting.

    C. Their way of life began to be less settled and more insecure.

    D. Their way of life began to be more settled and villages began to appear.

_____ 7. In what way are the religions of Islam, Judaism, and Christianity alike?

    A. They began in 2000 B.C.

    B. They are monotheistic.

    C. They are polytheistic.

    D. They regard Job as the messenger of God.

_____ 8. What people conquered Mesopotamia and Persia in the A.D. 1200s?

    A. Muslims

    B. Babylonians

    C. Ottomans

    D. Mongols

_____ 9. Following World War I, how did Britain and France divide the territory of the former Ottoman Empire?

    A. by setting boundaries based on historical divisions

    B. by creating boundaries that ignored ethnic backgrounds

    C. by creating boundaries based on population distribution

    D. by setting boundaries based on religious divisions

_____ 10. What event triggered the first Persian Gulf War in the 1990s?

    A. Iraq's invasion of Kuwait

    B. Iraq's invasion of Iran

    C. U.S. invasion of Afghanistan

    D. Israel's capture of the West Bank

Discovering World Geography

Lesson Quiz 3

Southwest Asia

networks

DIRECTIONS: True/False Indicate whether the statement is true (T) or false (F).

_____ **1.** Yemen is a highly urbanized country.

_____ **2.** The Arabian Desert is sparsely populated.

_____ **3.** Arabic is the most widespread language in Southwest Asia.

_____ **4.** Islam is the dominant religion in Southwest Asia.

_____ **5.** Afghanistan ranks among Southwest Asia's richest countries.

DIRECTIONS: Multiple Choice Indicate the answer choice that best answers the question.

_____ **6.** Which statement is the most accurate depiction of the population in Southwest Asia?

  A. The population in oil-rich countries is declining.

  B. Most countries in the region remain rural and isolated.

  C. A high percentage of the region's population is below 15 years of age.

  D. The total population of Southwest Asia is far less than that of the United States.

_____ **7.** What are the two main branches of Islam in Southwest Asia?

  A. Hazari and Afghani   **C.** Arabic and Persian

  B. Islamist and Kurdish   **D.** Sunni and Shia

_____ **8.** Which of the following is the holy month of fasting for Muslims?

  A. December   **C.** *Eid al-Fitr*

  B. Ramadan   **D.** Rosh Hashanah

_____ **9.** Which territories are at the heart of the Arab-Israeli conflict?

  A. Gaza Strip and West Bank

  B. Suez Canal and Golan Heights

  C. Syria and Jordan

  D. Lebanon and Sinai Peninsula

_____ **10.** What is the main reason that Syria and Iraq oppose dam-building projects along the Tigris and Euphrates Rivers in Turkey?

  A. They do not want Turkey to hire Kurdish workers to build the dams.

  B. They object to Turkey's use of foreign funds to build the dams.

  C. They fear that river flow will be reduced when the dams are built.

  D. They believe that Turkey will produce more electricity than they can.

DIRECTIONS: If the statement is true, write T. If the statement is false, write F.

_____ 1. Persian is spoken in a large area.

_____ 2. The Arabian Desert is sparsely populated.

_____ 3. Arabic is the most wide-spread language in Southwest Asia.

_____ 4. Gaza is the dominant region in Southwest Asia.

_____ 5. Afghanistan has a high population. Afghanistan is a landlocked country.

DIRECTIONS: Multiple Choice Indicate the answer choice that best answers the question or completes the statement.

_____ 6. Which statement is the most accurate description of the population of southwest Asia?

A. The population in southwest countries is decreasing.
B. Most countries have modern health systems, rural, and isolated.
C. A high percentage of the region's population is the over 65 years old.
D. The population of Southwest Asia is far less than that of the United States.

_____ 7. What are the two main branches of Islam in Southwest Asia?
A. Muslim and Afghan.   C. Arabic and Persia.
B. Islamist and Kurdish.   D. Sunni and Shia.

_____ 8. Which of the following is the holy month of respect for Muslims?
A. December.   C. Eid al-Fitr.
B. Ramadan.   D. Post-Ramadan.

_____ 9. Which territories are in dispute in the West Bank for all equity?
A. Gaza Strip and West Bank.
B. Gaza Strip and Golan Heights.
C. Syria and Jordan.
D. Lebanon and Saudi Arabia.

_____ 10. What, the multiple reasons that Syria and Iraq are each building is decreasing their land and fertile lands, rivers, or turkey?
A. Why do no water flow over the Turkish border in Southwest Asia.
B. They believe they always need to follow in the north of the dam dry.
C. The fresh from their flow will be solved with a fine dams are built.
D. They believe that some will produce more electricity than the year.

Chapter Test, Form A

netw⊙rks

Southwest Asia

DIRECTIONS: True/False Indicate whether the statement is true (T) or false (F). If the statement is false, rewrite it to make it true.

_____ 1. Turkey has coasts on the Mediterranean and Black Seas.

_____

_____ 2. The Tigris and Euphrates Rivers are often considered parts of the same river system.

_____

_____ 3. By about A.D. 800, Islam extended from northern Africa into most of France.

_____

_____ 4. Israel controls the West Bank and East Jerusalem.

_____

_____ 5. The population of Southwest Asia is less than that of the United States.

_____

DIRECTIONS: Matching Match each item with its description.

_____ 6. one area at the heart of the Arab-Israeli conflict

_____ 7. landform created by sediment deposited during floods

_____ 8. one of two main branches of Islam

_____ 9. holy month of fasting for Muslims

_____ 10. streambed that is dry for much of the year

A. alluvial plain

B. wadi

C. West Bank

D. Sunni

E. Ramadan

DIRECTIONS: Multiple Choice Indicate the answer choice that best answers the question.

_____ 11. What human-made feature has contributed greatly to the Red Sea becoming one of the world's busiest waterways?

    A. Strait of Hormuz

    B. Suez Canal

    C. Kuwait refinery complex

    D. hydroelectric dam

Discovering World Geography

_____ **12.** In which writing system was the poem known as the *Epic of Gilgamesh* created?

   A. Arabic

   B. Latin

   C. cuneiform

   D. Hindi

_____ **13.** What do the Dead Sea and the Caspian Sea have in common?

   A. Both are freshwater seas.

   B. Both seas are at high elevations.

   C. Both have straits that open to the Indian Ocean.

   D. Both seas are landlocked.

On September 11, 2001, an Islamist organization called al-Qaeda carried out terrorist attacks on U.S. soil that killed nearly 3,000 people. The United States determined that the Taliban, Afghanistan's Islamist ruling group, was supporting al-Qaeda and sheltering its leaders. In October, forces led by the United States and the United Kingdom invaded Afghanistan and removed the Taliban from power. Two years later, the Second Persian Gulf War began when U.S. and U.K. forces invaded Iraq and overthrew the government of Saddam Hussein, who was accused of supporting terrorists and possessing weapons of mass destruction, a suspicion that was ultimately not proven true.

—*Discovering World Geography*

_____ **14.** Based on the excerpt, from which country did the United States suspect that al-Qaeda operated?

   A. Pakistan

   B. Iraq

   C. Afghanistan

   D. United Kingdom

_____ **15.** Based on the excerpt, what was a reason that U.S. and U.K. forces invaded Iraq in 2003?

   A. They believed Iraq had weapons of mass destruction.

   B. They believed Iraq had joined forces with Iran.

   C. They believed Saddam Hussein was a leader of al-Qaeda.

   D. They believed Saddam Hussein had masterminded the attack on U.S. soil.

_____ **16.** What are the five duties required of followers of Islam called?

    A. Pillars of Islam

    B. Five Noble Truths

    C. Praises to Allah

    D. Rules of the Prophet

_____ **17.** What event triggered the invasion of Israel by Arab countries in 1948?

    A. removal of British troops from Israel

    B. Israel's declaration of independence

    C. an invasion of Syria by Israel

    D. the Holocaust

DIRECTIONS: Short Answer Answer each of the following questions.

18. In what ways does Islam play a central role in the daily lives of many Southwest Asians?

_____

_____

_____

_____

_____

19. Compare the climates in the mountainous and desert areas of Southwest Asia.

_____

_____

_____

_____

_____

DIRECTIONS: Essay Answer the following question on a separate piece of paper.

20. How has the discovery of oil deposits in Southwest Asia affected the region's economy and social order? Provide specific examples from your reading.

Chapter Test, Form B

Southwest Asia

networks

DIRECTIONS: True/False Indicate whether the statement is true (T) or false (F). If the statement is false, rewrite it to make it true.

_____ **1.** The Red Sea is one of the world's busiest waterways.

_____

_____ **2.** Most of Southwest Asia falls within a temperate climate zone.

_____

_____ **3.** The Sumerians were among the ancient Mesopotamian societies.

_____

_____ **4.** The Ottoman Empire was formally dissolved after World War II.

_____

_____ **5.** Arabs comprise the largest ethnic group in Southwest Asia.

_____

DIRECTIONS: Matching Match each item with its description.

_____ **6.** systematic murder of six million European Jews by Nazi Germany

_____ **7.** considered the father of monotheism by Jews, Christians, and Muslims

_____ **8.** wave of pro-democracy protests and uprisings in North Africa and Southwest Asia

_____ **9.** highest mountain range in Southwest Asia

_____ **10.** place where the Ottoman Empire originated in the A.D. 1200s

A. Hindu Kush

B. Abraham

C. Anatolian Peninsula

D. Holocaust

E. Arab Spring

DIRECTIONS: Multiple Choice Indicate the answer choice that best answers the question.

_____ **11.** Which present-day country occupies much of ancient Mesopotamia?

　　A. Yemen

　　B. Israel

　　C. Iraq

　　D. Saudi Arabia

Chapter Test, Form B *cont.*

Southwest Asia

networks

_____ **12.** The scarcity of which resource has shaped the history of Southwest Asia?

    A. oil   **C.** natural gas

    B. water   **D.** copper

_____ **13.** What is the Arab word for "God"?

    A. Muhammad   **C.** Kaaba

    B. Makkah   **D.** Allah

_____ **14.** Which of the following events spurred the movement for a Jewish state?

    A. Holocaust

    B. World War I

    C. Arab Spring

    D. Persian Gulf War

_____ **15.** Which of the following statements describes most accurately how many Southwest Asians identify themselves?

    A. They identify more with their state or province than with their nation.

    B. Their identify more with their employer than with their family.

    C. They identify more with their tribe than with their nation.

    D. They identify more with an ancient empire than with a modern-day ruler.

> The region of Southwest Asia takes its physical shape mostly from the bodies of water that surround it. Turkey has coasts on the Mediterranean and Black seas. Syria, Lebanon, Jordan, and Israel have coasts on the Mediterranean Sea. Jordan, Saudi Arabia, and Yemen border the long, narrow Red Sea. The Red Sea has been one of the world's busiest waterways since Egypt's Suez Canal was completed in 1869. To the southeast of the Arabian Peninsula lies a part of the Indian Ocean called the Arabian Sea. Yemen and its neighbor Oman have coasts along this sea.
>
> —*Discovering World Geography*

_____ **16.** Based on the excerpt, which of the following determines the physical shape of Southwest Asia?

    A. Arabian Peninsula

    B. bodies of water

    C. mountain ranges

    D. Egypt's Suez Canal

Discovering World Geography

_____ **17.** Based on the excerpt, which of the following countries has coasts on both the Red Sea and the Arabian Sea?

    A. Turkey

    B. Syria

    C. Israel

    D. Yemen

Over thousands of years, Mesopotamian societies such as the Sumerians and the Babylonians invented sophisticated irrigation and farming methods. They built impressive works of architecture, most notably huge, pyramid-shaped temple towers, and made advances in mathematics, astronomy, government, and law. Using a writing system called cuneiform (kew-NAY-ih-form), they produced great works of literature, including a poem known as the *Epic of Gilgamesh*. Mesopotamia's achievements helped shape later civilizations in Greece, Rome, and Western Europe.

—Discovering World Geography

_____ **18.** Based on the excerpt, what can be said about the early people of Mesopotamia?

    A. They focused almost exclusively on agriculture.

    B. They lacked a system of writing.

    C. They had an advanced civilization that shaped later civilizations.

    D. They knew little about architecture.

_____ **19.** Based on the excerpt, what is the best meaning of "sophisticated" as used in the first sentence?

    A. highly developed

    B. wise to the ways of the world

    C. very cultured

    D. intellectual

DIRECTIONS: Essay Answer the following question on a separate piece of paper.

20. How has the discovery of oil deposits in Southwest Asia affected the region's economy and social order? Provide specific examples from your reading.

Unit Test

networks

Africa

DIRECTIONS: True/False Indicate whether the statement is true (T) or false (F).

_____ **1.** The Egyptian civilization arose along the Nile River.

_____ **2.** Desertification turns desert land into farmland.

_____ **3.** Most of Central Africa's people make their living through subsistence farming.

_____ **4.** The Sahara's vast stretches of sand are called wadis.

_____ **5.** The rights of black South Africans were limited under apartheid.

DIRECTIONS: Matching Match each item with its description.

_____ **6.** ban on trade, such as that imposed on South Africa to oppose apartheid

_____ **7.** method of passing on stories about a group by word of mouth

_____ **8.** material used to make tools in ancient Central Africa

_____ **9.** tomb for ancient pharaohs

_____ **10.** parents with their children

A. pyramid

B. oral tradition

C. iron

D. nuclear family

E. embargo

DIRECTIONS: Multiple Choice Indicate the answer choice that best answers the question.

_____ **11.** Which body of water links North Africa to Southwest Asia and Europe?

   A. Arabian Sea

   B. Mediterranean Sea

   C. Indian Ocean

   D. Atlantic Ocean

_____ **12.** Which resource first attracted Portuguese explorers to the region of West Africa?

   A. copper

   B. iron ore

   C. hardwoods

   D. gold

_____ **13.** What is the longest river in the world?

   A. Amazon River

   C. Nile River

   B. Mississippi River

   D. Tigris River

_____ **14.** What is genocide?

    A. slaughter of an entire people on ethnic grounds

    B. pesticide that is sprayed on vegetation

    C. study of genetics

    D. poisonous gas

_____ **15.** Which type of power do the rapids and waterfalls on the Congo River provide?

    A. geothermal   **C.** solar

    B. hydroelectric   **D.** wind

_____ **16.** What was the purpose of barracoons, which were used during the early centuries of European contact with West Africa?

    A. to haul heavy loads overland

    B. to serve as currency for trade

    C. to travel inland waterways

    D. to temporarily hold captured enslaved persons

_____ **17.** On which body of water do many West African countries have coastlines?

    A. Indian Ocean   **C.** Atlantic Ocean

    B. Red Sea   **D.** Pacific Ocean

_____ **18.** What is the main way in which African countries have tried to stop the spread of the HIV virus?

    A. spraying pesticides to kill germs

    B. educating people about how to prevent infection

    C. building bigger hospitals to hold more patients

    D. controlling immigration to keep out HIV carriers

_____ **19.** Which of the following countries is located in the region of Southern Africa?

    A. Angola   **C.** Ghana

    B. Egypt   **D.** Nigeria

_____ **20.** Which of the following is a tropical disease carried by mosquitoes that is a problem for several countries in Southern Africa?

    A. dysentery   **C.** malaria

    B. cholera   **D.** HIV/AIDS

Lesson Quiz 1

networks

North Africa

DIRECTIONS: True/False Indicate whether the statement is true (T) or false (F).

_____ **1.** The lowland area located in Northwestern Egypt is called the Qattara Depression.

_____ **2.** The Aswān High Dam is the only dam on the Nile River that helps control flooding.

_____ **3.** For centuries, North Africa has been linked to other lands by the Mediterranean Sea.

_____ **4.** The Arabian Desert covers much of North Africa.

_____ **5.** Algeria, Libya, and Egypt all produce both oil and natural gas.

DIRECTIONS: Multiple Choice Indicate the answer choice that best answers the question.

_____ **6.** Which North African country lies directly west of Egypt?

    A. Libya   **C.** Morocco

    B. Tunisia   **D.** Algeria

_____ **7.** Which mountains form the longest mountain chain in Africa?

    A. Gebel Katherina

    B. Mount Kilimanjaro

    C. Apennine Mountains

    D. Atlas Mountains

_____ **8.** What are considered North Africa's most important bodies of water?

    A. Suez Canal and Red Sea

    B. Atlantic Ocean and Mediterranean Sea

    C. Mediterranean Sea and Nile River

    D. Nile River and Red Sea

_____ **9.** What sort of climate dominates North Africa's western coast?

    A. semiarid climate   **C.** arid climate

    B. Mediterranean climate   **D.** subtropical climate

_____ **10.** Why might future population growth pose a problem for North Africa?

    A. The region lacks open land for cities to expand.

    B. Demand for water could easily become greater than the supply.

    C. The region has too few energy resources to supply a larger population.

    D. Too many people may begin migrating from the region in search of a better life.

Lesson Quiz 2

networks

North Africa

DIRECTIONS: Matching Match each item with its description.

_____ 1. a system of writing that uses pictures to represent sounds or words

_____ 2. kings of ancient Egypt

_____ 3. belief in just one god

_____ 4. a fragrant substance taken from certain plants

_____ 5. figures with political and religious authority who ruled the Muslim empire

A. pharaohs

B. caliphs

C. monotheism

D. hieroglyphics

E. myrrh

DIRECTIONS: Multiple Choice Indicate the answer choice that best answers the question.

_____ 6. Which of the following statements about religion in ancient Egypt is accurate?

    A. Ancient Egyptians believed that the soul disintegrated into nothing after death.

    B. Ancient Egyptians practiced polytheism—the belief in many gods.

    C. Ancient Egyptians were called to prayer six times every day by the pharaoh.

    D. Ancient Egyptians believed in one god—the pharaoh.

_____ 7. The followers of which religion ruled all of North Africa by the A.D. 700s?

    A. Islam   **C.** Christianity

    B. Judaism   **D.** Buddhism

_____ 8. What was the first North African country to gain its independence?

    A. Algeria   **C.** Morocco

    B. Libya   **D.** Egypt

_____ 9. Why did many foreign nations want to control Egypt in the late 1800s?

    A. They wanted the riches that had been buried in the tombs of the pharaohs.

    B. They hoped to gain control over Egypt's vast reserves of oil.

    C. They wanted access to the recently built Suez Canal.

    D. They prized the rich agricultural fields of the Nile River delta.

_____ 10. Which North African country did military leader Muammar al-Qaddafi control for more than 40 years?

    A. Egypt   **C.** Morocco

    B. Tunisia   **D.** Libya

Discovering World Geography

Lesson Quiz 3

North Africa

networks

DIRECTIONS: True/False Indicate whether the statement is true (T) or false (F).

_____ **1.** Three main groups—Egyptians, Moroccans, and Turks—make up the population of North Africa.

_____ **2.** Farms in Libya are small and clustered around oases.

_____ **3.** Islam does not permit art to show the figures of animals or humans.

_____ **4.** In most North African countries, women have a high literacy rate.

_____ **5.** Morocco's government has close relations with the United States.

DIRECTIONS: Multiple Choice Indicate the answer choice that best answers the question.

_____ **6.** Which North African country has the highest rate of urbanization?

    A. Morocco   **C.** Egypt

    B. Algeria   **D.** Libya

_____ **7.** Which of the following activities is most likely to occur at a *souk*?

    A. Muslims worship and pray.

    B. Fruits and vegetables are sold.

    C. Sporting events are held.

    D. Children learn about Islam.

_____ **8.** Which European language are you most likely to hear in North Africa?

    A. German   **C.** French

    B. Arabic   **D.** Italian

_____ **9.** Why are many foreign companies unwilling to invest in Algeria?

    A. The Algerian government keeps tight control of businesses.

    B. Algeria has virtually no natural resources.

    C. Few skilled workers remain in Algeria because of emigration.

    D. Religious fundamentalists in the country discourage such investment.

_____ **10.** Which of the following statements about Islam in modern North Africa is accurate?

    A. Some strict Muslims want to change laws to conform to the rules set by Islam.

    B. North African women have fewer rights than women in other Muslim lands.

    C. Most strict Muslims welcome the influence of Western culture.

    D. The authority of Islam has decreased since the rise of the Internet.

Chapter Test, Form A

North Africa

networks

DIRECTIONS: True/False Indicate whether the statement is true (T) or false (F). If the statement is false, rewrite it to make it true.

_____ **1.** The easternmost country in North Africa is Morocco.

_____

_____ **2.** Egypt controls the important Suez Canal.

_____

_____ **3.** People first settled along the Nile River thousands of years ago.

_____

DIRECTIONS: Matching Match each item with its description.

_____ **4.** the poor farmers of Egypt

_____ **5.** area formed by soil deposits that build up as river water slows down

_____ **6.** chemical compounds often used in fertilizers; found in Morocco

_____ **7.** nuggets of steamed wheat that are the base of many Moroccan meals

_____ **8.** fine, rich soil that is excellent for farming

_____ **9.** vast stretches of sand, as are found in the Sahara

_____ **10.** North African open-air market

A. delta

B. fellaheen

C. silt

D. phosphates

E. couscous

F. souk

G. ergs

DIRECTIONS: Multiple Choice Indicate the answer choice that best answers the question.

_____ **11.** What religion is practiced by most of North Africa's people?

A. Christianity   **C.** Zoroastrianism

B. Islam   **D.** Judaism

_____ **12.** Which of the following was a result of the ancient Egyptians' belief in life after death?

A. Egyptians developed a way of writing using pictures.

B. The pharaohs had vast tombs built for themselves.

C. The ancient Egyptians created one of the world's earliest libraries.

D. People settled along the banks of the Nile River to farm and grow food.

Discovering World Geography

229

_____ **13.** Which North African country has the most diversified economy?

    A. Egypt   **C.** Algeria

    B. Tunisia   **D.** Morocco

_____ **14.** Which of the following was a direct result of the third Carthage War?

    A. Rome came to control western North Africa.

    B. Most North Africans became polytheists.

    C. Islam became the main religion of North Africa.

    D. Lebanese traders began doing business in western North Africa.

_____ **15.** Which of the following statements best describes Islamic fundamentalists?

    A. Muslims who encourage Western influences in North African society

    B. Muslims who want North Africa to retain ties to former European colonizers

    C. Muslims who want a government to follow the strict laws of Islam

    D. Muslims who cooperate with other religions to promote goodwill

---

Egypt broke ranks with other Muslim nations in 1979 when it signed a peace treaty with Israel. It has also developed close ties with the United States since then. That friendship has come under increasing criticism from Muslim fundamentalists. Morocco has also had close relations with the United States. Its government has been criticized for this reason, too. . . .

The situations in Algeria and Libya also are uncertain. Will new governments there be less willing to sell oil to the United States? For what purposes will they use the money they earn from selling oil? The answers to these questions will help to shape the future of North Africa and the world.

—*Discovering World Geography*

_____ **16.** Based on the excerpt, in what way might the governments of Algeria and Libya be able to exert great influence over the United States?

    A. These countries might align with Israel to control trade in the Mediterranean.

    B. These countries might join with Egypt to wage war on the United States.

    C. These countries might send missionaries to convert Americans to Islam.

    D. These countries might cut off oil shipments to the United States.

_____ **17.** Based on the excerpt, which countries developed close ties with the U.S.?

    A. Tunisia and Libya   **C.** Egypt and Morocco

    B. Libya and Algeria   **D.** Libya and Western Sahara

North African Independence

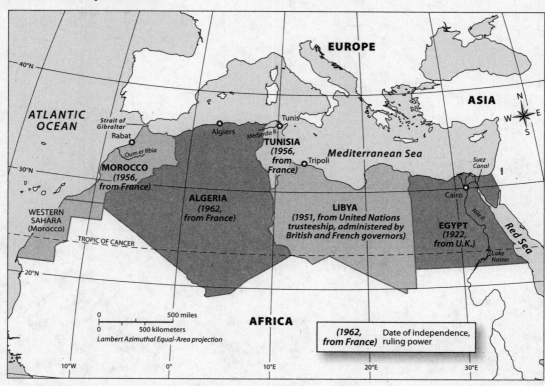

_____ **18.** Based on the map, which North African country was the last to become independent?

    A. Tunisia   **C.** Algeria

    B. Western Sahara   **D.** Egypt

_____ **19.** Based on the map, which of the following is a valid conclusion?

    A. Great Britain showed no interest in colonizing North Africa.

    B. Most of North Africa was once under the control of Italy.

    C. All of the countries of North Africa are controlled by dictatorships.

    D. France exerted a strong presence in colonial North Africa.

DIRECTIONS: Essay Answer the following question on a separate piece of paper.

20. In your opinion, what is the most precious natural resource in North Africa? Explain your answer.

Discovering World Geography

Chapter Test, Form B

networks

North Africa

DIRECTIONS: True/False Indicate whether the statement is true (T) or false (F). If the statement is false, rewrite it to make it true.

_____ **1.** All of North Africa has either a desert or semiarid climate.

_____

_____ **2.** Ancient Egyptians were skilled mathematicians and engineers.

_____

_____ **3.** In October 2011, Libyan rebels killed dictator Hosni Mubarak.

_____

_____ **4.** North Africa's largest city is Casablanca, Morocco.

_____

_____ **5.** Some rural North Africans still live a nomadic lifestyle.

_____

_____ **6.** Slow population growth is a major concern in Libya and Egypt.

_____

DIRECTIONS: Matching Match each item with its description.

_____ **7.** people who move about from place to place in search of food

_____ **8.** a course taken by a river as it flows

_____ **9.** a dry streamed in North Africa

_____ **10.** underground layers of rock in which water collects

A. wadi

B. channel

C. aquifers

D. nomads

DIRECTIONS: Multiple Choice Indicate the answer choice that best answers the question.

_____ **11.** The vast majority of Egyptians live within 12 miles (19 km) of what vital water source?

    A. Strait of Gibraltar   **C.** Suez Canal

    B. Red Sea   **D.** Nile River

_____ **12.** What are Tunisia's main natural resources?

    A. oil and natural gas   **C.** phosphates and iron ore

    B. fish and timber   **D.** coal and tin

Chapter Test, Form B *cont.*

netw**rks**

North Africa

North African Independence

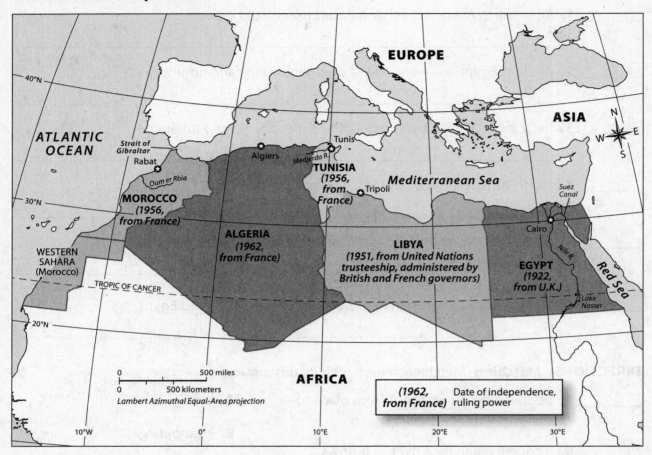

_____ 13. Based on the map, which country claims ownership of Western Sahara?

   A. Algeria

   B. Morocco

   C. Tunisia

   D. France

_____ 14. Based on the map, which of the following is a reasonable conclusion?

   A. The British once controlled the Suez Canal.

   B. Europeans who colonized North Africa shared power with local peoples.

   C. French is the official language of Egypt.

   D. French is rarely spoken in North Africa.

Discovering World Geography

Chapter Test, Form B *cont.*

North Africa

_____ **15.** How was Islamic rule of North Africa different from earlier Roman rule?

    A. Islamic rule had a greater impact on the culture of North Africans than Roman rule.

    B. Islamic rule isolated North Africa, while Roman rule encouraged outside contact.

    C. Under Islam, North Africans mostly spoke local languages rather than Latin.

    D. Trade flourished under Islamic rule, while Roman rule abolished it.

_____ **16.** In which North African country did the Arab Spring revolts begin?

    A. Algeria   **C.** Morocco

    B. Tunisia   **D.** Libya

_____ **17.** Which two political forces are especially strong in modern North Africa?

    A. calls for nuclear disarmament and for peace with Israel

    B. demands for women's rights and a stronger labor movement

    C. a push for democracy and rising Islamic fundamentalism

    D. growing secularism and increased interest in socialism

DIRECTIONS: Short Answer Answer each of the following questions.

18. Describe the rain shadow effect and how it affects the climate in North Africa.

_____

_____

_____

_____

19. Briefly describe a typical North African town or city.

_____

_____

_____

_____

DIRECTIONS: Essay Answer the following question on a separate piece of paper.

20. In your opinion, what is the most precious natural resource in North Africa? Explain your answer.

Lesson Quiz 1

networks

East Africa

DIRECTIONS: True/False Indicate whether the statement is true (T) or false (F).

_____ **1.** Ethiopia and Somalia are part of the Horn of Africa.

_____ **2.** Kilimanjaro is the tallest mountain in Africa.

_____ **3.** The source of the Nile River is still unknown.

_____ **4.** In many parts of East Africa, wet and dry seasons alternate.

_____ **5.** The soils in East Africa are ideal for farming.

DIRECTIONS: Multiple Choice Indicate the answer choice that best answers the question.

_____ **6.** To which of the following landforms was East Africa once connected?

    A. Mesopotamian Plain

    B. Deccan Plateau

    C. Arabian Peninsula

    D. Anatolian Peninsula

_____ **7.** Which of the following statements about Lake Victoria is accurate?

    A. It is the largest freshwater lake in the world.

    B. It is the largest lake in Africa.

    C. It is one of the deepest lakes in the world.

    D. It supports no fish life.

_____ **8.** In what way might climate change affect Mount Kilimanjaro?

    A. Kilimanjaro will probably erupt within the next 20 years.

    B. Its climate may change from highland to tropical over the next 20 years.

    C. New glaciers are likely to form in the highest mountain valleys.

    D. Kilimanjaro's glaciers may melt away over the next 20 years.

_____ **9.** Which alternative energy source comes from sources like hot springs in Kenya and Djibouti?

    A. geothermal   **C.** solar

    B. hydroelectric   **D.** wind

_____ **10.** Which of the following events draws thousands of tourists to East Africa each year?

    A. Northern Lights   **C.** Harvest Moon

    B. Great Migration   **D.** Mardi Gras

Lesson Quiz 2

networks

East Africa

DIRECTIONS: Matching Match each item with its description.

_____ **1.** regular tax payment by a weak country to a stronger country

_____ **2.** walled trade city founded in the A.D. 900s

_____ **3.** powerful civilization that arose in ancient Nubia

_____ **4.** actions by which stronger nations exert control over weaker nations

_____ **5.** language that is a mixture of Arabic and Bantu

A. Kush

B. Swahili

C. tribute

D. imperialism

E. Kilwa

DIRECTIONS: Multiple Choice Indicate the answer choice that best answers the question.

_____ **6.** Which burial custom did the Kushites adopt from the Egyptians?

    A. They made and lit funeral pyres for their dead.

    B. They held services in boats on the Nile River to honor their dead.

    C. They built pyramids to mark the tombs of their rulers and nobles.

    D. They made caskets of bronze and gold and buried their dead.

_____ **7.** In which area of East Africa did Arabs begin to settle in the A.D. 900s?

    A. on the Indian Ocean coast   **C.** around Lake Victoria

    B. along the Nile River   **D.** on the slopes of Mount Kilimanjaro

_____ **8.** Why did the Portuguese travel to India by sea not by land around 1500?

    A. The British and the Germans controlled the land routes.

    B. Travel by sea was easier and less costly.

    C. There were no land routes to India from Europe.

    D. The Portuguese lacked experience at overland travel.

_____ **9.** Which European country claimed it had the right to establish a "protectorate" in Ethiopia in 1889?

    A. Britain   **C.** Spain

    B. France   **D.** Italy

_____ **10.** How did the conflict in Somalia in 1992 affect Kenya?

    A. Civil war broke out in Kenya.

    B. Kenyans joined forces with Somalis against European control.

    C. Refugees from Somalia made their way to Kenya.

    D. The United States led an intervention force in Kenya.

Lesson Quiz 3

networks

East Africa

DIRECTIONS: True/False Indicate whether the statement is true (T) or false (F).

_____ **1.** Ethiopia has the largest population of the countries in East Africa.

_____ **2.** Most East Africans are either Christian or Muslim.

_____ **3.** Most East Africans live in cities.

_____ **4.** The earliest known human bones were found in East Africa.

_____ **5.** Industrialization has come quickly for East Africa.

DIRECTIONS: Multiple Choice Indicate the answer choice that best answers the question.

_____ **6.** Which East African country has the lowest population density?

    A. Rwanda   **C.** Uganda

    B. Kenya   **D.** Somalia

_____ **7.** Which of the following statements about the general population in East Africa is accurate?

    A. Most people live in cities.

    B. Most people have strong ties to their ethnic groups.

    C. Most people are nomadic.

    D. Most people have a strong national identity.

_____ **8.** Which of the following statements about rural people in East Africa is most accurate?

    A. Most rural people depend on agriculture to make a living.

    B. Most rural people live in brick houses and have modern appliances.

    C. Most rural people live on plantations that grow cash crops.

    D. Most rural people commute to the cities for their jobs.

_____ **9.** What is the main reason that East Africa's agriculture is heavily dependent on growing cash crops for export?

    A. The soil and climate in East Africa are ideal for growing cash crops.

    B. The governments have given land to those who want to start big farms.

    C. The focus on growing cash crops for export started in colonial times.

    D. Subsistence farms are less vulnerable to drought than larger farms.

_____ **10.** What has been one of the major causes of hunger and poor nutrition in East Africa?

    A. wildlife sanctuaries   **C.** ecotourism

    B. war and conflict   **D.** industrialization

Chapter Test, Form A

netw**rks**

East Africa

DIRECTIONS: True/False Indicate whether the statement is true (T) or false (F). If the statement is false, rewrite it to make it true.

_____**1.** The East African country of Rwanda is landlocked.

_____

_____**2.** The Nile River has two sets of headwaters: the Blue Nile and the White Nile.

_____

_____**3.** Well-known wildlife reserves are located on the Sudanese Plain, an area of tropical grasslands larger than the state of Connecticut.

_____

_____

_____**4.** Even before the 1800s, Europeans knew a great deal about Africa.

_____

_____**5.** Folktales and fables are part of East Africa's oral tradition.

_____

DIRECTIONS: Matching Match each item with its description.

_____ **6.** ethnic group that dominated the Rwandan government in the 1990s

_____ **7.** first prime minister of independent Kenya

_____ **8.** leading East African novelist who wrote *Weep Not, Child*

_____ **9.** group of related people descended from the same ancestor

_____ **10.** type of energy produced through the use of falling water

A. Ngugi wa Thiong'o

B. hydroelectric power

C. Hutu

D. clan

E. Jomo Kenyatta

DIRECTIONS: Multiple Choice Indicate the answer choice that best answers the question.

_____ **11.** What powerful force separated Africa from the Arabian Peninsula?

A. A volcano erupted and formed the Arabian Peninsula.

B. A tsunami filled the great valley now known as the Red Sea.

C. Shifting tectonic plates pulled the two areas apart.

D. Erosion over millions of years caused some land to sink and some to rise.

Discovering World Geography

241

Chapter Test, Form A *cont.*

East Africa

_____ **12.** What is one effect of the intermittent rainfall and high temperatures that occur in many areas of East Africa?

    A. East Africa must pipe in water from outside the region.

    B. Except for the Nile, East Africa has few important rivers.

    C. East Africa has no areas suitable for agriculture.

    D. East Africa's lakes are too small to support fishing.

_____ **13.** What mineral is taken in large amounts from Djibouti's Lake Assal?

    A. gold   **C.** gems

    B. tin   **D.** salt

Kenya also has a wide variety of spoken languages. Swahili and English are used by large numbers of people to communicate. Those two languages are the official languages of the Kenya National Assembly and of the courts.

Swahili is almost universal in Tanzania. The geographical location and colonial history of East African countries have often made an impact on the languages spoken there. For example, in Somalia the official language is Somali. However, Arabic is widely spoken in the northern area of the country, and Swahili is widespread in the south. In addition, English and Italian are used in the country's colleges and universities. In Djibouti, Arabic and French are important languages.

—Discovering World Geography

_____ **14.** According to the excerpt, in which East African country are English and Italian used in colleges and universities?

    A. Kenya   **C.** Tanzania

    B. Somalia   **D.** Djibouti

_____ **15.** Based on the excerpt, which two ethnic groups are likely to have played a large role in Djibouti's history?

    A. the English and the Italians   **C.** the French and the Italians

    B. the Italians and the Arabs   **D.** the Arabs and the French

_____ **16.** Through which economic activity did the people of Aksum attain their power and wealth?

    A. fishing   **C.** trading

    B. mining   **D.** farming

Discovering World Geography

_____ **17.** What was the purpose of David Livingstone's trip to Africa in the 1800s?

    A. to find the source of the Nile River

    B. to learn what had happened to Henry Morton Stanley

    C. to hunt for gold

    D. to begin an archaeological study of Aksum

DIRECTIONS: Short Answer Answer each of the following questions.

18. What was the purpose of the Jonglei Canal project began in the Sudd area in the 1970s? Why was the project suspended?

_____

_____

_____

_____

_____

19. What happened as a result of the ethnic tensions that afflicted Rwanda and Burundi in the 1990s?

_____

_____

_____

_____

_____

DIRECTIONS: Essay Answer the following question on a separate piece of paper.

20. How have the major health issues in East Africa affected the region's economy? Explain.

Chapter Test, Form B

networks

East Africa

DIRECTIONS: True/False Indicate whether the statement is true (T) or false (F). If the statement is false, rewrite it to make it true.

_____ **1.** Lake Victoria is the largest lake on the continent of Africa.

_____

_____ **2.** High mountains such as Kilimanjaro and the peaks of the Ruwenzori Range contain glaciers.

_____

_____ **3.** The kings of Aksum adopted Islam as their religion.

_____

_____ **4.** Kenya was a British colony.

_____

_____ **5.** Manufacturing is the main economic activity in East Africa.

_____

DIRECTIONS: Matching Match each item with its description.

_____ **6.** capital of Kenya

_____ **7.** ethnic group inhabiting the highlands of Kenya

_____ **8.** ancient region in northeastern Africa that was the home of the Kushites

_____ **9.** nomadic ethnic group of northern Tanzania and southern Kenya

_____ **10.** religious and military leader of rebellious forces in Sudan

A. Masai

B. Kikuyu

C. Nubia

D. Muhammad Ahmad

E. Nairobi

DIRECTIONS: Multiple Choice Indicate the answer choice that best answers the question.

_____ **11.** What is a distinguishing feature of the eastern Rift Valley of East Africa?

    A. Rain forests fill the valley.

    B. It is one of the hottest and driest places on Earth.

    C. When irrigated, the soils are fertile and ideal for farming.

    D. It is one of the wettest places on Earth.

_____ **12.** At what city do the Blue Nile and the White Nile meet?

    A. Nairobi   **C.** Mogadishu

    B. Kilwa   **D.** Khartoum

_____ **13.** How have droughts and unwise land use affected the Sahel?

    A. Farmers have installed irrigation systems.

    B. People are moving to the area to enjoy the drier air.

    C. The land is turning into desert.

    D. The land is turning into salt seas.

_____ **14.** Which group brought Christianity to Ethiopia?

    A. Greek soldiers in the A.D. 100s

    B. traders and missionaries from the Mediterranean region in the A.D. 300s

    C. Portuguese missionaries in the late 1400s

    D. Italian diplomats in the late 1880s

_____ **15.** Which of the following statements about the economic development of East Africa is accurate?

    A. The workforce is well educated and well trained.

    B. The emphasis is on primary industries.

    C. An extensive rail network has helped attract factories.

    D. The emphasis is on service industries.

> The history of Somalia since independence in 1960 offers another example of the problems East African countries have faced. Since the 1970s, Somalia has been scarred by civil war. Border disputes with Ethiopia have also increased instability. Rival clan factions have engaged in bitter feuds. Drought has brought famine to much of the country. In late 1992, the United States led a multinational intervention force in an effort to restore peace to the country. The civil war in Somalia, however, remained unresolved.
>
> The instability, misery, and violence in Somalia also have affected neighboring countries. Thousands of refugees, for example, have made their way into Kenya. A refugee is a person who flees to another country for safety.
>
> —*Discovering World Geography*

_____ **16.** Based on the excerpt, how did the civil war in Somalia affect neighboring countries?

    A. People who fled from Somalia were returned to their country.

    B. Migrants from Kenya flooded into Somalia.

    C. U.S. troops rescued refugees in neighboring countries.

    D. People from Somalia entered Kenya in search of safety.

_____ **17.** Based on the excerpt, why was there conflict between Somalia and Ethiopia?

    A. They each claimed the right to host U.S. troops.

    B. They quarreled over water rights.

    C. They could not agree on border lines.

    D. They were divided by ethnic tensions.

In the late 1970s, the swampy Sudd was the focus of a huge construction project called the Jonglei Canal. This channel was planned to bypass the Sudd. The goal was to allow the headstreams of the White Nile to flow more freely. Instead of the water spreading across the Sudd and slowly moving through it, the canal would allow more water to flow downstream and reach Sudan and Egypt. That would support more agriculture and better city services in those countries. But it would also damage the wetland environment of the Sudd. Fisheries could collapse and go extinct. Construction was suspended in 1983. The project could not continue because civil war in Sudan made it too dangerous.

—*Discovering World Geography*

_____ **18.** Based on the excerpt, what was the main purpose for building the Jonglei Canal?

    A. to supply more water to Sudan and Egypt

    B. to prevent flooding in the Sudd

    C. to expand the fisheries

    D. to preserve the wetland environment

_____ **19.** Based on the excerpt, why was the project suspended?

    A. Environmental groups protested the canal.

    B. Civil war broke out in Sudan.

    C. Rising costs of building materials made the project too costly.

    D. A severe drought disrupted the flow of water.

DIRECTIONS: Essay Answer the following question on a separate piece of paper.

20. How have the major health issues in East Africa affected the region's economy? Explain.

Lesson Quiz 1

networks

Central Africa

DIRECTIONS: True/False Indicate whether the statement is true (T) or false (F).

_____ **1.** The dominant landform of Central Africa is the Congo River watershed.

_____ **2.** In Central Africa, the farther one gets from the Equator, the more it rains.

_____ **3.** Experts say that clearing land for slash-and-burn agriculture may have increased the expanse of savanna in Central Africa.

_____ **4.** Central Africa has extensive modern transportation networks.

_____ **5.** Central Africa lacks any reserves of petroleum or natural gas.

DIRECTIONS: Multiple Choice Indicate the answer choice that best answers the question.

_____ **6.** How does São Tomé and Príncipe differ from all the other Central African nations?

    A. It is the only Central African nation that is not located near the Equator.

    B. It is the largest nation in Central Africa.

    C. It is the only landlocked Central African nation.

    D. It is the only island nation in Central Africa.

_____ **7.** Why is the Congo River not navigable for its entire course?

    A. Rebel groups have blocked portions of the river to ship traffic.

    B. Several series of cataracts and rapids occur along the river.

    C. The river is severely polluted in many areas.

    D. Parts of the river are too narrow to allow for ship traffic.

_____ **8.** Which of the following countries is the largest in Central Africa?

    A. Gabon   **C.** Democratic Republic of the Congo

    B. Cameroon   **D.** Central African Republic

_____ **9.** Why are few plants found at ground level in Central African rain forests?

    A. The forest floor consists mostly of clay soil and gravel.

    B. Because of the forest canopy, very little sunlight filters through to the forest floor.

    C. The animals of the forest eat most of the ground-level plants.

    D. The forest does not get enough precipitation to support ground-level plant life.

_____ **10.** Which activity produces 90 percent of the total exports of the Democratic Republic of the Congo?

    A. mining   **C.** fishing

    B. agriculture   **D.** tourism

Lesson Quiz 2

networks

Central Africa

DIRECTIONS: True/False Indicate whether the statement is true (T) or false (F).

_____ **1.** Throughout prehistoric times, Central Africans were farmers and herders.

_____ **2.** The slave trade in Central Africa provided workers for plantations in the Americas.

_____ **3.** An important goal of colonialism is profit for the controlling power.

_____ **4.** France ruled the colonies of the Republic of the Congo, Gabon, and Cameroon in the region of Central Africa.

_____ **5.** Gabon and the Republic of the Congo have achieved relative stability.

DIRECTIONS: Multiple Choice Indicate the answer choice that best answers the question.

_____ **6.** How did palm oil affect the lives of the early peoples of Central Africa?

    A. Palm oil became an important part of the religious rituals practiced by the people.

    B. Central Africans traded the oil to nearby civilizations for other products.

    C. Proteins and vitamins in the oil made people healthier, boosting the population.

    D. The oil was used in lamps, allowing the people to work at night.

_____ **7.** Why were stone tools not completely replaced by iron tools in early Central Africa?

    A. Iron tools were more difficult to make.

    B. Iron was expensive and access to iron ore was limited.

    C. Only religious leaders and tribal chiefs were permitted to use iron tools.

    D. The stone tools worked much better than those made of iron.

_____ **8.** Which European country was the first to become actively involved in the Central African slave trade?

    A. Belgium   **C.** Spain

    B. France   **D.** Portugal

_____ **9.** Which two plants had an important effect on farming and diet in Central Africa after the rise of colonialism?

    A. sugar cane and yams   **C.** potatoes and tobacco

    B. millet and barley   **D.** cassava and maize

_____ **10.** Which statement best describes the role of Belgium's King Leopold II in the history of Central Africa?

    A. He sought to improve the working conditions of Africans.

    B. He was the first European to grant independence to a Central African colony.

    C. He strongly supported the idea of dividing Africa into European colonies for profit.

    D. He sent missionaries who converted most Central Africans to Christianity.

Discovering World Geography

Lesson Quiz 3

networks

Central Africa

DIRECTIONS: True/False Indicate whether the statement is true (T) or false (F).

_____ **1.** Life expectancy at birth varies widely among Central African countries.

_____ **2.** Most of Central Africa's people live in urban areas such as Kinshasa.

_____ **3.** Almost all Central Africans follow traditional African religions.

_____ **4.** Music, visual arts, and literature are important in Central African culture.

_____ **5.** Environmentalists and commercial interests usually work together to promote economic growth in Central Africa.

DIRECTIONS: Multiple Choice Indicate the answer choice that best answers the question.

_____ **6.** Which of the following statements about the population of Central Africa is accurate?

    A. The region has a very large population, relative to its size.

    B. People over the age of 55 make up most of the population.

    C. The population growth rate is high.

    D. The region has a high population density.

_____ **7.** What is especially notable about the Bambuti people of the Congo forests?

    A. Their diet consists entirely of meat and fish.

    B. They are extremely short in stature.

    C. They have no spoken language.

    D. They were the first Christian converts in Central Africa.

_____ **8.** Why did French become the most common trade language in Central Africa?

    A. The language is a remnant of French and Belgian colonialism.

    B. France is the most important trading partner of most Central African nations.

    C. France is the only European country that recognizes the independence of Central African nations.

    D. Most Central African nations follow French laws and government structures.

_____ **9.** What vegetable is a staple in the diet of most Central Africans?

    A. beets   **C.** green beans

    B. okra   **D.** spinach

_____ **10.** For what musical style is the city of Kinshasa in the Democratic Republic of the Congo noted?

    A. electronic music   **C.** African jazz

    B. flute music   **D.** Afrobeat

Discovering World Geography

Chapter Test, Form A

networks

Central Africa

DIRECTIONS: True/False Indicate whether the statement is true (T) or false (F). If the statement is false, rewrite it to make it true.

_____ 1. The eastern part of Central Africa runs along the Great Rift Valley and features rugged mountain ranges and long, narrow lakes.

_____

_____ 2. Some Central African countries have been plagued by political instability and corruption.

_____

_____ 3. Central Africans who flee war and conflict are known as *nomads*.

_____

_____ 4. In rural Central Africa, most people work as miners.

_____

DIRECTIONS: Matching Match each item with its description.

_____ 5. tuberous plant grown for its edible roots

_____ 6. area of grassland with a mixture of trees and shrubs

_____ 7. land drained by a river and its system of tributaries

_____ 8. grass that produces edible seeds in a short growing season

_____ 9. passage in which freshwater meets salt water

_____ 10. wide variety of life on Earth

A. watershed

B. savanna

C. estuary

D. millet

E. biodiversity

F. cassava

DIRECTIONS: Multiple Choice Indicate the answer choice that best answers the question.

_____ 11. How does the Central African Republic differ from all the other Central African nations?

    A. It is the only Central African nation that is not located near the Equator.

    B. It is the largest nation in Central Africa.

    C. It is the only landlocked Central African nation.

    D. It is the only island nation in Central Africa.

_____ 12. Which is the most populous country in Central Africa?

    A. Cameroon

    B. Equatorial Guinea

    C. Central African Republic

    D. Democratic Republic of the Congo

_____ **13.** Which of the following correctly identifies a stage of the "triangular trade"?

    A. Cotton, sugar, and molasses were shipped from Africa to the Americas.

    B. Millet, palm oil, and cassava came to Africa from the Americas.

    C. Slaves were shipped from Africa to Europe.

    D. Cloth, beads, and guns came to Africa from Europe.

_____ **14.** How does daily life for women in rural Central Africa differ from that for men?

    A. Women mainly grow crops such as coffee and cotton for sale.

    B. Women typically gather and prepare food.

    C. Women usually do the hunting, trapping, and fishing.

    D. Women are mainly responsible for building family homes.

_____ **15.** The Yaka people of Central Africa are known for what type of art?

    A. pottery and sculpture

    B. statues depicting motherhood

    C. decorative masks and figurines

    D. stone and nail-studded statues

Around 10,000 years ago, Earth's climate entered a dry phase. Vegetation patterns changed in response and led to the movement of people. The changes also intensified the struggle for survival: The region's inhabitants were forced to find ways to get more food from a smaller area of their environment.

Gradually, a transformation that historians call the agricultural revolution swept through the region, beginning in the north. People began to collect plants—especially roots and tubers—on a more regular basis. This led to the invention of specialized digging tools, such as stone hoes. Over time, the hunters and gatherers turned into farmers. They learned how to clear plots of fertile land and plant a piece of each root or tuber that they ate.

—*Discovering World Geography*

_____ **16.** Based on the excerpt, which event was the primary cause of the agricultural revolution in the region?

    A. Earth's climate changed, forcing people to find new ways to feed themselves.

    B. Central Africans invented stone tools.

    C. People began settling near reliable sources of water.

    D. People learned to clear plots of fertile land.

Discovering World Geography

_____ **17.** Based on the excerpt, what is the principal way in which stone hoes helped people in the struggle for survival?

   A. People used them to kill game to provide meat.

   B. People used them to dig roots and clear ground.

   C. People used them as weapons for defending their communities.

   D. People used them to harvest millet for grain.

DIRECTIONS: Short Answer Answer each of the following questions.

18. Give three reasons why the Congo River is important to Central Africa.

_____

_____

_____

_____

_____

19. Provide an example of how the environment of Central Africa influences the types of housing found there.

_____

_____

_____

_____

_____

DIRECTIONS: Essay Answer the following question on a separate piece of paper.

20. Explain what led to the development of the slave trade in Central Africa in the 1400s. Then summarize how the slave trade was a part of what was called the "triangular trade."

Chapter Test, Form B

netw⊙rks

Central Africa

DIRECTIONS: True/False Indicate whether the statement is true (T) or false (F). If the statement is false, rewrite it to make it true.

_____ **1.** The agricultural revolution in Central Africa laid the foundation for village life and also for the development of crafts.

_____

_____ **2.** Central Africans make tapioca and flour from potatoes.

_____

_____ **3.** In Central Africa, more and more people are moving into cities.

_____

_____ **4.** Hundreds of different languages are spoken across Central Africa.

_____

_____ **5.** In the Democratic Republic of the Congo, about half of the people are Muslim.

_____

DIRECTIONS: Matching Match each item with its description.

_____ **6.** slaves were shipped from Africa to the Americas

_____ **7.** country that is one of the world's leading producers of manganese

_____ **8.** country that gets nearly half its export earnings from diamonds

_____ **9.** country with the region's most abundant natural resources

_____ **10.** country whose capital is Brazzaville

A. Democratic Republic of the Congo

B. Gabon

C. Middle Passage

D. Republic of the Congo

E. Central African Republic

DIRECTIONS: Multiple Choice Indicate the answer choice that best answers the question.

_____ **11.** Which Central African nation served as one of the most important centers of the slave trade?

A. Republic of the Congo   **C.** Equatorial Guinea

B. Central African Republic   **D.** Gabon

_____ **12.** In what field have Central Africans Clémentine Madiya Faik-Nzuji, Ntumb Diur, and Kama Kamanda gained international fame?

A. photography   **C.** literature

B. music   **D.** motion pictures

Discovering World Geography   **257**

Chapter Test, Form B *cont.*

Central Africa

_____ **13.** Which of the following statements about the Congo River is accurate?

    A. It is navigable for its entire course.

    B. It is the longest river in Africa.

    C. It empties into the Indian Ocean.

    D. It is the world's third-largest river when measured by water flow.

_____ **14.** How did Europeans often justify the colonization of Central Africa?

    A. They believed that whites were morally entitled to the region's riches.

    B. They promised to share the riches they made with the people of Central Africa.

    C. They claimed their goal was to promote civilization and to spread Christianity.

    D. They argued that they needed the region's resources more than local people did.

_____ **15.** Which of the following statements about Central Africa's population is accurate?

    A. Children and teenagers make up about half of the region's population.

    B. The life expectancy for Central Africans is the highest in the world.

    C. The region's rate of population growth is falling rapidly.

    D. Central Africa is the most densely populated region in the world.

> With great population growth comes the need for economic development. The economies of many countries in Central Africa depend heavily on agriculture, logging, and mining. Coastal countries with rain forests, such as Gabon, export significant amounts of valuable hardwoods, including Rhodesian teak, ebony, African walnut, and rosewood.
>
> In general, economic development depends on economic growth. Economic growth usually means that more resources are used and more pollution and waste are produced. Some economic activities, particularly mining and lumbering, take place in areas with high biodiversity. Some critics of mining and timber cutting argue that biodiversity needs to be conserved.
>
> —*Discovering World Geography*

_____ **16.** Based on the excerpt, which of the following is a reasonable conclusion?

    A. All Central Africans are committed to protecting the region's biodiversity.

    B. Central African nations can never take full advantage of their natural resources.

    C. There is tension between those who promote economic growth in Central Africa and those who favor environmental conservation.

    D. Building up Central Africa's economy requires improved agricultural techniques.

Chapter Test, Form B *cont.*

Central Africa

_____ **17.** Based on the excerpt, which of the following is currently the least important part of the economies of most Central African nations?

    A. farming   **C.** mining

    B. heavy industry   **D.** logging

Independence for Central African Countries

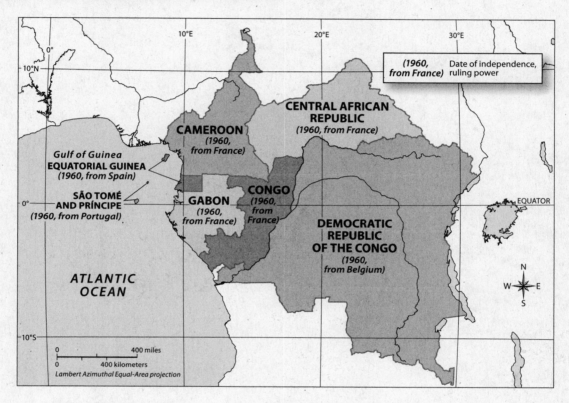

_____ **18.** Based on the map, which Central African country was once a colonial possession of Spain?

    A. Central African Republic   **C.** Cameroon

    B. Equatorial Guinea   **D.** São Tomé and Príncipe

_____ **19.** Based on the map, which of the following European countries had the greatest colonial presence in Central Africa?

    A. France   **C.** Germany

    B. Spain   **D.** Portugal

DIRECTIONS: Essay Answer the following question on a separate piece of paper.

20. Explain what led to the development of the slave trade in Central Africa in the 1400s. Then summarize how the slave trade was a part of what was called the "triangular trade."

Discovering World Geography

Lesson Quiz 1

networks

West Africa

DIRECTIONS: True/False Indicate whether the statement is true (T) or false (F).

_____ **1.** West Africa has no major mountain ranges.

_____ **2.** Lake Chad is one of the world's largest artificial lakes.

_____ **3.** The savanna receives more rainfall than the Sahel.

_____ **4.** Though gold first attracted Europeans to the region, gold mining is no longer important to West Africa.

_____ **5.** Most of Benin's rain forest has been cleared of hardwoods.

DIRECTIONS: Multiple Choice Indicate the answer choice that best answers the question.

_____ **6.** What do the countries of Mali, Niger, and Chad have in common?

    A. They all have a coastline on the Atlantic Ocean.

    B. No mountains are located within their borders.

    C. They are all landlocked countries.

    D. They are all island nations.

_____ **7.** Which of the following is West Africa's longest and most important river?

    A. Niger River

    B. Senegal River

    C. Nile River

    D. Black Volta River

_____ **8.** Which of the following correctly lists the climate zones of West Africa from north to south?

    A. savanna, rain forest, semiarid Sahel, arid desert

    B. arid desert, semiarid Sahel, savanna, rain forest

    C. semiarid Sahel, rain forest, savanna, arid desert

    D. rain forest, savannah, semiarid Sahel, arid desert

_____ **9.** Which body of water is the main source for the fishing industry in Mali?

    A. Lake Chad   **C.** Lake Volta

    B. Senegal River   **D.** Niger River

_____ **10.** In which natural resource is Nigeria especially rich?

    A. silver   **C.** manganese

    B. oil   **D.** salt

Lesson Quiz 2

networks

West Africa

DIRECTIONS: True/False Indicate whether the statement is true (T) or false (F).

_____ **1.** The Almoravids were North African Christians who conquered ancient Ghana.

_____ **2.** The Ghana Empire was West Africa's first trading kingdom.

_____ **3.** Liberia was founded in 1822 as a home for freed American slaves.

_____ **4.** Since the Biafran war ended, Nigeria has been ruled by freely elected governments.

_____ **5.** By 1961, all of France's West African colonies had achieved independence.

DIRECTIONS: Multiple Choice Indicate the answer choice that best answers the question.

_____ **6.** How did the Sahara of 10,000 years ago differ from the Sahara of today?

    A. Even fewer plant and animal species lived there.

    B. Great cities with thousands of inhabitants existed there.

    C. It had grasslands and was more like a savanna than a desert.

    D. It was mostly tropical rainforest.

_____ **7.** Which of the following allowed the Bantu to expand easily into areas occupied by hunter-gatherer groups?

    A. their Muslim religion   **C.** their great wealth

    B. their farming practices   **D.** their knowledge of the Sahara

_____ **8.** Which is the best explanation for the collapse of the Ghana Empire?

    A. The region's gold reserves became depleted.

    B. The conquering Almoravids brought infectious disease.

    C. Trading routes shifted to other parts of West Africa.

    D. The empire grew weak because it could not feed its growing population.

_____ **9.** From what activity did the small African kingdoms along the West African coast become rich beginning around the 1500s?

    A. slave trade   **C.** sale of oil and natural gas

    B. sale of tobacco   **D.** gold-for-salt trade

_____ **10.** Which of the following statements about the European colonization of West Africa is accurate?

    A. Europeans colonized only the coastal regions.

    B. Europeans made the important decisions about how Africans lived.

    C. Europeans left the most fertile land for the Africans to use for their farms.

    D. Germany and Portugal claimed the most territory in West Africa.

          Discovering World Geography

Lesson Quiz 3

networks

West Africa

DIRECTIONS: True/False Indicate whether the statement is true (T) or false (F).

_____ **1.** West Africa is the least populous region of Africa.

_____ **2.** European languages are the official languages of most of West Africa.

_____ **3.** Villages in West Africa represent the homesteads of extended families.

_____ **4.** The colonial powers built West African economies on a wide variety of resources and industries.

_____ **5.** The HIV virus is a serious problem in West Africa.

DIRECTIONS: Multiple Choice Indicate the answer choice that best answers the question.

_____ **6.** Which of the following statements about languages in West Africa is accurate?

    A. Most traditional, ethnic languages of West Africa have died out.

    B. Arabic is almost unheard of in West Africa.

    C. In some places, people speak a blend of European and African languages.

    D. In most of West Africa, it is illegal for people to speak a traditional language.

_____ **7.** What is animism?

    A. the belief in only one god

    B. the belief in spirits of one's ancestors, the air, the earth, and rivers

    C. the belief in a god who is not wholly good and is possibly evil

    D. the belief that one's ruler is a god

_____ **8.** Which is the largest city in West Africa?

    A. Bamako, Mali   **C.** Dakar, Senegal

    B. Lagos, Nigeria   **D.** Accra, Ghana

_____ **9.** What is one way life in rural West Africa differs from life in cities there?

    A. The nuclear family structure is more common in rural areas.

    B. Rural dwellers are far more likely to deal with a wide variety of people every day.

    C. Rural West Africans speak English or French almost exclusively.

    D. Rural dwellers are more likely to wear traditional clothing.

_____ **10.** What is the most popular form of recreation in West Africa?

    A. dance   **C.** sports

    B. music   **D.** visual arts

Chapter Test, Form A

networks

West Africa

DIRECTIONS: True/False Indicate whether the statement is true (T) or false (F). If the statement is false, rewrite it to make it true.

_____ **1.** Recent drought has contributed to the shrinking of Lake Chad.

_____

_____ **2.** In early times, the main barrier to contact between West Africa and North Africa was the Niger River.

_____

_____ **3.** In 1989, Charles Taylor led an invasion of Nigeria to depose the president.

_____

_____ **4.** West Africa had few large towns until the colonial period.

_____

_____ **5.** Chinua Achebe is a famous writer from Nigeria.

_____

DIRECTIONS: Matching Match each item with its description.

_____ **6.** semiarid region between the Sahara desert and the savanna

_____ **7.** depressed area of land drained by a river and its tributaries

_____ **8.** blend of two or more languages that becomes the language of a region

_____ **9.** arid desert plateau region near Chad's eastern border

_____ **10.** simplified language used by people who cannot speak each other's languages

A. basin

B. Sahel

C. pidgin

D. Ennedi

E. creole

DIRECTIONS: Multiple Choice Indicate the answer choice that best answers the question.

_____ **11.** The Fouta Djallon, a highland region of savanna and deciduous forest, is located in which country?

    A. Guinea

    B. Mali

    C. Niger

    D. Chad

_____ **12.** What is the key characteristic of the climates throughout West Africa?

    A. cold season and hot season

    B. seasons of high and low humidity

    C. wet season and dry season

    D. seasons of high and low barometric pressure

European countries that carved up Africa to add to their overseas empires had their own reasons for setting colonial borders where they did. They did not consider the borders of the different ethnic groups of the Africans who already lived on the land they colonized. As a result, the European colonies in Africa contained populations that were ethnically diverse. When African countries declared independence, the new national borders closely followed the old colonial borders, preserving that diversity.

Establishing a sense of national unity is difficult, however. Many people have a stronger identification with their ethnic group than with the country they live in. For example, the Hausa are citizens of Nigeria, but many feel closer ties to the people and culture of the Hausa than to the country of Nigeria.

Another factor working against national unity is that a West African ethnic group does not typically live in only one country. Some Yoruba people, for example, live in Nigeria. Other Yoruba live in Benin. No matter where they live, the Yoruba feel a closer connection to other Yoruba people than to Nigeria or Benin.

—Discovering World Geography

_____ **13.** Based on the excerpt, what effects did colonial borders created by Europeans have on ethnic groups in West Africa?

    A. Traditional enemies were kept away from one another to lessen tensions.

    B. Ethnic differences ceased to matter in post-colonial West Africa.

    C. Ethnic groups often were divided by national borders.

    D. Traditional languages quickly died out, replaced by English or French.

_____ **14.** Based on the excerpt, which of the following is a reasonable conclusion?

    A. The map of West Africa would look much different if national boundaries followed ethnic divisions.

    B. Most West Africans feel closer ties to their country than to their ethnic groups.

    C. The borders drawn by European powers have helped to promote national unity among West Africans.

    D. West Africans have very little loyalty to their ethnic group.

_____ **15.** Which domesticated animals were ideal for desert dwellers due to their ability to survive without water for long periods of time?

    A. cattle   **C.** goats

    B. sheep   **D.** camels

_____ **16.** Which of the following shows the major West African trading kingdoms in correct chronological order?

    A. Bantu, Songhai, Ghana   **C.** Songhai, Ghana, Bantu

    B. Ghana, Mali, Songhai   **D.** Mali, Ghana, Songhai

_____ **17.** Which of the following statements about the population of West Africa as it compares to most of the rest of the world is accurate?

    A. The population is much older.

    B. The birthrate is considerably lower.

    C. The population is growing more slowly.

    D. Life expectancy is shorter.

DIRECTIONS: Short Answer Answer each of the following questions.

18. Which three parts of Bantu culture were spread through the Bantu migration?

_____

_____

_____

_____

19. In what way is the hardwood industry of Benin similar to the iron ore industry of Mauritania?

_____

_____

_____

DIRECTIONS: Essay Answer the following question on a separate piece of paper.

20. Discuss the political and social development of modern Nigeria. How did the country's colonial history and religious and ethnic differences contribute to the instability there?

Chapter Test, Form B

networks

West Africa

DIRECTIONS: True/False Indicate whether the statement is true (T) or false (F). If the statement is false, rewrite it to make it true.

_____ **1.** Cape Verde and Tristan da Cunha are landlocked nations of West Africa.

_____

_____ **2.** Ghana's main sources of electricity are two dams on the Volta River.

_____

_____ **3.** The empire of Mali reached its height under the emperor Mansa Musa.

_____

_____ **4.** In rural West Africa, ethnicity and tradition help to preserve traditional languages and culture.

_____

_____ **5.** The British government legalized the slave trade in 1807.

_____

DIRECTIONS: Matching Match each item with its description.

_____ **6.** to formally withdraw from a political union

_____ **7.** hot winter wind that blows up dust in the Sahara

_____ **8.** the practice of seizing political control of other places to create an empire

_____ **9.** the underlying framework of an area, such as roads and bridges

_____ **10.** colorful, handwoven traditional fabric from Ghana

A. imperialism

B. harmattan

C. kente

D. secede

E. infrastructure

DIRECTIONS: Multiple Choice Indicate the answer choice that best answers the question.

_____ **11.** What waterway marks the border between Mauritania and Senegal?

A. Niger River

B. White Volta River

C. Lake Chad

D. Senegal River

_____ **12.** How are the natural resources of Ghana and Burkina Faso similar?

A. Both nations contain gold deposits.

B. Iron ore deposits in both nations have been depleted.

C. Both are leaders in the production of hardwoods.

D. Salt mining is the leading industry in both nations.

Chapter Test, Form B *cont.*

netw⊙rks

West Africa

Trading Kingdoms of West Africa

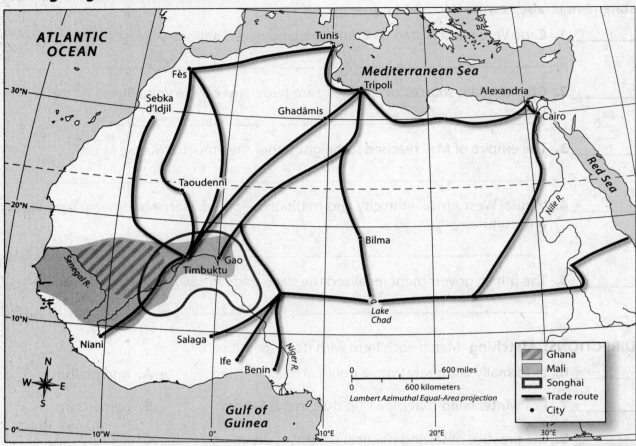

_____ **13.** Based on the map, which city was located in the Kingdom of Mali?

    A. Timbuktu   **C.** Benin

    B. Taodenni   **D.** Bilma

_____ **14.** Based on the map, how did the Mali and Ghana Empires differ?

    A. Gold was not an important trading commodity in the Mali Empire.

    B. The Ghana Empire extended to the Atlantic coast.

    C. Fewer trading routes passed through the Mali Empire.

    D. The Mali Empire was larger than the Ghana Empire.

_____ **15.** Why was salt such an important trade good in West Africa?

    A. Salt was used in the animist religious rituals of the West African people.

    B. West Africans used it to preserve food.

    C. Salt was used by West African families as a cleansing agent.

    D. West Africans gave salt to their animals to help them retain fluids.

                                          Discovering World Geography

_____ **16.** Which two events in 1869 increased European interest in Africa?

    A. the discovery of gold in Ghana and the opening of the Suez Canal

    B. the closing of the slave trade and the rise of the Songhai Empire

    C. the opening of the Suez Canal and the discovery of diamonds in South Africa

    D. the discovery of rubber trees in Central Africa and the discovery of oil in Nigeria

_____ **17.** Besides English, which of the following European languages is most widely used in West Africa?

    A. Italian

    B. German

    C. French

    D. Greek

The Sahel is a semiarid region that runs between the arid Sahara and the savanna. Beginning in northern Senegal and stretching west into East Africa, the Sahel has a short rainy season. Annual rainfall ranges from only 8 inches to 20 inches (20 cm to 51 cm). This climate supports low grasses, thorny shrubs, and a few trees. The grasses are plentiful enough to support grazing livestock, such as cattle, sheep, camels, and pack oxen. It is important, however, that the herds do not grow too large. Too many animals leads to overgrazing and permanent damage to the grasslands. Overgrazing and too much farming result in desertification, the process in which semiarid lands become drier and more desertlike.

            —*Discovering World Geography*

_____ **18.** Based on the excerpt, which description best characterizes the Sahel?

    A. mountainous zone

    B. dry zone

    C. rainless zone

    D. forest zone

_____ **19.** Based on the excerpt, which is the most reasonable conclusion?

    A. Most of West Africa's crops are grown in the Sahel.

    B. The Sahel does not support herding.

    C. Desertification is potentially a serious problem in the Sahel.

    D. West Africa's largest cities are located in the Sahel.

DIRECTIONS: Essay Answer the following question on a separate piece of paper.

20. Discuss the political and social development of modern Nigeria. How did the country's colonial history and religious and ethnic differences contribute to the instability there?

Lesson Quiz 1

networks

Southern Africa

DIRECTIONS: True/False Indicate whether the statement is true (T) or false (F).

_____ **1.** The Indian Ocean borders Southern Africa on the west.

_____ **2.** The Kalahari Desert is a vast, sand-covered plateau.

_____ **3.** The Orange River is Southern Africa's longest river.

_____ **4.** The northern half of Southern Africa lies in the Tropics.

_____ **5.** The Republic of South Africa has a thriving mining industry.

DIRECTIONS: Multiple Choice Indicate the answer choice that best answers the question.

_____ **6.** At which location do the Indian and Atlantic oceans meet in Southern Africa?

    A. Great Escarpment   **C.** Kalahari Desert

    B. Cape of Good Hope   **D.** Madagascar

_____ **7.** Why do the native people call Victoria Falls *Mosi-oa-Tunya*, or "The Smoke That Thunders"?

    A. because of the veil of mist that rises from the gorge into which the falls flow

    B. because the waters have a dark gray color

    C. because the area around the falls is dry and prone to fires

    D. because people dump and burn their trash in the gorge

_____ **8.** Why is Southern Africa's western coast called the "Skeleton Coast"?

    A. Large fish are washed ashore in high tide and die, leaving their bones.

    B. Its sands are bleached white by the sun.

    C. The fog there is so thick that many ships have run aground, and the sailors did not survive in the desert.

    D. Pirates used to attack and rob ships as they sailed along the coast.

_____ **9.** What are "blood diamonds"?

    A. diamonds that are red in color

    B. diamonds that are used for industrial purposes

    C. diamonds that cost many lives when a mine caves in

    D. diamonds that are mined to pay for rebellions and other conflicts

_____ **10.** What is Malawi's most important natural resource?

    A. gold   **C.** iron ore

    B. fertile soil   **D.** copper

Discovering World Geography

Lesson Quiz 2

netw⊙rks

DIRECTIONS: Matching Match each item with its description.

_____ **1.** rebel leader in Rhodesia, later president of Zimbabwe

A. Shaka

_____ **2.** Dutch settlers who founded Cape Colony

B. Boers

_____ **3.** Shona word meaning "stone houses"

C. Madagascar

_____ **4.** early Zulu leader

D. Robert Mugabe

_____ **5.** Southern African country that gained independence from France in 1960

E. Zimbabwe

DIRECTIONS: Multiple Choice Indicate the answer choice that best answers the question.

_____ **6.** What is one possible explanation for the Shona's abandonment of their city of Great Zimbabwe in the 1400s?

    A. They retreated into the hills when the Zulu attacked them.

    B. They no longer had enough food and water supplies for all their people.

    C. Most of the Shona people died in an epidemic, and the others fled the city.

    D. A huge fire swept through the city, burning it to the ground.

_____ **7.** What European country gained control of Cape Colony from the Dutch?

    A. Britain   **C.** France

    B. Portugal   **D.** Germany

_____ **8.** What was the main reason a guerrilla war began in Rhodesia during the 1970s?

    A. The Zulu wanted to reclaim their land.

    B. Black Rhodesians wanted control of the mining industry.

    C. The government refused to give the African population the right to vote.

    D. The Portuguese wanted control of the mining industry.

_____ **9.** Around what time period did the Shona people build a kingdom in what is now Zimbabwe and Mozambique?

    A. 1000 B.C.   **C.** A.D. 900

    B. 500 B.C.   **D.** A.D. 1500

_____ **10.** How did some countries place pressure on South Africa over the issue of apartheid?

    A. They began a campaign of civil disobedience.

    B. They placed embargos, or bans, on trade with South Africa.

    C. They gave black South Africans money and arms.

    D. They lowered the prices they offered for South African minerals.

Discovering World Geography

Lesson Quiz 3

networks

Southern Africa

DIRECTIONS: True/False Indicate whether the statement is true (T) or false (F).

_____ **1.** South Africa has the largest white minority in Southern Africa.

_____ **2.** In South Africa and Angola, most people live in rural areas.

_____ **3.** In almost every country in Southern Africa, most people are Muslim.

_____ **4.** In Southern Africa, the hope of jobs draws many people to the cities.

_____ **5.** The rate of infant death is high in Southern Africa.

DIRECTIONS: Multiple Choice Indicate the answer choice that best answers the question.

_____ **6.** Which Southern African country has the highest population density?

    A. Malawi

    B. South Africa

    C. Angola

    D. Mozambique

_____ **7.** Which of the following statements about the languages spoken in Southern Africa is accurate?

    A. Most people speak Portuguese.

    B. Most people speak English.

    C. Most people speak indigenous languages.

    D. Most people speak Afrikaans.

_____ **8.** Which of the following statements about the cities of Southern Africa is accurate?

    A. There are no shantytowns in the cities.

    B. Some cities lack adequate public utility services for their growing population.

    C. Since apartheid ended, South Africa's suburbs are for whites only.

    D. All areas have electricity and clean water supplies.

_____ **9.** Which health issue has a higher rate in Southern Africa than in any other region in Africa?

    A. HIV/AIDS   **C.** heart disease

    B. diabetes   **D.** smallpox

_____ **10.** Which country in Southern Africa is the region's most industrial and wealthiest?

    A. Angola   **C.** South Africa

    B. Mozambique   **D.** Zimbabwe

Chapter Test, Form A

network

Southern Africa

DIRECTIONS: True/False Indicate whether the statement is true (T) or false (F). If the statement is false, rewrite it to make it true.

_____ **1.** Southern Africa is bordered by the Indian Ocean and the Atlantic Ocean.

_____

_____ **2.** Victoria Falls is about twice the width and height of Niagara Falls.

_____

_____ **3.** Great Zimbabwe, the capital city of the Shona people, was abandoned in the 1900s.

_____

_____ **4.** "Boers" is the Dutch word for "farmers."

_____

_____ **5.** Malawi is Southern Africa's most urban nation.

_____

DIRECTIONS: Matching Match each item with its description.

_____ **6.** open-air trading site held at regular intervals

_____ **7.** steep cliff separating a higher surface from a lower surface

_____ **8.** the practice of illegally killing game

_____ **9.** artificial lake created by a dam

_____ **10.** Dutch settlement founded in 1652 at the southern tip of Africa

A. escarpment

B. reservoir

C. poaching

D. Cape Colony

E. periodic market

DIRECTIONS: Multiple Choice Indicate the answer choice that best answers the question.

_____ **11.** Which word best describes the physical geography of Southern Africa?

    A. low   **C.** coastal

    B. swampy   **D.** high

_____ **12.** What is Southern Africa's longest river?

    A. Orange River   **C.** Zambezi River

    B. Limpopo River   **D.** Nile River

Population of Southern Africa

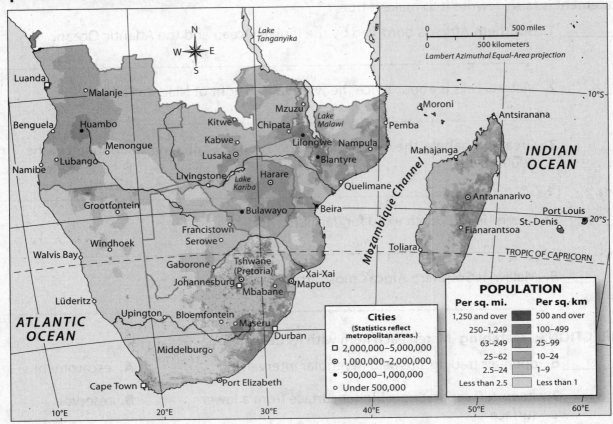

_____ **13.** Based on the map, what in general can be said about the population of Southern Africa?

    A. The population is more dense in the western half than the northern half of the region.

    B. The population is less dense in the eastern half of the region.

    C. The population is more dense in the western half of the region.

    D. The population is more dense in the eastern half of the region.

_____ **14.** Based on the map, which of the following cities has a population of two to five million?

    A. Durban   **C.** Lusaka

    B. Capetown   **D.** Walvis Bay

_____ **15.** Western South Africa, western Namibia, and much of Botswana have which type of climate?

    A. arid   **C.** tropical

    B. temperate   **D.** semiarid

_____ **16.** Which of the following statements about the first European settlements in Southern Africa is accurate?

    A. The British were never interested in Cape Colony.

    B. The first settlements were mostly trading posts and supply stations.

    C. The Portuguese founded the settlement of Cape Colony.

    D. The Dutch had no colonies in Southern Africa.

_____ **17.** Who was elected president of South Africa in 1994?

    A. P.W. Botha

    B. Robert Mugabe

    C. Nelson Mandela

    D. David Livingstone

DIRECTIONS: Short Answer Answer each of the following questions.

18. Describe the energy resources found in the countries of Southern Africa.

_____

_____

_____

_____

_____

19. What was the Great Trek and why did it occur?

_____

_____

_____

_____

_____

DIRECTIONS: Essay Answer the following question on a separate piece of paper.

20. Summarize what led to the rise and fall of apartheid in South Africa, including Nelson Mandela's role in the fight for equal rights.

Chapter Test, Form B

netw⊛rks

Southern Africa

DIRECTIONS: True/False Indicate whether the statement is true (T) or false (F). If the statement is false, rewrite it to make it true.

_____ **1.** The country of Madagascar occupies one of the world's largest islands.

_____

_____ **2.** The largest lake in Southern Africa is Lake Zambezi.

_____

_____ **3.** Arab and Muslim culture influenced some early kingdoms in Madagascar.

_____

_____ **4.** Most people in Southern Africa live in cities.

_____

_____ **5.** Most large Southern African cities have shantytowns.

_____

DIRECTIONS: Matching Match each item with its description.

_____ **6.** flat basin that contains a huge expanse of salt in northern Namibia

_____ **7.** mining, manufacturing, and financial center in South Africa

_____ **8.** South Africa's largest ethnic group

_____ **9.** landlocked country in Southern Africa

_____ **10.** South African president, elected after the end of apartheid

A. Swaziland

B. Etosha Pan

C. Nelson Mandela

D. Zulu

E. Johannesburg

DIRECTIONS: Multiple Choice Indicate the answer choice that best answers the question.

_____ **11.** Which of the following is a leading export for Zimbabwe?

A. copper

B. natural gas

C. gold

D. tobacco

_____ **12.** Which Europeans founded Cape Colony?

A. English

B. Dutch

C. Portuguese

D. French

_____ **13.** Which statement accurately describes the climates in Southern Africa?

    A. There are no desert regions in Southern Africa.

    B. Southern Africa's climates range from humid to arid and from hot to cool.

    C. The southern half of Southern Africa lies in the Tropics.

    D. There are no distinct seasons in any of the region's climates.

_____ **14.** Which statement accurately describes rainfall in the Namib Desert?

    A. Rain falls at least three times each year.

    B. Along the coast, the Namib Desert receives heavy rains most of the year.

    C. It never rains in the Namib Desert.

    D. In some years, no rain falls along the coast of the Namib Desert.

_____ **15.** What feature distinguished the Shona's stone buildings?

    A. The large stones were cut and fit into place without any mortar.

    B. The buildings had glass windows.

    C. The buildings had very low ceilings.

    D. The odd-sized stones were held in place with cement.

While other European nations gave up their African colonies, Portugal refused to do so. Revolts for independence broke out in Angola in 1961 and in Mozambique in 1964. The thousands of troops Portugal sent to crush these revolts failed to do so.

By 1974, the Portuguese had grown tired of these bloody and expensive wars. The army overthrew Portugal's government and pulled the troops out of Africa. Angola and Mozambique became independent countries in 1975 as a result. Fighting continued, however, as rebel groups in each country competed for control. Mozambique's long civil war ended when a peace agreement was reached in 1994. Peace was not finally achieved in Angola until 2002.

—*Discovering World Geography*

_____ **16.** Based on the excerpt, what in general can be said about the quest for independence in Portuguese colonies in Southern Africa?

    A. Portugal was the first European nation to grant freedom to its colonies.

    B. The rebel groups in Portugal's colonies cooperated after achieving freedom.

    C. Angola achieved independence peacefully.

    D. The Portuguese colonies' quest for independence was marked by bloody revolts.

_____ **17.** Based on the excerpt, why did Portugal pull its troops out of Africa?

    A. The government had run out of resources to pay for the costly wars.

    B. They were pressured to pull out by other European countries.

    C. Portugal's army overthrew the government and pulled the troops from Africa.

    D. The United Nations ordered Portugal to grant their colonies independence.

> Malawi is just one-third the size of Zimbabwe and one-sixth the size of Zambia, yet it exceeds both in population. With some 16 million people living in an area roughly the size of Pennsylvania, it is the region's most densely populated country. On average, every square mile holds more than 250 people.
>
> Surprisingly, Malawi is also Southern Africa's most rural nation. Only 20 percent of its people live in cities. Its small size and large rural population mean that most of its farms are small. Most farm villages are not able to produce much more than what they need. As a result, Malawi is the region's poorest country. The average Malawian earns less than $350 per year.
>
> —*Discovering World Geography*

_____ **18.** Based on the excerpt, which statement accurately describes Malawi?

    A. Most Malawians earn more than the average Southern African.

    B. Malawi is the most densely populated, most rural, and poorest country in Southern Africa.

    C. Zimbabwe is more densely populated than Malawi.

    D. Farm villages in Malawi produce cash crops.

_____ **19.** Based on the excerpt, why are most Malawian farms so small?

    A. Malawi has a small area and a large rural population.

    B. The land is so poor that farmers cannot afford large farms.

    C. There are not enough people in Malawi to manage large farms.

    D. Malawi's economy is based on service industries, not on farming.

DIRECTIONS: Essay Answer the following question on a separate piece of paper.

20. Summarize what led to the rise and fall of apartheid in South Africa, including Nelson Mandela's role in the fight for equal rights.

Unit Test

networks

Oceania, Australia, New Zealand, and Antarctica

DIRECTIONS: True/False Indicate whether the statement is true (T) or false (F).

_____ 1. The main islands of New Zealand are called East Island and West Island.

_____ 2. Australia and New Zealand are home to some of the best universities in the world.

_____ 3. Antarctica was first sighted by explorers in 1820.

_____ 4. Oceania's low islands have many large trees that are used for timber, rubber, and other products.

_____ 5. Many countries in Oceania have lagged in economic development because of limited resources.

DIRECTIONS: Matching Match each item with its description.

_____ 6. traditional Maori art form combining music, dance, singing, and facial expressions

_____ 7. traditional Samoan home made of wood poles, with a thatched roof

_____ 8. base where scientists live and work, as in Antarctica

_____ 9. huge spout of hot water that shoots from the ground

_____ 10. thick layer of ice and compressed snow that forms a crust over land

A. geyser

B. kapahaka

C. fale

D. ice sheet

E. research station

DIRECTIONS: Multiple Choice Indicate the answer choice that best answers the question.

_____ 11. How much of Australia is covered by deserts?

    A. one-quarter   **C.** one-half

    B. one-third   **D.** two-thirds

_____ 12. Which European country colonized Australia in the late 1700s?

    A. Britain   **C.** Spain

    B. France   **D.** Portugal

_____ 13. Which of the following goods are exported by New Zealand?

    A. beef and wool

    B. steel and oil

    C. electronics and silver

    D. coffee and wine

_____ **14.** How does the climate of New Guinea differ from that of the smaller islands of Oceania?

    A. New Guinea has a subtropical climate; the smaller islands all have tropical climates.

    B. Monsoons are uncommon on New Guinea, but common on the smaller islands.

    C. New Guinea includes a highland climate zone, unlike the smaller islands.

    D. Drought is unheard of in New Guinea but common in the smaller islands.

_____ **15.** Which of the following statements about the ethnic groups in Oceania is accurate?

    A. There are five major ethnic groups.

    B. There are several different ethnic groups, but they all have similar cultures.

    C. Papau New Guinea is the least diverse country in Oceania.

    D. There are so many different ethnic groups that they cannot all be classified.

_____ **16.** Which of the following statements about Antarctica's land size is the most accurate?

    A. It is the world's second-largest continent.

    B. It is the same size as the United States.

    C. It is the world's smallest continent.

    D. It is larger than either Australia or Europe.

_____ **17.** Which type of climate is found on most of Oceania's islands?

    A. arid   **C.** tropical

    B. semiarid   **D.** temperate

_____ **18.** Which country is by far the most populous in Oceania?

    A. Guam   **C.** Samoa

    B. Papua New Guinea   **D.** Wake Island

_____ **19.** Which of the following statements about Antarctica's climate is accurate?

    A. Temperatures in Antarctica are coldest near the coasts, warmest in the interior.

    B. Antarctica has an extremely dry climate.

    C. Antarctica is the least windy continent on Earth.

    D. It snows almost every day in Antarctica.

_____ **20.** Which of the following statements accurately describes Antarctica's population?

    A. Antarctica has no permanent residents.

    B. Antarctica's permanent residents serve as support staff at research stations.

    C. The indigenous residents of Antarctica died off under colonial rule.

    D. Most of Antarctica's permanent residents immigrated from Australia.

Lesson Quiz 1

networks

Australia and New Zealand

DIRECTIONS: True/False Indicate whether the statement is true (T) or false (F).

_____ **1.** Australia is the world's smallest continent.

_____ **2.** The Great Barrier Reef is a living coral reef.

_____ **3.** Most of Australia has a wet climate.

_____ **4.** Australia and New Zealand are located in the Northern Hemisphere.

_____ **5.** A kangaroo is a type of mammal known as a marsupial.

DIRECTIONS: Multiple Choice Indicate the answer choice that best answers the question.

_____ **6.** Why is Australia nicknamed "The Land Down Under"?

     A. because it is south of, or under, Asia

     B. because of its fertile soils

     C. because it is located south of, or under, the Equator

     D. because the continent is usually covered under a dense fog

_____ **7.** How many main islands does New Zealand have?

     A. one   **C.** three

     B. two   **D.** four

_____ **8.** Why does Australia depend on underground aquifers for nearly one-third of its water?

     A. Most of the lakes near Australia's cities are salt lakes.

     B. Rain is scanty in much of Australia and there are few large rivers.

     C. No part of Australia receives more than a few inches of rain a year.

     D. Dust storms make the water in reservoirs too muddy to use.

_____ **9.** Which months are Australia's and New Zealand's winter months?

     A. June, July, and August   **C.** December, January, and February

     B. March, April, and May   **D.** September, October, and November

_____ **10.** What makes New Zealand's kiwi different from most other birds?

     A. The kiwi's feathers are of very vivid colors.

     B. The kiwi eats only one type of insect, a beetle.

     C. The kiwi is a flightless bird.

     D. It is the male kiwi that lays the eggs.

Lesson Quiz 2

networks

Australia and New Zealand

DIRECTIONS: Matching Match each item with its description.

_____ **1.** species of domestic dog brought to Australia about 4,000 years ago

_____ **2.** largely self-governing country within the British Empire

_____ **3.** vast ranches in the Outback and other areas

_____ **4.** flat, bent, wooden weapon developed by Aboriginal hunters

_____ **5.** first humans to live on the islands of New Zealand

A. boomerang

B. dingoes

C. Maori

D. stations

E. dominion

DIRECTIONS: Multiple Choice Indicate the answer choice that best answers the question.

_____ **6.** How did the first people to migrate to Australia from what is now New Guinea travel?

    A. in small canoes

    B. by horseback

    C. in large ships

    D. over land bridges and peninsulas

_____ **7.** Captain Cook, who explored Australia and New Zealand, was from which country?

    A. Norway

    B. Britain

    C. Holland

    D. Spain

_____ **8.** Which of the following statements about the first European colonists of Australia is accurate?

    A. Most came to Australia in search of gold.

    B. Most were servants who worked on large ranches.

    C. Most were convicted criminals from the British Isles.

    D. Most came to Australia for religious freedom.

_____ **9.** Which country gained legal ownership of New Zealand with the signing of the Treaty of Waitangi?

    A. Great Britain

    B. United States

    C. Canada

    D. France

_____ **10.** Why were Australia and New Zealand pulled into the two world wars?

    A. They were bound by treaty to help defend the United States.

    B. They were part of the British Empire with close ties to Great Britain.

    C. German forces invaded their countries.

    D. They did not want to be left out of the eventual peace settlement.

Lesson Quiz 3

networks

Australia and New Zealand

DIRECTIONS: True/False Indicate whether the statement is true (T) or false (F).

_____ **1.** Australia's population is more diverse than the population of New Zealand.

_____ **2.** Most people in Australia and New Zealand live in the cities and suburbs.

_____ **3.** Australia has only a few natural resources.

_____ **4.** The New Zealand government agreed to pay the Maori for lost land and lost fishing rights.

_____ **5.** Both Australia and New Zealand have low birthrates and low death rates.

DIRECTIONS: Multiple Choice Indicate the answer choice that best answers the question.

_____ **6.** Which of the following statements about the populations of Australia and New Zealand is accurate?

    A. Rural settlements in New Zealand are more remote than they are in Australia.

    B. People's lifestyles are very different from those in the United States.

    C. The highest populations are concentrated in small land areas.

    D. Most people live in the Australian Outback.

_____ **7.** What is another name for Australian English?

    A. Strine   **C.** Bush

    B. Aussie   **D.** Kiwi

_____ **8.** By what means do many students living in the remote Australian Outback receive their lessons?

    A. by international mail   **C.** by attending classes once a week

    B. over the Internet   **D.** from teachers at nearby schools

_____ **9.** How has New Zealand's economy changed during the past two decades?

    A. It is now more farm-based and depends on cash crops.

    B. It is increasingly guided by central directives from the government.

    C. It once was farm-based, but now it depends mostly on tourism.

    D. It once was farm-based, but it is now based increasingly on industry.

_____ **10.** What is the main reason that many organisms in the Great Barrier Reef are dying?

    A. The ocean waters have become less salty.

    B. Waves from more frequent storms have broken the reef apart.

    C. Global warming has made temperatures in the oceans rise.

    D. Introduced species of fish have attacked the reef's corals.

Discovering World Geography

Chapter Test, Form A

Australia and New Zealand

netw rks

DIRECTIONS: True/False Indicate whether the statement is true (T) or false (F). If the statement is false, rewrite it to make it true.

_____ **1.** Overall, Australia has a high elevation compared to other continents.

_____

_____ **2.** New Zealand has geysers—spouts of hot water that shoot from the ground.

_____

_____ **3.** It is thought that the first people in Australia arrived by walking across land bridges when sea levels were low.

_____

_____ **4.** The French colonized Australia and New Zealand.

_____

_____ **5.** Living in the Australian Outback is often referred to as living "in the bush."

_____

DIRECTIONS: Matching Match each item with its description.

_____ **6.** Dutch explorer who sailed around Australia in the 1600s

_____ **7.** massive, solid stone such as Ayers Rock (Uluru)

_____ **8.** Aboriginal musical instrument that creates a vibrating sound

_____ **9.** British explorer who visited Australia in the 1700s

_____ **10.** the most rural and isolated parts of the Central Lowlands in Australia

A. Outback

B. monolith

C. Abel Tasman

D. James Cook

E. didgeridoo

DIRECTIONS: Multiple Choice Indicate the answer choice that best answers the question.

_____ **11.** What sort of activity created landforms such as the huge plateau at the center of the North Island of New Zealand?

    A. oxidation

    B. volcanic

    C. erosion

    D. glacial

_____ **12.** Why does New Zealand experience frequent earthquakes?

    A. New Zealand is part of the Ring of Fire with its active tectonic plates.

    B. New Zealand is located in the Northern Hemisphere, which has more earthquakes.

    C. New Zealand is located just below the Equator, which causes more earthquakes.

    D. The landmass of New Zealand was rifted from the land mass of Australia.

_____ **13.** What is a marsupial?

    A. reptile that buries its eggs in the sand

    B. insect that burrows in the ground

    C. mammal that raises its young in a pouch

    D. bird that cannot fly

Traditional Aboriginal culture takes many forms. Aboriginal peoples living in different parts of Australia developed their own languages, religions, traditions, and ways of life. It was difficult for separate tribes of native people to communicate with one another, because about 400 different languages were spoken across Australia. Yet, many of Australia's native people share a number of common beliefs and cultural traditions. Aboriginal culture is closely connected to the natural world. Aboriginal people have traditional beliefs about the creation of Earth and of plants and animals. . . . The Dreaming tells how the Spirit Ancestors created the land, the universe, and the laws of life, death, and society. The concept of Dreaming is central to many Aboriginal peoples' social structures and belief systems.

—*Discovering World Geography*

_____ **14.** Based on the excerpt, what in general can be said about Aboriginal peoples and their culture?

    A. Aboriginal culture is based on a study of science.

    B. Aboriginal peoples shared a common language.

    C. Aboriginal peoples believed "the Dreaming" told of bad times.

    D. Aboriginal peoples were of many unique tribes.

_____ **15.** Based on the excerpt, in Aboriginal belief, who created the laws of life, death, and society?

    A. nature   **C.** the first tribes to settle Australia

    B. Spirit Ancestors   **D.** Earth

Chapter Test, Form A *cont.*

networks

Australia and New Zealand

> Rural areas in New Zealand are not as remote as those in Australia, because New Zealand has a much smaller land area. Lush pasture lands can feed herds of sheep and cattle on fewer acres than the dry Australian Outback. As a result, New Zealand farms are located closer together, and farm families have more contact with friends and neighbors. Many people in rural areas live near small towns, where they can shop and interact with others. In recent decades, the populations of New Zealand's small towns have been shrinking as more and more rural people move to cities.
>
> —*Discovering World Geography*

_____ **16.** Based on the excerpt, what can you infer about rural life in the Australian Outback?

  A. Rural life is more isolated in the Australian Outback than it is in New Zealand.

  B. Rural life is much the same in the Australian Outback as it is in New Zealand.

  C. In the Australian Outback, farms are located close together.

  D. In the Australian Outback, rural people live close to small towns.

_____ **17.** Based on the excerpt, which comparison of New Zealand and Australia is accurate?

  A. The rural areas in New Zealand are more remote than those in Australia.

  B. Pastures in New Zealand are not as lush as those in Australia.

  C. Rural residents in New Zealand live closer to towns than residents in Australia's Outback.

  D. Farms in New Zealand are not as close together as they are in Australia.

DIRECTIONS: Short Answer Answer each of the following questions.

18. What is a drought? How can a drought affect life in Australia?

_____

_____

19. Discuss Australia and New Zealand's low birth- and death rates. Why are they occurring and how will they affect the countries?

_____

_____

_____

DIRECTIONS: Essay Answer the following question on a separate piece of paper.

20. What are "introduced species"? What impact have they had on Australia's environment?

Chapter Test, Form B

networks

Australia and New Zealand

DIRECTIONS: True/False Indicate whether the statement is true (T) or false (F). If the statement is false, rewrite it to make it true.

_____ **1.** Islam is the most common religion in Australia and New Zealand.

_____

_____ **2.** New Zealand is located within the Pacific Ocean's Ring of Fire.

_____

_____ **3.** Explorers from other European countries sailed around Australia and New Zealand after the British arrived.

_____

_____ **4.** During the 1850s, thousands of people went to Australia in search of gold.

_____

_____ **5.** The kiwifruit has become a symbol of New Zealand.

_____

DIRECTIONS: Matching Match each item with its description.

_____ **6.** one of New Zealand's largest cities

_____ **7.** landform that makes up half of Australia

_____ **8.** type of energy produced by extremely hot liquid rock in Earth's upper mantle

_____ **9.** one of Australia's largest cities

_____ **10.** traditional Maori customs and traditions

A. Western Plateau

B. Sydney

C. tikanga

D. Auckland

E. geothermal

DIRECTIONS: Multiple Choice Indicate the answer choice that best answers the question.

_____ **11.** Which of the following statements about the climate in New Zealand is accurate?

    A. It never snows in New Zealand.

    B. New Zealand's climate is as varied as its land.

    C. Little rain falls in New Zealand.

    D. Most of New Zealand has a subantarctic climate.

_____ **12.** What type of food do koalas eat?

    A. bark from beech trees   **C.** leaves from eucalyptus trees

    B. stems from wildflowers   **D.** boysenberries and blackberries

_____ **13.** On what concept is the Maori spiritual belief system based?

  A. The Maori are the chosen people.

  B. A happy life depends on forgetting the past.

  C. One who keeps the peace shall be at peace.

  D. All life in the universe is connected.

_____ **14.** Why did the Maori language nearly die out?

  A. The government banned the language in schools.

  B. The tribal elders encouraged people to speak English.

  C. Fewer and fewer Maori spoke the language, even in their homes.

  D. English was a far easier language to speak.

_____ **15.** What are Australia's three leading exports?

  A. beef, sugar cane, and gold

  B. steel, sugar cane, and coal

  C. wood, wool, and wheat

  D. coal, iron ore, and gold

Australia is the driest inhabited continent in the world. Only the icy continent of Antarctica receives less precipitation than Australia. A major problem in the dry areas is that long periods of little or no rain can result in drought.

Droughts are common in Australia and threaten the survival of wildlife, livestock, and farm crops. Low water reserves can lead to poor-quality drinking water for humans. Geographers can now predict some droughts by monitoring climate changes caused by El Niño. El Niño occurs every few years when global winds and ocean currents shift, affecting global rainfall patterns.

—*Discovering World Geography*

_____ **16.** Based on the excerpt, what in general can be said about droughts?

  A. El Niño has no effect on rainfall patterns or droughts.

  B. Droughts do not affect the health of humans.

  C. Droughts result from a lack of rain over long periods.

  D. Geographers have no way to predict droughts.

_____ **17.** Based on the excerpt, what is El Niño?

    A. period of drought that comes at regular intervals

    B. seasonal shift in global winds and ocean currents

    C. long period of rainfall that ends a drought

    D. shift in global winds and ocean currents that occurs every few years

---

Australia's population began to grow for other reasons, as well. When resources such as coal, tin, and copper were discovered, workers came for mining jobs. Business owners built shops and hotels wherever there were people to spend money. Small towns grew into cities. Farmers planted crops in Australia's most fertile areas. Ranchers brought sheep and cattle from overseas, and Australia's ranching industry was born. Vast ranches called stations covered millions of acres in the Outback and other areas. Today, millions of sheep and cattle live on ranches all across Australia.

—*Discovering World Geography*

_____ **18.** Based on the excerpt, what can you infer about Australia's economy?

    A. Ranching continues to be an important economic activity in Australia.

    B. The Outback lacks significant economic activities.

    C. Few ranches exist today.

    D. Agriculture was never a big part of Australia's economy.

_____ **19.** Based on the excerpt, which of the following statements is most accurate?

    A. There were already enough sheep and cattle on the continent to help start the ranching industry.

    B. Business owners located their businesses in places where there were enough people to sell to.

    C. Very few jobs were available to miners.

    D. The ranches were relatively small and only built near existing towns.

DIRECTIONS: Essay Answer the following question on a separate piece of paper.

20. What are "introduced species"? What impact have they had on Australia's environment?

Lesson Quiz 1

netw❍rks

Oceania

DIRECTIONS: True/False Indicate whether the statement is true (T) or false (F).

_____ **1.** Geographers divide Oceania into two sections, Micronesia and Macronesia.

_____ **2.** England, France, and the United States have island territories in Oceania.

_____ **3.** If sea levels continue to rise, some of Oceania's low islands could disappear below the water.

_____ **4.** The majority of high islands in Oceania were formed by underwater volcanoes.

_____ **5.** Fish are the chief export for most islands in Oceania.

DIRECTIONS: Multiple Choice Indicate the answer choice that best answers the question.

_____ **6.** Which of the following is located in Micronesia?

A. Niue   **C.** the Solomon Islands

B. Guam   **D.** Kiribati

_____ **7.** What is unique about the island of New Guinea in Oceania?

A. It is the only territory in Oceania that is not an island.

B. Unlike other parts of Oceania, New Guinea contains no mountains.

C. It is the only independent country in Oceania.

D. Not all of the island is considered part of Oceania.

_____ **8.** How are high islands different from low islands?

A. High islands are much sandier than low islands.

B. High islands can support human populations, unlike low islands.

C. High islands are typically smaller and flatter than low islands.

D. High islands are generally greener and larger than low islands.

_____ **9.** Since the islands of Samoa and Tonga are located south of the Equator, which of the following is a reasonable conclusion?

A. Neither Samoa nor Tonga receives much annual rainfall.

B. Samoa and Tonga are much cooler than other parts of Oceania.

C. Samoa and Tonga have a wet season from December to April.

D. These islands are the only areas in Oceania that are affected by monsoon winds.

_____ **10.** Which of the following natural resources are plentiful throughout Oceania?

A. solar energy and wind   **C.** gold and copper

B. oil and natural gas   **D.** emeralds and diamonds

Discovering World Geography

Lesson Quiz 2

networks

Oceania

DIRECTIONS: True/False Indicate whether the statement is true (T) or false (F).

_____ **1.** Historians believe the first settlers in Oceania came from Australia.

_____ **2.** Many islands in Oceania allow foreign governments to use their land or resources in exchange for military protection and economic aid.

_____ **3.** More than 800 different languages are spoken in Papua New Guinea.

_____ **4.** Many traditional Polynesian and Micronesian cultures practiced tattooing.

_____ **5.** A luau is a traditional Samoan home made of wood poles and thatched roof.

DIRECTIONS: Multiple Choice Indicate the answer choice that best answers the question.

_____ **6.** What navigation method was used by the first Polynesian settlers?

     A. orienteering   **C.** tracking

     B. spelunking   **D.** wayfinding

_____ **7.** How did people in Oceania respond to Christian missionaries?

     A. They readily embraced the Christian religion.

     B. After resisting at first, many converted to Christianity.

     C. In most places, the people chased the missionaries away.

     D. They persuaded the missionaries that traditional island religions were better.

_____ **8.** When did many island colonies in Oceania begin to demand independence?

     A. in the late 1800s   **C.** after World War I

     B. after the Vietnam War   **D.** after World War II

_____ **9.** Which of the following facts about Papua New Guinea best illustrates the traditional folk saying, "For every village, a different culture"?

     A. A small percentage of the country's population lives in urban areas.

     B. Highland areas have relatively high population densities.

     C. Thousands of distinct tribal groups live in remote villages on the islands.

     D. The population density along the coastal plains is fairly low.

_____ **10.** What hunting method, not used by other traditional cultures in Oceania, was used by Melanesians?

     A. They hunted with bows and arrows.

     B. They trapped animals in deep pits.

     C. They used slingshots to knock birds and other animals unconscious.

     D. They chased animals into nets so others could grab them.

Lesson Quiz 3

net☀rks

Oceania

DIRECTIONS: True/False Indicate whether the statement is true (T) or false (F).

_____ 1. Papua New Guinea has the most valuable resources in Oceania.

_____ 2. Some island countries in Oceania earn revenue by selling fishing rights to other countries.

_____ 3. The tourism industry in most of Oceania is minor and undeveloped.

_____ 4. The economy of American Samoa was badly damaged by a 2009 earthquake and tsunami.

_____ 5. A major challenge facing Oceania is that too many people are migrating into the region.

DIRECTIONS: Multiple Choice Indicate the answer choice that best answers the question.

_____ 6. What is the biggest challenge facing the economy of Papua New Guinea?

    A. The country's best agricultural areas are slowly being reclaimed by the ocean.

    B. It is difficult to locate and move resources through the country's wild terrain.

    C. Because the island is based on coral, it contains few deposits of metal ores.

    D. The country lacks a tourist industry to draw visitors and employ workers.

_____ 7. How do most people in Papua New Guinea earn a living?

    A. mining   **C.** subsistence farming

    B. logging   **D.** tourist trade

_____ 8. Why does the island country of Tuvalu import far more than it exports?

    A. Tuvalu is a small nation with poor soil and few natural resources.

    B. Subsistence farming is not an important economic activity on Tuvalu.

    C. The people of Tuvalu are not efficient workers.

    D. The government of Tuvalu places heavy taxes on mineral exports.

_____ 9. Which country has seen unrest between native peoples and immigrants from India?

    A. Kiribati   **C.** Tonga

    B. the Solomon Islands   **D.** Fiji

_____ 10. What may occur in Oceania as a consequence of global warming?

    A. An increasing number of earthquakes could damage farmland on some islands.

    B. Increased vegetation growth could overrun towns and cities.

    C. Some low islands could be submerged by the ocean.

    D. Decreased rainfall could threaten many islands with desertification.

Present

DIRECTIONS: True/False Indicate whether the statement is true (T) or false (F).

_____ 1. Papua New Guinea has the most valuable resource in Oceania.

_____ 2. Some island countries in Oceania earn revenue by selling fishing rights to other countries.

_____ 3. The manufacturing is most of Oceania is minor and undeveloped.

_____ 4. The economy of American Samoa was badly damaged by a 2009 earthquake and tsunami.

_____ 5. A major challenge facing Oceania is that too many people are migrating into the region.

DIRECTIONS: Multiple Choice Indicate the answer choice that best answers the question.

_____ 6. What are the biggest challenges facing the economy of Oceania today?
   A. The economy's high agricultural areas are slowly being reclaimed by the ocean.
   B. It is difficult to locate and move resources through the continent's eastward terrain.
   C. Because the island is based on coral, it cannot grow vegetables, fruits, or nuts.
   D. The country lacks a country infrastructure, few materials, and a dry landscape.

_____ 7. How do most people in Papua New Guinea earn a living?
   A. mining   C. subsistence farming
   B. logging   D. tourist trade

_____ 8. Why does the island country of Tuvalu import far more than it exports?
   A. Tuvalu is a small nation with poor soil and few natural resources.
   B. Subsistence farming is not an important economic activity on Tuvalu.
   C. The people of Tuvalu are not efficient workers.
   D. The government of Tuvalu places heavy taxes on imported goods.

_____ 9. Which country has seen conflict between two people's communities in recent years?
   A. Kiribati   C. Tonga
   B. the Solomon Islands   D. Fiji

_____ 10. What may occur if Oceania feels a consequence of global warming?
   A. An increase in powerful earthquakes could damage rainforests in some places.
   B. Increased vegetation in which could overrun farms and towns.
   C. Some low islands could be submerged by the oceans.
   D. Decreasing rainfall could cause drought conditions in desert regions.

Chapter Test, Form A

netw⊙rks

Oceania

DIRECTIONS: True/False Indicate whether the statement is true (T) or false (F). If the statement is false, rewrite it to make it true.

_____ **1.** The smallest inhabited island nation in Oceania is Samoa.

_____

_____ **2.** Once Europeans began colonizing Oceania in the 1600s, colonists and native people lived together peacefully.

_____

_____ **3.** Life in the villages of Oceania is based on tradition.

_____

_____ **4.** Mining and farming provide jobs for many people in Papua New Guinea.

_____

_____ **5.** The countries of Oceania often need to buy food, energy resources, and raw materials from other countries.

_____

DIRECTIONS: Matching Match each item with its description.

_____ **6.** a territory occupied or controlled by a foreign government

_____ **7.** method of navigation that relies on observing the natural world

_____ **8.** money transferred by a foreign worker to his or her family

_____ **9.** a territory that has been placed under the governing authority of another country by the United Nations

_____ **10.** a group of islands clustered together or closely scattered across an area

A. remittance

B. wayfinding

C. possession

D. archipelago

E. trust territory

DIRECTIONS: Multiple Choice Indicate the answer choice that best answers the question.

_____ **11.** What of the following statements about Polynesia is most accurate?

    A. Guam is part of the Polynesian islands.

    B. Most of the islands in Polynesia are high islands.

    C. Polynesia contains Oceania's largest island.

    D. Polynesia is located in the central Pacific Ocean.

_____ **12.** What two climate zones are found in New Guinea?

    A. tropical and highland

    B. arid and semiarid

    C. highland and steppe

    D. tropical and Mediterranean

Many of the islands of Oceania with less-developed economies are known as *MIRAB economies*. MIRAB is an acronym for migration, remittances, aid, and bureaucracy. Island countries with MIRAB economies are not able to fully support the needs of their people through their own resources and labor. These countries depend on outside aid and remittances from workers who have migrated to overseas areas. One example of a MIRAB economy is the Polynesian island nation of Tonga. Tonga raises a few export crops, such as squash, vanilla beans, and root vegetables. The tourist industry also brings in some revenue. Still, the most important source of income for most Tongans is remittances. Seventy-five percent of all Tongan families receive money from family members who live and work elsewhere.

—*Discovering World Geography*

_____ **13.** Based on the passage, which is an example of the "M" in MIRAB?

    A. The United States sends foreign aid to Samoa.

    B. A native Tongan moves to the United States to find a job.

    C. Guam builds new facilities to attract tourists.

    D. The United States builds a military base on Wake Island.

_____ **14.** Based on the passage, which of the following is a reasonable conclusion?

    A. The most prosperous countries can be characterized as MIRAB economies.

    B. People who live in countries with MIRAB economies are unskilled at agriculture.

    C. Countries with MIRAB economies are relatively poor.

    D. MIRAB economies export far more than they import.

_____ **15.** Which is an accurate description of the many island cultures of Oceania?

    A. Most island residents see no value in continuing traditional ways.

    B. People follow a mixture of traditional and modern practices, beliefs, and lifestyles.

    C. Oceania can be called the most culturally modern region in the world.

    D. The island cultures are remarkably similar.

_____ **16.** Which of the following industries is important to the economies of the countries of Oceania?

    A. tourism

    B. banking

    C. technology

    D. manufacturing

_____ **17.** With which of the following natural disasters are the islands of Oceania frequently threatened?

    A. avalanches

    B. tornadoes

    C. blizzards

    D. tsunamis

DIRECTIONS: Short Answer Answer each of the following questions.

18. Describe how Oceania's low and high islands were formed.

_____

_____

_____

_____

_____

19. Describe the positive and negative effects of Papua New Guinea's widely diverse cultures.

_____

_____

_____

_____

_____

DIRECTIONS: Essay Answer the following question on a separate piece of paper.

20. Which type of islands in Oceania do you think are more likely to have prosperous economies—high islands or low islands? Explain your answer.

Chapter Test, Form B

networks

Oceania

DIRECTIONS: True/False Indicate whether the statement is true (T) or false (F). If the statement is false, rewrite it to make it true.

_____ **1.** People from areas such as the Philippines and Indonesia settled the islands of Oceania over a period of many centuries.

_____

_____ **2.** In general, the lowlands and coastal plains of Papua New Guinea have higher population densities than the highland areas.

_____

_____ **3.** A simplified language that is used for communication between people who speak different languages is called a dialect.

_____

_____ **4.** Crops grown or gathered to sell for profit are called cash crops.

_____

_____ **5.** Most islands in Oceania export far more than they import.

_____

_____ **6.** Commercial fishing threatens the survival of local fishing industries in Oceania.

_____

DIRECTIONS: Matching Match each item with its description.

_____ **7.** an island characterized by steep slopes and diverse plant and animal life

_____ **8.** a shallow pool at the center area of an island

_____ **9.** a coral island made up of a reef island with a pool at the center

_____ **10.** the typical "desert island" described in books and seen in films

A. high island

B. low island

C. lagoon

D. atoll

DIRECTIONS: Multiple Choice Indicate the answer choice that best answers the question.

_____ **11.** The Owen Stanley Range is considered the "backbone" of which country in Oceania?

    A. Samoa

    B. Papua New Guinea

    C. Tahiti

    D. Vanuatu

_____ **12.** Which of the following can be classified as a possession?

    A. French Polynesia   **C.** Palau

    B. the Marshall Islands   **D.** Papua New Guinea

_____ **13.** Which of the following is an accurate statement about low islands?

    A. Low islands have abundant mineral resources.

    B. Agriculture is a key part of the economies of low islands.

    C. Low islands have limited mineral resources.

    D. The economies of low islands are based entirely on mining.

_____ **14.** What are Papua New Guinea's most profitable resources?

    A. oil and natural gas

    B. coffee and tea

    C. gold and copper

    D. timber and rubber

_____ **15.** How are Guam and Wake Island similar?

    A. They are both independent nations.

    B. Agriculture is the main economic activity on both islands.

    C. Mining is an important activity for each nation's economy.

    D. They are both home to U.S. military bases.

Traditional celebrations are practiced throughout Oceania. Some traditional events, such as the Hawaiian luau, have become more modern in recent decades. Luaus were traditionally ritual ceremonies and feasts celebrating important events, such as victories in battle. Centuries ago, men and women ate in separate areas during luaus, and only chiefs ate certain foods. Some luaus were attended only by men. Today, luaus are banquets of traditional and modern foods eaten on a low table.

—Discovering World Geography

_____ **16.** Based on the excerpt, which activity are you likely to find at a luau?

    A. painting   **C.** gaming

    B. feasting   **D.** fighting

Chapter Test, Form B *cont.*

Oceania

_____ **17.** Based on the excerpt, which of the following is a reasonable conclusion?

    A. Younger people in Oceania are quickly abandoning their traditional cultures.

    B. Men and women are strictly segregated in the region's societies.

    C. Maintaining elements of traditional cultures is important to the people of Oceania.

    D. There are no traces of modern life on most islands in Oceania.

> Tourists come from all over the world to enjoy the sunshine, warm ocean waters, and panoramic views. Resorts provide comfortable lodging, food, recreation, and entertainment. Most resorts are located in beautiful natural areas, such as tropical beaches, mountains, and forests. Tourist businesses employ thousands of people. Without the revenue from tourism, many small island countries would be at risk of economic collapse.
>
> —*Discovering World Geography*

_____ **18.** Based on the excerpt, which of the following is most likely a popular tourist activity in Oceania?

    A. visiting museums

    B. skiing

    C. horse racing

    D. swimming

_____ **19.** Based on the excerpt, which is most likely to jeopardize the tourism economy of Oceania?

    A. regional pollution and natural disasters

    B. the discovery of precious metals in the region

    C. the cultivation of more cash crops on the islands

    D. population increase in the region

DIRECTIONS: Essay Answer the following question on a separate piece of paper.

20. Which type of islands in Oceania do you think are more likely to have prosperous economies—high islands or low islands? Explain your answer.

Lesson Quiz 1

networks

Antarctica

DIRECTIONS: Matching Match each item with its description.

_____ 1. plants that usually grow on solid, rocky surfaces

A. iceberg

_____ 2. tiny organisms floating near the water's surface

B. katabatic winds

_____ 3. large chunk of freshwater ice that breaks free of an ice shelf or a glacier

C. lichens

_____ 4. tiny crustaceans similar to shrimp

D. krill

_____ 5. powerful gusts driven by the force of gravity

E. plankton

DIRECTIONS: Multiple Choice Indicate the answer choice that best answers the question.

_____ 6. Which body of water surrounds Antarctica on all sides?

    A. Atlantic Ocean   **C.** Indian Ocean

    B. Pacific Ocean   **D.** Southern Ocean

_____ 7. What feature of an iceberg makes it so dangerous to ships?

    A. An iceberg moves at high speeds due to water currents.

    B. Most of an iceberg's mass is below the surface of the water.

    C. An iceberg is usually so small that ships just plow over it.

    D. An iceberg always appears larger than it actually is.

_____ 8. In what way does Antarctica help maintain the global climate balance?

    A. Plentiful rains help restore Earth's water supply.

    B. The ice absorbs the sunlight and helps warm Earth.

    C. The ice reflects the sunlight and helps cool Earth.

    D. Antarctica's extreme cold helps to balance the heat from the Equator.

_____ 9. Which statement best describes plant and animal life found in Antarctica?

    A. Only a few plants grow in Antarctica and most land animals are insects or mites.

    B. Antarctica has no plant or animal life.

    C. No animal stays in Antarctica year-round.

    D. Antarctica teems with animal life year-round.

_____ 10. Which statement best describes the natural resources of Antarctica?

    A. All the resources there are nonrenewable.

    B. Whatever mineral resources might exist are buried under the thick ice sheet.

    C. Extensive mining operations are underway to reach Antarctica's mineral resources.

    D. The continent does not have any natural resources.

Lesson Quiz 2

networks

Antarctica

DIRECTIONS: True/False Indicate whether the statement is true (T) or false (F).

_____ **1.** Antarctica has a small native population.

_____ **2.** One purpose of the Antarctic Treaty is to protect Antarctica's environment.

_____ **3.** Summer is the best time for scientists to work in Antarctica.

_____ **4.** The levels of ozone in the atmosphere are lowest over the Arctic Circle and over Antarctica and the Southern Ocean.

_____ **5.** Geographers cannot tell if the Antarctic ice sheet is shrinking.

DIRECTIONS: Multiple Choice Indicate the answer choice that best answers the question.

_____ **6.** Which of the following statements about the explorers Roald Amundsen and Robert Scott is accurate?

  A. Both men had much experience dealing with cold and snow.

  B. Both men were explorers from Norway.

  C. Both men were explorers from Great Britain.

  D. Both men wanted to be the first to reach the South Pole.

_____ **7.** Which group decides how Antarctica's lands and resources are used?

  A. Southern Oceanic Watch Team

  B. Antarctic Treaty System

  C. United Nations

  D. Amundsen-Scott Memorial Fund

_____ **8.** How much food and other supplies do Antarctic research stations store?

  A. enough for a year or more   **C.** enough for two months

  B. enough for six months   **D.** enough for three years

_____ **9.** What do we call the technology by which scientists study rock formations below ice sheets?

  A. global positioning system   **C.** remote sensing

  B. three-dimensional maps   **D.** magnetic resonance imaging

_____ **10.** In what way is climate change affecting Antarctica?

  A. The ice shelf is thickening and growing.

  B. The amount of plankton and krill is decreasing.

  C. Fewer icebergs are found in the waters.

  D. There is more ship traffic in the area.

Discovering World Geography

Chapter Test, Form A

networks

Antarctica

DIRECTIONS: True/False Indicate whether the statement is true (T) or false (F). If the statement is false, rewrite it to make it true.

_____ **1.** Antarctica is located in the Northern Hemisphere.

_____

_____ **2.** During winter, the seawater next to Antarctica's ice shelves actually freezes.

_____

_____ **3.** Antarctica has an extremely wet climate.

_____

_____ **4.** Some countries have made claims to large sections of Antarctica.

_____

_____ **5.** During the summer, the sun shines 24 hours a day in Antarctica.

_____

DIRECTIONS: Matching Match each item with its description.

_____ **6.** English explorer who traveled to the South Pole

_____ **7.** gas in atmosphere that absorbs harmful ultraviolet radiation

_____ **8.** Norwegian explorer who traveled to the South Pole

_____ **9.** international agreement to protect Antarctica's wildlife

_____ **10.** process of ice breaking free from an ice shelf or glacier

A. Roald Amundsen

B. calving

C. Robert Scott

D. Antarctic Conservation Act

E. ozone

DIRECTIONS: Multiple Choice Indicate the answer choice that best answers the question.

_____ **11.** Why is Antarctica called the highest continent?

    A. Because it is located in the Northern Hemisphere.

    B. Because it has the highest overall elevation of any continent.

    C. Because wind currents travel from the highest elevation to the lowest elevation.

    D. Because it has the largest, tallest ice shelf.

_____ **12.** Why does Antarctica seem to double in size every winter?

    A. The ice shelves break into large chunks and float around the coast.

    B. The heavy snow in the winter covers the frozen waters.

    C. Coastal water freezes into ice shelves during the winter.

    D. The ice shelves melt enough to show much of the land beneath them.

_____ **13.** Why are most plants in Antarctica found on the Antarctic Peninsula and the islands that surround it?

    A. These are the warmest, wettest areas on the continent.

    B. These areas have hot springs and are warm.

    C. These are the coldest, driest areas on the continent.

    D. The mountains protect the area from the katabatic winds.

Although the land of Antarctica is not home to many living things, the Antarctic seas are filled with life. Many kinds of seals, dolphins, fish, and other marine animals live in waters surrounding Antarctica. Whales come to the Southern Ocean to feed during the summer. Sea mammals and seabirds eat krill, tiny crustaceans similar to shrimp. Krill thrive in the waters of the Southern Ocean, feeding on even smaller life-forms called plankton.

Plankton are tiny organisms floating near the water's surface. Some types of plankton are single-celled bacteria; others are plants such as algae. Plankton, krill, fish, sea mammals, seabirds, and land animals are part of Antarctica's ecosystem. These creatures are essential parts of the food chain that supports life on the continent.

—Discovering World Geography

_____ **14.** Based on the excerpt, what in general can be said about Antarctica's sea and land life?

    A. Plankton feed off the krill.

    B. The seas around Antarctica are too cold to support much marine life.

    C. Whales feed in the Southern Ocean during the winter months.

    D. All of the sea, land, and flying creatures in Antarctica are essential parts of the food chain.

_____ **15.** Based on the excerpt, what would happen if the supply of plankton sharply decreased?

    A. The krill would find another source of food.

    B. It would have no effect on the ecosystem of Antarctica.

    C. The food chain would be severely disrupted.

    D. Krill would multiply and take over the seas.

Discovering World Geography

Chapter Test, Form A *cont.*

Antarctica

> Nations including Argentina, Australia, Great Britain, New Zealand, and Norway still claim large sections of the continent as territories, but not all governments acknowledge these claims. Because Antarctica is not considered a nation or a country and it has no government, issues relating to the continent's use and protection are decided by the Antarctic Treaty System. This is a group of representatives from 48 countries that have interests in Antarctica. Important decisions affecting Antarctica's environment, wildlife, and resident scientists are made by annual meetings of the Antarctic Treaty System.
>
> —*Discovering World Geography*

_____ **16.** Based on the excerpt, what in general can be said about the governance of Antarctica?

    A. The continent has no government.

    B. Resident scientists make all decisions about the continent's environment.

    C. Countries are not allowed to make claims in Antarctica.

    D. The country with the largest claim governs the continent.

_____ **17.** Based on the excerpt, who has authority over the resident scientists?

    A. the scientists themselves   **C.** Great Britain

    B. Antarctic Treaty System   **D.** Australia

DIRECTIONS: Short Answer Answer each of the following questions.

18. Explain how the weather affects the time of year that most scientists live in Antarctica.

_____

_____

_____

19. Explain why very little of the sun's heat energy reaches Antarctica.

_____

_____

_____

DIRECTIONS: Essay Answer the following question on a separate piece of paper.

20. Describe how climate change has affected Antarctica. What impact does this have on the rest of the world?

Chapter Test, Form B

netw🌐rks

Antarctica

DIRECTIONS: True/False Indicate whether the statement is true (T) or false (F). If the statement is false, rewrite it to make it true.

_____ 1. One nickname for Antarctica is "the bottom of the world."

_____

_____ 2. Icebergs look larger than they really are.

_____

_____ 3. Antarctic hair grass is the only flowering plant that grows in Antarctica.

_____

_____ 4. Antarctica is the only continent that has no permanent human settlement.

_____

_____ 5. Thinning of the ozone layer may be harmful to life on Earth.

_____

DIRECTIONS: Matching Match each item with its description.

_____ 6. group making decisions on Antarctica's environment, wildlife, and resident scientists

_____ 7. thick slab of ice that is attached to a coastline but floats on the ocean

_____ 8. landmass from which Antarctica, Asia, and Africa broke away

_____ 9. technology that collects data about Earth from scientific instruments far above the surface

_____ 10. highest point in Antarctica

A. ice shelf

B. Vinson Massif

C. Antarctic Treaty System

D. remote sensing

E. Gondwana

DIRECTIONS: Multiple Choice Indicate the answer choice that best answers the question.

_____ 11. Which of the following statements about Antarctica's ice is accurate?

    A. Most of Antarctica's ice melts each summer and refreezes each winter.

    B. All of Antarctica's mountains lie beneath an ice sheet.

    C. About two-thirds of Earth's freshwater is frozen in the Antarctic ice sheet.

    D. About half of Antarctica's land surface lies under an ice sheet.

_____ **12.** Which of the following statements about the landmass of Antarctica is accurate?

    A. The Antarctic landmass has no mountain ranges.

    B. Antarctica has no lands with extremes of high and low elevation.

    C. Antarctica is the lowest continent on Earth.

    D. Antarctica has a central landmass and an archipelago of rocky islands.

_____ **13.** How did the icy seas that surround Antarctica get their names?

    A. They were named for the new species of marine animals found in them.

    B. They were named by explorers and scientists who studied and mapped the region.

    C. The countries making claim to the territories named the seas.

    D. The native peoples of Antarctica named the seas.

> Because of its high latitude, Antarctica never receives direct rays from the sun, even when the Southern Hemisphere is tilted toward the sun. Thus, the sun's energy is spread out over a wider surface than at lower-latitude places such as the Equator. The result is that very little heat energy reaches the surface of the land. In addition, being south of the Antarctic Circle, most of Antarctica receives no sunlight at all and is completely dark for at least three months of the year.
>
> The high elevation across Antarctica affects its climate, as well. Strong, fast winds blow colder air down from high interior lands toward the coasts. These powerful gusts, called katabatic winds, are driven by the force of Earth's gravity.
>
> All of these factors combined produce an intensely cold climate. Temperatures are coldest in the interior highlands and warmest near the coasts.
>
> —*Discovering World Geography*

_____ **14.** Based on the excerpt, why is Antarctica completely dark for at least three months of the year?

    A. Because it is located near the Equator.

    B. Because it is located north of the Antarctic Circle.

    C. Because it is located south of the Antarctic Circle.

    D. Because it is located in the Northern Hemisphere.

_____ **15.** Based on the excerpt, what force drives the katabatic winds?

    A. Earth's gravity

    B. location south of Antarctic Circle

    C. heat from the sun

    D. location in Southern Hemisphere

_____ **16.** Which of the following statements about the Antarctic Treaty of 1959 is accurate?

    A. The treaty divided Antarctica among Australia, Great Britain, and New Zealand.

    B. The treaty set rules for how Antarctica's land and resources are to be managed.

    C. The treaty granted countries the right to test weapons in Antarctica.

    D. The treaty set the rules for how resident scientists could do their studies.

_____ **17.** What makes Antarctica a good place for scientific research?

    A. Antarctica's elevation is ideal for communications.

    B. Antarctica's climate is mild, especially in the winter.

    C. Scientists can easily travel to and within Antarctica.

    D. Antarctica has a largely unspoiled environment.

> One important area of study focuses on the ozone layer that is high in Earth's atmosphere. Ozone is a gas in the atmosphere that absorbs harmful ultraviolet radiation from the sun. Through decades of research and study, scientists discovered that the layer of ozone in our planet's atmosphere had thinned and decreased. This means that less ozone exists to protect Earth and life on Earth from damaging solar radiation. The two locations on Earth where levels of ozone are the lowest are over the Arctic Circle and over Antarctica and the Southern Ocean. Loss of ozone affects all life on the planet. Scientists in Antarctica and other parts of the world are working to find a way to protect and preserve the ozone layer.
>
> —*Discovering World Geography*

_____ **18.** Based on the excerpt, what can you infer about the ozone layer today?

    A. Because of our conservation efforts, the ozone layer is thickening and increasing.

    B. There is more harmful solar radiation over the Equator than over the Arctic Circle.

    C. The ozone layer is thinning, and we need to find ways to protect and preserve it.

    D. There is little concern about the thinning of the ozone layer today.

_____ **19.** Based on the excerpt, if the ozone layer continues to thin, how will it affect life on Earth?

    A. Only life in and around the Arctic Circle and Antarctica will be affected.

    B. All life on Earth will be exposed to more harmful solar radiation.

    C. The ozone layer will adequately protect life on Earth for many years to come.

    D. The thinning of the ozone layer should not harm life on Earth.

DIRECTIONS: Essay Answer the following question on a separate piece of paper.

20. Describe how climate change has affected Antarctica. What impact does this have on the rest of the world?

Answer Key

The World
UNIT TEST
True/False

1. False   2. True   3. False
4. True   5. False

Matching

6. D   7. C   8. E   9. A   10. B

Multiple Choice

11. C   12. B   13. D   14. A   15. C
16. D   17. A   18. B   19. B   20. A

The Geographer's World
LESSON QUIZ 1
True/False

1. False   2. True   3. False
4. True   5. True

Multiple Choice

6. B   7. A   8. C   9. A   10. D

LESSON QUIZ 2
True/False

1. True   2. True   3. False
4. True   5. False

Multiple Choice

6. C   7. A   8. A   9. B   10. D

CHAPTER TEST, FORM A
True/False

1. True
2. False. A map is less accurate than a globe because it does distort physical reality.
3. False. The map feature that indicates north, south, east, and west is the compass rose.
4. True
5. True

Matching

6. E   7. A   8. B   9. D   10. C

Multiple Choice

11. B   12. A   13. C   14. A   15. D
16. A   17. C

Short Answer

18. Students' responses will vary. Possible response: One way people affect the environment is through pollution, which can destroy trees and crops and make the land and water unfit for habitation. Deforestation is a second way people affect the environment, reducing natural habitats for animals, damaging the water cycle, and contributing to soil erosion.

    One way the environment affects people is through climate; the types of houses people build and the clothes they wear depend in large part on the climate they live in. The environment can also influence how people make a living; for example, mining and not agriculture would likely predominate in a region rich in coal.

19. A globe is more accurate than a flat map because it mimics the spherical shape of Earth. Copying the features of the round Earth onto a flat surface introduces distortions. A globe can represent surface features, directions, and distances more accurately than a flat map.

Essay

20. Students' responses will vary. Possible response: If geospatial technologies stopped working, large parts of the economy would be at risk. Travel might become more difficult because people could not use their GPS to find places. Aircraft and ships could become lost due to the GPS satellites not working. Delivery of goods would be slowed because delivery people could no longer rely on GPS to help them find their way. Earth imaging would become more difficult, so mapping Web sites such as Google Earth would probably be unavailable. Also, severe storms would be less predictable, which could put people's lives at risk. Communications would also be affected because cell phone companies use GPS to provide services.

CHAPTER TEST, FORM B
True/False

1. False. Relative location uses the cardinal directions—north, south, east, and west.
2. True
3. True
4. False. General-purpose maps usually show either the human-made features of an area or its natural features, but not both.
5. True
6. True

Matching

7. B **8.** C **9.** D **10.** A

Multiple Choice

11. B **12.** C **13.** A **14.** A **15.** C

16. B **17.** D **18.** B **19.** D

Essay

20. Students' responses will vary. Possible response: If geospatial technologies stopped working, large parts of the economy would be at risk. Travel might become more difficult because people could not use their GPS to find places. Aircraft and ships could become lost due to the GPS satellites not working. Delivery of goods would be slowed because delivery people could no longer rely on GPS to help them find their way. Earth imaging would become more difficult, so mapping Web sites such as Google Earth would probably be unavailable. Also, severe storms would be unpredictable, which could put people's lives at risk. Communications would also be affected because cell phones companies use GPS to provide services.

Physical Geography

LESSON QUIZ 1

True/False

1. True **2.** False **3.** True

4. True **5.** False

Multiple Choice

6. B **7.** D **8.** B **9.** C **10.** D

LESSON QUIZ 2

Matching

1. D **2.** C **3.** E **4.** B **5.** A

Multiple Choice

6. C **7.** A **8.** D **9.** C **10.** B

LESSON QUIZ 3

True/False

1. False **2.** True **3.** False **4.** True **5.** True

Multiple Choice

6. A **7.** D **8.** D **9.** C **10.** A

CHAPTER TEST, FORM A

True/False

1. False. The sun's gravity causes Earth to constantly orbit around it.

2. True

3. False. Earth's crust is made up of **16** enormous tectonic plates.

4. False. Ice sheets cover most of Greenland and Antarctica.

5. True

Matching

6. C **7.** D **8.** A **9.** E **10.** B

Multiple Choice

11. C **12.** B **13.** D **14.** B

15. A **16.** C

Short Answer

17. Twain heard a "great rattle" and "a heavy grinding noise." He felt the ground rolling under him "in waves" and then a "violent joggling up and down."

18. Students' responses will vary but might note that Twain was most likely fearful during the earthquake and indicated this by using words such as "terrific," "grinding," and "violent."

19. Earthquakes can trigger other natural disasters, such as tsunamis. The earthquake that hit Japan in 2011 caused a tsunami that triggered a nuclear accident.

Essay

20. Students' essays will vary. Essays may include: Human actions have caused much damage to the world's water supply. Factories dump waste into waterways. Chemicals used on lawns or in farm fields to control pests and weeds run off into waterways or seep into wells that hold drinking water. As a result, many of our rivers, lakes, and oceans and even our groundwater are polluted or poisoned. This pollution results in death of fish, fowl, and animals, including humans, or causes deadly diseases. Also, the fossil fuels we burn release poisonous gases into the air that, when mixed with water vapor in the air, create toxins that fall back to Earth in the form of acid rain. This is a deadly mixture that pollutes the water, damages the trees and other plants, and kills plant and animal life in bodies of water.

The government should have stronger laws to prevent factories from dumping toxic waste into waterways. Pesticides and other chemicals for weed control should be developed that are not toxic to other plant and animal life. More attention should be given to the production and operation of vehicles, aircraft, trains, and ships that run on alternative fuels such as alcohol, electricity, or hydrogen. Individuals can help, too, by not throwing trash or debris of any kind into waterways. People can water their lawns and wash their cars less frequently, fix dripping faucets and pipes, and take steps every day to conserve fresh water.

CHAPTER TEST, FORM B

True/False

1. False. We define a year as 365¼ days.
2. False. Cold temperate climates have a short summer season.
3. True
4. False. The Panama Canal connects the Atlantic and Pacific oceans.
5. True

Matching

6. E   7. D   8. C   9. B   10. A

Multiple Choice

11. B   12. A   13. D   14. B   15. D
16. C   17. B   18. C   19. D

Essay

20. Students' essays will vary. Essays may include: Human actions have caused much damage to the world's water supply. Factories dump waste into waterways. Chemicals used on lawns or in farm fields to control pests and weeds run off into waterways or seep into wells that hold drinking water. As a result, many of our rivers, lakes, and oceans and even our groundwater are polluted or poisoned. This pollution results in death of fish, fowl, and animals, including humans, or causes deadly diseases. Also, the fossil fuels we burn release poisonous gases into the air that, when mixed with water vapor in the air, create toxins that fall back to Earth in the form of acid rain. This is a deadly mixture that pollutes the water, damages the trees and other plants, and kills plant and animal life in bodies of water.

The government should have stronger laws to prevent factories from dumping toxic waste into waterways. Pesticides and other chemicals for

weed control should be developed that are not toxic to other plant and animal life. More attention should be given to the production and operation of vehicles, aircraft, trains, and ships that run on alternative fuels such as alcohol, electricity, or hydrogen. Individuals can help, too, by not throwing trash or debris of any kind into waterways. People can water their lawns and wash their cars less frequently, fix dripping faucets and pipes, and take steps every day to conserve fresh water.

Human Geography

LESSON QUIZ 1

True/False

1. True   2. True   3. False
4. True   5. False

Multiple Choice

6. D   7. C   8. B   9. C   10. A

LESSON QUIZ 2

True/False

1. False   2. False   3. True
4. True   5. False

Multiple Choice

6. B   7. D   8. C   9. B   10. C

LESSON QUIZ 3

True/False

1. True   2. False   3. True
4. True   5. False

Multiple Choice

6. B   7. C   8. D   9. C   10. A

CHAPTER TEST, FORM A

True/False

1. False. On any given day around the world, more births than deaths occur.
2. True
3. True
4. False. People who live in a dictatorship often have few rights.
5. True
6. False. The United States has a mixed market economy.

Matching

7. D   **8.** A   **9.** B   **10.** C

Multiple Choice

11. B   **12.** C   **13.** A   **14.** D   **15.** C
16. A   **17.** B

Short Answer

18. Students' responses will vary. Possible response: Rapid population growth has had a negative effect on the environment. For example, it is responsible for the clearing of much of the world's forests, the decrease in global nonrenewable resources, an increase in pollution, and the deterioration of much of the world's water supply.

19. Students' responses will vary. Possible response: Language and culture are closely related. Language is a verbal expression of culture. People use language to communicate information and experiences. Language maintains and conveys cultural beliefs and traditions. For example, a cultural group might use certain words that are unfamiliar to people outside the group.

Essay

20. All students should recognize that the United States has a mixed market economy, but their explanations may vary. Possible response: The United States has a mixed market economy. It is a market economy because individuals and companies are able to decide what they will produce, how they will produce their goods and services, and how they will distribute those goods and services. The economy is mixed because, although private individuals own the factors of production, the government does get involved in economic decisions. For example, the government determines what infrastructure will be built, and the government has passed laws putting many restrictions and regulations upon private industry. Some examples of these regulations include the minimum wage laws and anti-pollution laws.

CHAPTER TEST, FORM B

True/False

1. False. Human populations grow at different rates in different areas of the world.

2. True

3. True

4. False. A cultural region is a geographic area in which people have certain traits in common.

5. False. Human rights are the same for every human in every culture.

6. False. Employees are an example of labor.

Matching

7. A   **8.** C   **9.** B   **10.** D

Multiple Choice

11. C   **12.** B   **13.** D   **14.** A   **15.** C
16. B   **17.** D   **18.** B   **19.** C

Essay

20. All students should recognize that the United States has a mixed market economy, but their explanations may vary. Possible response: The United States has a mixed market economy. It is a market economy because individuals and companies are able to decide what they will produce, how they will produce their goods and services, and how they will distribute those goods and services. The economy is mixed because, although private individuals own the factors of production, the government does get involved in economic decisions. For example, the government determines what infrastructure will be built, and the government has passed laws putting many restrictions and regulations upon private industry. Some examples of these regulations include the minimum wage laws and anti-pollution laws.

North America
UNIT TEST
True/False

1. True   **2.** False   **3.** True   **4.** False   **5.** True

Matching

6. D   **7.** A   **8.** C   **9.** E   **10.** B

Multiple Choice

11. B   **12.** A   **13.** C   **14.** D   **15.** B
16. D   **17.** C   **18.** A   **19.** B   **20.** C

The United States East of the Mississippi River
LESSON QUIZ 1
True/False

1. True   **2.** False   **3.** False   **4.** True   **5.** True

Discovering World Geography

Multiple Choice

6. C   7. B   8. A   9. B   10. D

LESSON QUIZ 2
Matching

1. D   2. E   3. A   4. B   5. C

Multiple Choice

6. B   7. D   8. C   9. D   10. A

LESSON QUIZ 3
True/False

1. True   2. False   3. True
4. True   5. False

Multiple Choice

6. A   7. C   8. C   9. D   10. B

CHAPTER TEST, FORM A
True/False

1. False. The Mississippi River divides the United States into two main regions.
2. True
3. True
4. True
5. False. The president can set aside land for use as a national park.

Matching

6. D   7. E   8. A   9. C   10. B

Multiple Choice

11. C   12. A   13. B   14. D   15. C
16. B   17. D

Short Answer

18. Students' responses will vary. Possible response: The first English colonists settled along the Atlantic coast of North America. The earliest settlements were in Jamestown, Virginia, and Plymouth, Massachusetts. As more Europeans arrived, the colonies grew from 52,000 colonists in 1650 to approximately 1.7 million in 1760. Small settlements grew to large cities, such as Boston and New York. By the mid-1700s, there were 13 English colonies in North America.

19. Students' responses will vary. Possible response: After the Civil War, many states in the Southeast passed laws that took away many of the rights

that freed African Americans had gained. Many African Americans moved to the North, especially to the cities, to find jobs and to have a better life. The population of the North increased as a result of this migration, called the Great Migration.

Essay

20. Students' responses will vary. Possible response: Native Americans and early colonists learned how to adapt to their environments. Native Americans had long mastered living off the land. They used the plants, animals, stones, woods, water, and soil to meet their needs. Those who lived in wooded areas, for example, made their shelters from bark and wood, and they burned wood to heat their shelters during the colder months. Those who lived in warmer climates made their shelters of vines or grasses for more open-air structures. Others used stones or molded earth to build more solid, insulated shelters. Native Americans hunted game, cooked and preserved their meat, and used their skins to make blankets and clothing.

The colonists had to learn to live off the land as well, or else they would have died of starvation. When their supplies from their native European country ran out, they learned how to plant crops, hunt for food, and preserve that food. They had to make and grow everything that they needed. They made essential supplies such as candles, soap, clothing, tools, and medicine from other materials and natural resources.

Life was hard for both Native Americans and early colonists. Once the colonists adapted to their environment, they learned more about the Native American way of life: live off the land but treat that land with respect.

CHAPTER TEST, FORM B
True/False

1. False. The state of New York is in the Mid-Atlantic subregion.
2. True
3. False. The Great Migration increased during the 1900s.
4. True
5. True

Matching

6. B   7. D   8. C   9. A   10. E

Multiple Choice

11. C **12.** A **13.** D **14.** B **15.** D

16. B **17.** D **18.** B **19.** C

Essay

20. Students' responses will vary. Possible response: Native Americans and early colonists learned how to adapt to their environments. Native Americans had long mastered living off the land. They used the plants, animals, stones, woods, water, and soil to meet their needs. Those who lived in wooded areas, for example, made their shelters from bark and wood, and they burned wood to heat their shelters during the colder months. Those who lived in warmer climates made their shelters of vines or grasses for more open-air structures. Others used stones or molded earth to build more solid, insulated shelters. Native Americans hunted game, cooked and preserved their meat, and used their skins to make blankets and clothing.

The colonists had to learn to live off the land as well, or else they would have died of starvation. When their supplies from their native European country ran out, they learned how to plant crops, hunt for food, and preserve that food. They had to make and grow everything that they needed. They made essential supplies such as candles, soap, clothing, tools, and medicine from other materials and natural resources.

Life was hard for both Native Americans and early colonists. Once the colonists adapted to their environment, they learned more about the Native American way of life: live off the land but treat that land with respect.

The United States West of the Mississippi River

LESSON QUIZ 1

Matching

1. C **2.** B **3.** E **4.** A **5.** D

Multiple Choice

6. B **7.** D **8.** C **9.** A **10.** B

LESSON QUIZ 2

True/False

1. False **2.** True **3.** True

4. False **5.** False

Multiple Choice

6. B **7.** D **8.** A **9.** C **10.** D

LESSON QUIZ 3

Matching

1. C **2.** A **3.** D **4.** B **5.** E

Multiple Choice

6. B **7.** D **8.** D **9.** C **10.** A

CHAPTER TEST, FORM A

True/False

1. True

2. False. Of the states west of the Mississippi River, Alaska is the largest in land area.

3. False. New Orleans was a French settlement.

4. True

5. False. In California, non-Hispanic whites are in the minority and Latinos constitute a large part of the population.

Matching

6. C **7.** B **8.** D **9.** A **10.** E

Multiple Choice

11. B **12.** D **13.** C **14.** C **15.** B

16. A **17.** C

Short Answer

18. Students' responses will vary. Possible response: California's Central Valley lies in the rain shadow of the coastal ranges. That is, it lies east of the coastal ranges, and that location would normally make it dry. However, it is also located near the Sierra Nevada range, which is west facing and receives rain and snow from Pacific Ocean storms. Farmers in the Central Valley use rainwater from the Sierra Nevada to irrigate their crops.

19. Students' responses will vary. Possible response: Because of their global locations, Alaska and Hawaii have very different climates. With a climate that is generally moderate but cool to cold, Alaska has areas in the south and southeast that have more moderate temperatures and significant snowfall. The areas to the north, however, have colder temperatures; those in the far north, very cold temperatures. In comparison, Hawaii has a tropical rain forest climate with high temperatures and heavy rainfall, especially in the winter.

Although the temperatures are high, the steady ocean breezes keep the air comfortable.

Essay

20. Students' essays will vary. Possible response: Water is essential for every living thing and when there is not enough water, that area suffers economically. During the Dust Bowl between the 1930s and 1940s, crops withered and the land itself blew away in huge dust storms. As a result, the area suffered an economic meltdown, and people moved to other regions in search of work. Population growth is having an even greater impact on water supplies for the western states, especially in the major cities that generally do not have an adequate supply of water to begin with.

To address the growing need for water, scientists are researching and developing ways to use seawater through desalination. It is an expensive process, but it may be the long-term solution. People themselves can help increase the water supply by reducing their consumption of it. Water-saving toilets, washing machines, and showerheads do not cost that much, and they cut down on the consumption of water. Turning off the tap when brushing teeth, taking shorter showers, washing the car less often, watering the lawn fewer times during dry weather—all of these are rather simple measures that ordinary people can take to conserve water.

CHAPTER TEST, FORM B

True/False

1. False. The area west of the Mississippi is larger than the area to the east.
2. True
3. True
4. False. To reach Oregon, settlers traveled the Oregon Trail.
5. False. Most Mormons settled in Utah.

Matching

6. B   7. A   8. E   9. C   10. D

Multiple Choice

11. D   12. B   13. A   14. B   15. C
16. B   17. C   18. C   19. B

Essay

20. Students' essays will vary. Possible response:

Water is essential for every living thing and when there is not enough water, that area suffers economically. During the Dust Bowl between the 1930s and 1940s, crops withered and the land itself blew away in huge dust storms. As a result, the area suffered an economic meltdown, and people moved to other regions in search of work. Population growth is having an even greater impact on water supplies for the western states, especially in the major cities that generally do not have an adequate supply of water to begin with.

To address the growing need for water, scientists are researching and developing ways to use seawater through desalination. It is an expensive process, but it may be the long-term solution. People themselves can help increase the water supply by reducing their consumption of it. Water-saving toilets, washing machines, and showerheads do not cost that much, and they cut down on the consumption of water. Turning off the tap when brushing teeth, taking shorter showers, washing the car less often, watering the lawn fewer times during dry weather—all of these are rather simple measures that ordinary people can take to conserve water.

Canada

LESSON QUIZ 1

True/False

1. True   2. False   3. False
4. True   5. False

Multiple Choice

6. D   7. C   8. B   9. C   10. B

LESSON QUIZ 2

Matching

1. C   2. B   3. E   4. A   5. D

Multiple Choice

6. B   7. C   8. A   9. D   10. A

LESSON QUIZ 3

True/False

1. False   2. True   3. True
4. False   5. True

Multiple Choice

6. B   7. C   8. A   9. C   10. B

CHAPTER TEST, FORM A

True/False

1. False. In land size, Russia is the largest nation in the world.
2. True
3. False. The Vikings settled in what is now Newfoundland.
4. True
5. True

Matching

6. B   7. E   8. A   9. C   10. D

Multiple Choice

11. A   12. B   13. A   14. B   15. C
16. B   17. D

Short Answer

18. Students' responses will vary. Possible response: The Prairie Provinces of Canada are covered mostly by plains, which extend northward from the United States. As in the United States, these plains are tilted from west to east.

19. Students' responses will vary. Possible response: Canada has a national and regional government, much like the United States. Provinces are the regions in Canada; whereas in the United States, states are the regions. However, the similarities between the governments of Canada and the United States end there. Canada's government is modeled after the United Kingdom's, with a parliamentary system and a prime minister. Canada and the United Kingdom even share the same king and queen.

Essay

20. Students' responses will vary. Possible response: When the first people from Asia came to Canada, they traveled southward. At that time, Canada was covered in ice, and living there would have been hard if not impossible. Yet when Canada warmed and the ice melted, people began migrating north and settled in various areas of the land. Some lived in the eastern woodlands, some went to the Pacific coast, and others settled farther north. Their way of life depended on the resources of the area they chose as their homes.

The people who settled in the eastern woodlands lived by hunting, fishing, and farming. They lived in the villages they made, and they traded with

one another. Those who settled along the Pacific coast had even more resources from which to fashion their way of life. The ocean and the rivers provided water and fish. The people hunted game in the forests and used the wood to make their houses and their canoes. The canoes provided them a means to hunt and to fish. Those who settled farther north had a more difficult life. Few plants or trees grew in the northern lands, and the people had to find other sources of food and to build their houses from materials other than wood. They also had to endure cold temperatures. From the caribou they hunted on land and from the seals and whales they hunted on water, these people found sources of food and used caribou hides to make their clothing and shoes.

The early people adapted to their environment and used what that environment offered to fashion their way of life. In other words, they learned to make their environment work for them.

CHAPTER TEST, FORM B

True/False

1. True
2. False. The Grand Banks is one of the world's great fisheries.
3. True
4. False. Newfoundland and Labrador was the last territory to join Canada as a province.
5. True

Matching

6. E   7. A   8. D   9. B   10. C

Multiple Choice

11. D   12. B   13. C   14. D   15. C
16. C   17. D   18. D   19. A

Essay

20. Students' responses will vary. Possible response: When the first people from Asia came to Canada, they traveled southward. At that time, Canada was covered in ice, and life would have been hard if not impossible there. Yet, when Canada warmed and the ice melted, people began migrating north and settled in various areas of the land. Some lived in the eastern woodlands, some went to the Pacific coast, and others settled farther north. Their way of life depended on the resources of the area they chose as their homes.

Discovering World Geography

Answer Key *cont.*

The people who settled in the eastern woodlands lived by hunting, fishing, and farming. They lived in the villages they made, and they traded with one another. Those who settled along the Pacific coast had even more resources from which to fashion their way of life. The ocean and the rivers provided water and fish. The people hunted game in the forests and used the wood to make their houses and their canoes. The canoes provided them a means to hunt and to fish. Those who settled farther north had a more difficult life. Few plants or trees grew in the northern lands, and the people had to find other sources of food and to build their houses from materials other than wood. They also had to endure cold temperatures. From the caribou they hunted on land and from the seals and whales they hunted on water, these people found sources of food and used caribou hides to make their clothing and shoes.

The early people adapted to their environment and used what that environment offered to fashion their way of life. In other words, they learned to make their environment work for them.

Mexico, Central America, and the Caribbean Islands

LESSON QUIZ 1

True/False

1. False 2. False 3. True
4. False 5. True

Multiple Choice

6. C   7. D   8. B   9. A   10. C

LESSON QUIZ 2

Matching

1. C   2. D   3. A   4. E   5. B

Multiple Choice

6. C   7. D   8. B   9. C   10. D

LESSON QUIZ 3

Matching

1. B   2. A   3. E   4. C   5. D

Multiple Choice

6. C   7. A   8. D   9. A   10. D

CHAPTER TEST, FORM A

True/False

1. True
2. False. The largest Latin American country is Mexico.
3. True
4. True
5. False. The biggest challenge for the Caribbean islands is to develop economically.

Matching

6. D   7. E   8. B   9. A   10. C

Multiple Choice

11. B   12. D   13. A   14. D   15. C
16. C   17. B

Short Answer

18. Students' responses will vary. Possible response: As a conquered people, Native Americans were often forced to work on plantations. Many were overworked and died; others died of starvation. They also suffered from diseases that the Europeans brought with them. Their numbers dwindled quickly, and the Europeans needed another source of labor. The Columbian Exchange provided the Europeans with enslaved Africans.

19. Students' responses will vary. Possible response: Mexico City is densely populated, with more than 21 million people. Because of the number of people in the city, a great deal of exhaust from the cars that people drive is released into the air. Add to that the fact that Mexico City is industrialized. Factories in the city release pollutants into the air, and the mountains around the city and the colder air in the higher atmosphere hold the polluted air in place. This can be a serious health threat to many people.

Essay

20. Students' responses will vary. Possible response: Although their number far exceeded those of the Spanish conquistadors, and even if they were fearsome warriors, the Aztec were no match for the foreign force. The Spanish had guns and armor; the Aztec only had spears and other basic weapons. Also, the Aztec had little resistance to the diseases the Spanish brought with them; thousands of Aztec died. The Aztec had few allies among other native peoples, who resented being under Aztec rule. The conquistadors played on this resentment and won more native peoples to their side.

After their defeat by the Spanish, life in Mexico changed dramatically. Mexico was now a colony of Spain, which controlled the government, economy, and society. The native peoples were converted to Catholicism by Roman Catholic priests. The people were also forced to work on farms or in mines by the Spanish conquistadors. The wealthiest people in colonial Mexico were now the settlers from Spain.

CHAPTER TEST, FORM B

True/False

1. False. Mexico and Central America form an isthmus between North and South America.
2. True
3. True
4. True
5. False. Cuba has a poor economy.

Matching

6. A   7. D   8. E   9. B   10. C

Multiple Choice

11. B   12. D   13. A   14. B   15. D
16. C   17. B   18. B   19. C

Essay

20. Students' responses will vary. Possible response: Although their number far exceeded those of the Spanish conquistadors, and even if they were fearsome warriors, the Aztec were no match for the foreign force. The Spanish had guns and armor; the Aztec only had spears and other basic weapons. Also, the Aztec had little resistance to the diseases the Spanish brought with them; thousands of Aztec died. The Aztec had few allies among other native peoples, who resented being under Aztec rule. The conquistadors played on this resentment and won more native peoples to their side.

   After their defeat by the Spanish, life in Mexico changed dramatically. Mexico was now a colony of Spain, which controlled the government, economy, and society. The native peoples were converted to Catholicism by Roman Catholic priests. The people were also forced to work on farms or in mines by the Spanish conquistadors. The wealthiest people in colonial Mexico were now the settlers from Spain.

South America

UNIT TEST

True/False

1. True   2. False   3. True
4. True   5. False

Matching

6. C   7. A   8. E   9. D   10. B

Multiple Choice

11. A   12. C   13. A   14. D   15. B
16. C   17. B   18. A   19. D   20. C

Brazil

LESSON QUIZ 1

True/False

1. False   2. True   3. True
4. False   5. False

Multiple Choice

6. B   7. C   8. A   9. C   10. D

LESSON QUIZ 2

True/False

1. True   2. True   3. False   4. True   5. True

Multiple Choice

6. C   7. A   8. D   9. B   10. B

LESSON QUIZ 3

True/False

1. True   2. False   3. False
4. True   5. False

Multiple Choice

6. A   7. B   8. D   9. C   10. A

CHAPTER TEST, FORM A

True/False

1. True
2. False. Slavery was outlawed in Brazil in 1888.
3. False. The largest group of multiethnic Brazilians shares European and African ancestry.
4. False. Portuguese is Brazil's official language.
5. True

Matching

6. E   **7.** A   **8.** D   **9.** C   **10.** B

Multiple Choice

11. C   **12.** D   **13.** A   **14.** C   **15.** B
16. B   **17.** D

Short Answer

18. Napoleon invaded Portugal in 1807, causing the Portuguese royal family to flee to Brazil. After Napoleon was defeated, most of the royal family returned to Portugal but the king's son, Pedro, stayed behind in Brazil. When Pedro was ordered back to Portugal, he refused to go and declared Brazil independent and himself emperor. If Napoleon had not invaded Portugal, these events would not likely have occurred. This is how he indirectly influenced the independence of Brazil.

19. People from many different ethnic groups live in Brazil. They have introduced new, non-Portuguese words into the language. In addition, many Native American languages are still spoken in Brazil. This mixing of languages has made Brazilian Portuguese much different from the language spoken in Portugal itself.

Essay

20. Spain and Portugal disputed each other's claims in the New World. To resolve their differences, the countries asked the Pope to find a solution. The Pope decided that all claims to the west of a certain line were to belong to Spain. Everything to the east was Portugal's. The two countries agreed to this division and signed the Treaty of Tordesillas in 1494. However, the division was not very equal. Most of the Americas lay west of the line and, as a result, became Spanish territory.

Students' responses as to which country benefited the most from the treaty may vary. Possible response: The treaty gave Portugal only a small portion of South America, while Spain was given almost all of South and Central America. For this reason, I believe the treaty benefited Spain the most.

CHAPTER TEST, FORM B

True/False

1. False. The Amazon is the largest river in terms of the amount of freshwater it carries.

2. True

3. True

4. False. Brazil got its name from the brazilwood that became highly valued in sixteenth-century Europe.

5. True

6. False. Today, Brazil is a democratic republic; the people elect a president and other leaders.

Matching

7. A   **8.** D   **9.** C   **10.** B

Multiple Choice

11. D   **12.** C   **13.** A   **14.** D   **15.** B
16. D   **17.** A   **18.** C   **19.** B

Essay

20. Spain and Portugal disputed each other's claims in the New World. To resolve their differences, the countries asked the Pope to find a solution. The Pope decided that all claims to the west of a certain line were to belong to Spain. Everything to the east was Portugal's. The two countries agreed to this division and signed the Treaty of Tordesillas in 1494. However, the division was not very equal. Most of the Americas lay west of the line and, as a result, became Spanish territory.

Students' responses as to which country benefited the most from the treaty may vary. Possible response: The treaty gave Portugal only a small portion of South America, while Spain was given almost all of South and Central America. For this reason, I believe the treaty benefited Spain the most.

The Tropical North

LESSON QUIZ 1

True/False

1. False   **2.** True   **3.** False
4. True   **5.** False

Multiple Choice

6. B   **7.** C   **8.** D   **9.** A   **10.** B

LESSON QUIZ 2

Matching

1. D   **2.** C   **3.** E   **4.** A   **5.** B

Multiple Choice

6. B   **7.** D   **8.** C   **9.** A   **10.** B

LESSON QUIZ 3

Matching

1. C   **2.** E   **3.** B   **4.** D   **5.** A

Multiple Choice

6. A   **7.** C   **8.** B   **9.** D   **10.** B

CHAPTER TEST, FORM A

True/False

1. False. The Tropical North is composed of five independent nations plus the colony of French Guiana.

2. False. Angel Falls is more than 20 times higher than Niagara Falls.

3. True

4. True

5. False. Colombia's Pacific coast region is sparsely populated.

Matching

6. C   **7.** A   **8.** E   **9.** D   **10.** B

Multiple Choice

11. C   **12.** A   **13.** B   **14.** C   **15.** B
16. C   **17.** D

Short Answer

18. Students' responses will vary. Possible response: The system of *encomienda* allowed Spanish colonists to force Native Americans to work for them. Native Americans were put to work in Spanish mines and on Spanish estates.

19. Students' responses will vary. Possible response: The countries of the Tropical North have diverse physical geography, ranging from mountain peaks that exceed 18,000 feet to extensive lowlands. The high peaks of the Andes tend to be very cold, and may be snow-covered all year, despite the fact that they lie in the Tropics. In contrast, the lowlands have more typical tropical weather featuring year-round warmth.

Essay

20. Students' responses will vary. Possible response: Relations between the United States and nations of the Tropical North are getting better, although there are still strains.

The United States and Colombia have been working together to fight drug trafficking. This has helped to soothe Colombian anger at U.S. actions that helped Panama to break away from Colombia a century ago.

U.S. relations with Venezuela, on the other hand, have been more troubled, particularly in the wake of Hugo Chávez's seizure of U.S. oil companies working in his country. Chávez's frequent criticisms of the United States and closeness to countries like Cuba and Iran have also strained relations.

CHAPTER TEST, FORM B

True/False

1. False. In the Tropical North, French Guiana has the least amount of land.

2. True

3. True

4. True

5. False. The official language of Ecuador is Spanish.

Matching

6. C   **7.** B   **8.** E   **9.** A   **10.** D

Multiple Choice

11. B   **12.** D   **13.** C   **14.** A   **15.** B
16. D   **17.** B   **18.** C   **19.** A

Essay

20. Students' responses will vary. Possible response: Relations between the United States and nations of the Tropical North are getting better, although there are still strains.

The United States and Colombia have been working together to fight drug trafficking. This has helped to soothe Colombian anger at U.S. actions that helped Panama to break away from Colombia a century ago.

U.S. relations with Venezuela, on the other hand, have been more troubled, particularly in the wake of Hugo Chávez's seizure of U.S. oil companies working in his country. Chávez's frequent criticisms of the United States and closeness to countries like Cuba and Iran have also strained relations.

Andes and Midlatitude Countries

LESSON QUIZ 1

True/False

1. True   2. True   3. False   4. False   5. True

Multiple Choice

6. C **7.** B **8.** D **9.** A **10.** C

LESSON QUIZ 2

True/False

1. True **2.** False **3.** False **4.** True **5.** True

Multiple Choice

6. B **7.** C **8.** C **9.** A **10.** D

LESSON QUIZ 3

True/False

1. False **2.** True **3.** False **4.** True **5.** True

Multiple Choice

6. D **7.** D **8.** C **9.** C **10.** A

CHAPTER TEST, FORM A

True/False

1. True

2. False. During the centuries of Spanish colonization, the Roman Catholic Church was one of the most important institutions in the Andean region.

3. False. Soccer [football] is the most popular sport in the Andean and midlatitude regions of South America.

Matching

4. G **5.** A **6.** D **7.** E **8.** C

9. F **10.** B

Multiple Choice

11. A **12.** D **13.** C **14.** C **15.** B

16. B **17.** D

Short Answer

18. The Andes were formed by the uplift caused by the collision of tectonic plates along the rim of the Pacific Ocean, leading to earthquakes and volcanic eruptions.

19. In the early 1900s, multinational companies of the United States and Europe exploited the region's raw materials. They began mining and smelting operations in the region. The operations were profitable and allowed owners to become very wealthy and powerful. However, most workers did not share in the profits and remained very poor.

Essay

20. El Niños are caused when weak cold winds come from the east. Without these cold winds, the central Pacific Ocean grows warmer than usual. More water evaporates, and more clouds form. As a result of an El Niño, thick bands of clouds form that change wind and rain patterns. During an El Niño, the climate along the Pacific coast of South America becomes much warmer and wetter than normal. Floods occur in some places, especially along the coast of Peru. Some areas receive heavier-than-normal rains. Other areas, however, have less-than normal rainfall.

CHAPTER TEST, FORM B

True/False

1. False. A series of knotted cords used by the Inca for record keeping was called a quipu.

2. True

3. True

4. True

5. False. Pachamanca is a mixture of lamb, pork, and chicken baked in an earthen oven.

6. True

Matching

7. C **8.** B **9.** D **10.** A

Multiple Choice

11. C **12.** C **13.** B **14.** A **15.** D

16. A **17.** B **18.** D **19.** C

Essay

20. El Niños are caused when weak cold winds come from the east. Without these cold winds, the central Pacific Ocean grows warmer than usual. More water evaporates, and more clouds form. As a result of an El Niño, thick bands of clouds form that change wind and rain patterns. During an El Niño, the climate along the Pacific coast of South America becomes much warmer and wetter than normal. Floods occur in some places, especially along the coast of Peru. Some areas receive heavier-than-normal rains. Other areas, however, have less-than-normal rainfall.

Europe
UNIT TEST
True/False

1. True **2.** False **3.** False **4.** True **5.** True

Matching

6. C **7.** E **8.** A **9.** D **10.** B

Multiple Choice

11. C **12.** D **13.** C **14.** B **15.** A
16. B **17.** D **18.** C **19.** A **20.** B

Western Europe
LESSON QUIZ 1
Matching

1. C **2.** E **3.** A **4.** D **5.** B

Multiple Choice

6. D **7.** B **8.** C **9.** D **10.** A

LESSON QUIZ 2
True/False

1. False **2.** True **3.** False **4.** True **5.** True

Multiple Choice

6. C **7.** D **8.** B **9.** A **10.** C

LESSON QUIZ 3
True/False

1. False **2.** True **3.** True **4.** True **5.** True

Multiple Choice

6. D **7.** C **8.** B **9.** A **10.** C

CHAPTER TEST, FORM A
True/False

1. True
2. False. The English Channel separates southern England from France.
3. True
4. True
5. False. The high-speed rail lines in France connect to other high-speed rail lines that go to London, the Netherlands, and Belgium.

Matching

6. C **7.** E **8.** A **9.** D **10.** B

Multiple Choice

11. A **12.** C **13.** D **14.** B **15.** C
16. A **17.** B

Short Answer

18. Students' responses will vary. Possible response: The Gulf Stream moves warm tropical waters northward, flowing across the Atlantic Ocean. Its eastern extension, the North Atlantic Current, moves along the European coast and heats the air above it. The warm, moist air is then carried by the Westerlies and brings mild temperatures and rain to most of Western Europe all year long. This is why the summers are cool and the winters are mild in most of Western Europe.

19. Students' responses will vary. Possible response: For more than 40 years, the United States and the Soviet Union engaged in a conflict that never erupted into war. Yet, the threat of war always existed. During this time, both nations stockpiled nuclear weapons as a show of their strength. The Soviet Union's influence began to weaken in the 1980s. The Cold War ended when the government of the Soviet Union collapsed in 1991.

Essay

20. Students' responses will vary. Possible response: At the end of World War I, Germany was blamed for starting the war. The winning nations forced Germany to pay them for damages, placing a heavy burden on war-torn Germany. The defeat and these payments weakened Germany's economy; they also angered the German people. Germans believed that they were being punished too severely.

Adolf Hitler played on the German people's anger and stirred up aggressive feelings. He became dictator and proposed a new German empire, peopled with the superior race of Germans. He and his Nazi Party began building a strong military force to make their new German empire a reality. War came when Hitler's armed forces invaded and took control of other countries to expand his empire. As war raged, the Nazis carried out the Holocaust, murdering 6 million Jews. World War II extended beyond Western Europe and involved all the world powers. At its end, World War II claimed the lives of between 40 million and 60 million people, the majority of which were civilians.

CHAPTER TEST, FORM B

True/False

1. False. The island of Britain contains England, Wales, and Scotland.
2. True
3. True
4. False. Following World War I, the victorious countries demanded that Germany pay for damages.
5. True

Matching

6. B   **7.** D   **8.** E   **9.** A   **10.** C

Multiple Choice

11. D   **12.** B   **13.** A   **14.** C   **15.** B
16. D   **17.** A   **18.** C   **19.** B

Essay

20. Students' responses will vary. Possible response: At the end of World War I, Germany was blamed for starting the war. The winning nations forced Germany to pay them for damages, placing a heavy burden on war-torn Germany. The defeat and these payments weakened Germany's economy; they also angered the German people. Germans believed that they were being punished too severely.

   Adolf Hitler played on the German people's anger and stirred up aggressive feelings. He became dictator and proposed a new German empire, peopled with the superior race of Germans. He and his Nazi Party began building a strong military force to make their new German empire a reality. War came when Hitler's armed forces invaded and took control of other countries to expand his empire. As war raged, the Nazis carried out the Holocaust, murdering 6 million Jews. World War II extended beyond Western Europe and involved all the world powers. At its end, World War II claimed the lives of between 40 million and 60 million people, the majority of which were civilians.

Northern and Southern Europe

LESSON QUIZ 1

Matching

1. C   **2.** E   **3.** A   **4.** D   **5.** B

Multiple Choice

6. C   **7.** D   **8.** A   **9.** B   **10.** D

LESSON QUIZ 2

Matching

1. D   **2.** A   **3.** C   **4.** E   **5.** B

Multiple Choice

6. C   **7.** D   **8.** B   **9.** A   **10.** D

LESSON QUIZ 3

True/False

1. False   **2.** True   **3.** True
4. True   **5.** False

Multiple Choice

6. C   **7.** A   **8.** B   **9.** D   **10.** C

CHAPTER TEST, FORM A

True/False

1. True
2. False. The Mediterranean Sea is the most important body of water in Southern Europe.
3. True
4. False. After fighting a civil war in the 1930s, Spain did not fight in World War II.
5. True

Matching

6. B   **7.** E   **8.** A   **9.** D   **10.** C

Multiple Choice

11. D   **12.** C   **13.** B   **14.** C   **15.** A
16. B   **17.** D

Short Answer

18. Students' responses will vary. Possible response: When a country's infant mortality rate decreases, that means that fewer infants die. Normally that would mean there would be more younger people in the population. But if older people lived longer, the population could still be aging overall. That might also be the case if the birth rate dropped and fewer infants were being born.

19. Students' responses will vary. Possible response: The Protestant Reformation had greater impact in Northern Europe than in Southern Europe. As a result of the Reformation, many Northern European kingdoms broke away from the

Roman Catholic Church and made Protestantism their official religion. Today more than three-quarters of the people in Northern Europe are Lutheran. In contrast, the Roman Catholic Church continues to have more impact in Southern Europe, except in Greece, where the Greek Orthodox Church is dominant.

Essay

20. Students' responses will vary. Possible response: Many Northern European countries have some form of welfare capitalism in place. Citizens pay the price of this practice through taxes, which are high. The governments use these taxes to provide many services to their citizens. These services include health care and education, the essential aspects of life that should be available to all people, including those who might not be able to afford them otherwise.

Welfare capitalism seems to work well for Northern Europe. For example, the literacy rate in Norway, Sweden, and Denmark is nearly 100 percent. The government gives strong support to education, and most schooling is free. Every citizen also has health insurance. This provision makes access to medical care and services far easier and should result in better preventative care and screenings.

CHAPTER TEST, FORM B

True/False

1. True
2. False. Norway is Europe's biggest exporter of oil.
3. False. The Vikings were excellent seafarers.
4. True
5. False. There are more Roman Catholics in Southern Europe than there are Protestants.

Matching

6. D   7. A   8. E   9. B   10. C

Multiple Choice

11. B   12. C   13. D   14. B   15. A
16. C   17. D   18. B   19. A

Essay

20. Students' responses will vary. Possible response: Many Northern European countries have some form of welfare capitalism in place. Citizens pay the price of this practice through taxes, which are

high. The governments use these taxes to provide many services to their citizens. These services include health care and education, the essential aspects of life that should be available to all people, including those who might not be able to afford them otherwise.

Welfare capitalism seems to work well for Northern Europe. For example, the literacy rate in Norway, Sweden, and Denmark is nearly 100 percent. The government gives strong support to education, and most schooling is free. Every citizen also has health insurance. This provision makes access to medical care and services far easier and should result in better preventative care and screenings.

Eastern Europe and Western Russia
LESSON QUIZ 1

True/False

1. True   2. False   3. True
4. False   5. False

Multiple Choice

6. C   7. A   8. D   9. B   10. B

LESSON QUIZ 2

True/False

1. True   2. True   3. False
4. True   5. False

Multiple Choice

6. A   7. C   8. B   9. B   10. D

LESSON QUIZ 3

True/False

1. True   2. False   3. False
4. True   5. False

Multiple Choice

6. D   7. C   8. A   9. A   10. B

CHAPTER TEST, FORM A

True/False

1. False. The northern Ural Mountains are covered with forests and glaciers.
2. False. Early Slavs migrated from Asia and settled in the area that now includes Ukraine and Poland.
3. True

4. False. The dominant religion in Russia and most Eastern European countries is the Eastern Orthodox Church.

5. True

Matching

6. B   7. D   8. C   9. E   10. A

Multiple Choice

11. C   12. D   13. A   14. D   15. B
16. C   17. B

Short Answer

18. The Balkan Peninsula is very mountainous. This makes it difficult for people to travel easily throughout the region. Therefore, human settlements in the Balkans are isolated from one another, resulting in cultural and ethnic diversity.

19. By the end of World War II, the Soviet army had pushed Germany out of Eastern Europe and was already in control of the region. Though the Soviet Union promised free elections in Eastern European countries, it soon installed (and dominated) communist governments there. The countries of Eastern Europe thus became Soviet satellites.

Essay

20. Because Russia is located between Asia and Western Europe, its history and culture have been influenced by developments in both regions.

   It has been attacked by Mongols from Asia and Germans from the west, among others. It has been influenced by European culture and made its own contributions to European art and literature. Also, Russia was influenced by the Ottoman Empire to its south. In short, Russian culture can be described as a mix of Western European and Asian influences.

CHAPTER TEST, FORM B

True/False

1. True

2. False. The southern coast of Ukraine is bordered by the Black Sea.

3. True

4. False. Most of Russia's vast coal, oil, and natural gas reserves are in Siberia.

5. True

Matching

6. E   7. A   8. D   9. C   10. B

Multiple Choice

11. B   12. C   13. D   14. A   15. C
16. B   17. D   18. B   19. A

Essay

20. Because Russia is located between Asia and Western Europe, its history and culture have been influenced by developments in both regions. It has been attacked by Mongols from Asia and Germans from the west, among others. It has been influenced by European culture and made its own contributions to European art and literature. Also, Russia was influenced by the Ottoman Empire to its south. In short, Russian culture can be described as a mix of Western European and Asian influences.

Asia

UNIT TEST

True/False

1. True   2. True   3. False   4. False   5. True

Matching

6. E   7. D   8. A   9. C   10. B

Multiple Choice

11. B   12. A   13. B   14. C   15. D
16. A   17. B   18. A   19. A   20. D

East Asia

LESSON QUIZ 1

True/False

1. True   2. False   3. True
4. False   5. True

Multiple Choice

6. D   7. B   8. C   9. A   10. B

LESSON QUIZ 2

Matching

1. D   2. C   3. A   4. E   5. B

Multiple Choice

6. B   7. D   8. C   9. A   10. D

LESSON QUIZ 3

True/False

1. False **2.** True **3.** True

4. True **5.** False

Multiple Choice

6. B   **7.** C   **8.** A   **9.** D   **10.** C

CHAPTER TEST, FORM A

True/False

1. True

2. False. The climates in the countries of East Asia are of a wide range.

3. False. The Chinese built the Great Wall of China to stop invaders from the north.

4. True

5. True

Matching

6. C   **7.** A   **8.** E   **9.** D   **10.** B

Multiple Choice

11. A   **12.** C   **13.** B   **14.** D   **15.** D

16. B   **17.** D

Short Answer

18. Students' responses will vary. Possible response: East Asia has a range of climates, from hot and rainy to cold and dry. This is partly due to the vast size of the region and its range of elevations. Many lands in the region lie in different latitudes and have different elevations. The more northern areas and areas of high elevation typically have colder climates. Polar air masses spread southward and bring in colder, drier air. Air masses from the Pacific Ocean spread inland and bring warmer, moist air.

19. Students' responses will vary. Possible response: The Chinese invented woodblock printing. They developed a way to use blocks of wood and clay to print characters on a page. With this invention, the Chinese could print a large number of books much more quickly than before. Woodblock printing allowed ideas to spread more easily through China and to other areas of East Asia and beyond.

Essay

20. Students' responses will vary. Possible response: Rapid economic growth often results in problems. One problem is how it affects a country's environment. Both China and Japan have become

major economic powers, and both countries now face environmental issues.

China uses coal to power its plants. Vehicles clog the roads. Both factories and vehicles have contributed to dramatic increases in air pollution. The water supply is contaminated with waste from factories, sewage, and farm chemicals. Urban areas have expanded into what was once farmland, and many of the larger urban areas face water shortages.

Japan has similar environmental issues. More developed than China, Japan has also been industrialized longer. As a result, Japan has taken stronger measures to protect its environment. However, the polluted air from its many plants has produced acid rain and caused many other problems. Along with these problems, Japan faced a nuclear incident in 2011. A powerful earthquake and tsunami killed thousands of people. In addition, several nuclear power plants were badly damaged.

A country may be an economic power, yet pollution and other industrial dangers must be overcome in order for the country to truly prosper.

CHAPTER TEST, FORM B

True/False

1. False. Russia lies to the north of East Asia.

2. True

3. True

4. False. Japan has a lower gross national product than China.

5. True

Matching

6. D   **7.** C   **8.** B   **9.** E   **10.** A

Multiple Choice

11. B   **12.** C   **13.** A   **14.** D   **15.** B

16. C   **17.** A   **18.** D   **19.** B

Essay

20. Students' responses will vary. Possible response: Rapid economic growth often results in problems. One problem is how it affects a country's environment. Both China and Japan have become major economic powers, and both countries now face environmental issues.

Discovering World Geography

China uses coal to power its plants. Vehicles clog the roads. Both factories and vehicles have contributed to dramatic increases in air pollution. The water supply is contaminated with waste from factories, sewage, and farm chemicals. Urban areas have expanded into what was once farmland, and many of the larger urban areas face water shortages.

Japan has similar environmental issues. More developed than China, Japan has also been industrialized longer. As a result, Japan has taken stronger measures to protect its environment. However, the polluted air from its many plants has produced acid rain and caused many other problems. Along with these problems, Japan faced a nuclear incident in 2011. A powerful earthquake and tsunami killed thousands of people. In addition, several nuclear power plants were badly damaged.

A country may be an economic power, yet pollution and other industrial dangers must be overcome in order for the country to truly prosper.

Southeast Asia

LESSON QUIZ 1

True/False

1. True   **2.** False   **3.** False
4. True   **5.** True

Multiple Choice

6. A   **7.** C   **8.** A   **9.** D   **10.** B

LESSON QUIZ 2

True/False

1. True   **2.** False   **3.** True
4. False   **5.** True

Multiple Choice

6. C   **7.** B   **8.** D   **9.** A   **10.** C

LESSON QUIZ 3

True/False

1. False   **2.** False   **3.** False
4. True   **5.** True

Multiple Choice

6. D   **7.** B   **8.** A   **9.** B   **10.** C

CHAPTER TEST, FORM A

True/False

1. True

2. False. Funan, one of the first important trade-based states in Southeast Asia, covered parts of present-day Cambodia, Thailand, and Vietnam.

3. True

4. True

5. False. The Association of Southeast Asian Nations (ASEAN) includes all countries in the region except East Timor.

Matching

6. C   **7.** A   **8.** E   **9.** B   **10.** D

Multiple Choice

11. C   **12.** D   **13.** A   **14.** B   **15.** B
16. C   **17.** B

Short Answer

18. Students' responses will vary. Possible response: One way this location has enriched the region is that trade has exposed the region to many different cultural influences. One way it has harmed the region is that foreign countries seeking wealth and power have attempted to control the area.

19. Four major tectonic plates meet in Southeast Asia, causing the region to experience frequent earthquakes and volcanoes. The four plates are the Eurasian Plate, the Indo-Australian Plate, the Pacific Plate, and the Indian Plate. The pressures and tensions produced by the meeting of these plates have fractured Earth's crust into many smaller plates across the region and produced the region's many islands and volcanoes.

Essay

20. Students' responses may vary. Possible response: Economic activity is negatively affecting Southeast Asia's environment in numerous ways. For example, tin mining has created huge wastelands in parts of the area. Commercial logging is contributing to deforestation, threatening the region's diverse flora and fauna.

While industrial growth creates environmental problems, it also provides much-needed jobs in a region plagued with widespread poverty. However, if the environment is not protected, the resources that provide jobs may be used up quickly.

Answer Key *cont.*

CHAPTER TEST, FORM B

True/False

1. True
2. False. Indonesia, Malaysia, and Thailand rank among the world's top tin producers.
3. True
4. False. The port of Malacca was the center of an important Islamic kingdom
5. False. In the 1970s, a rural communist movement called the Khmer Rouge terrorized the people of Cambodia.
6. True

Matching

| 7. D | 8. A | 9. C | 10. B |

Multiple Choice

| 11. B | 12. C | 13. D | 14. A | 15. C |
| 16. B | 17. D | 18. B | 19. C |

Essay

20. Students' responses may vary. Possible response: Economic activity is negatively affecting Southeast Asia's environment in numerous ways. For example, tin mining has created huge wastelands in parts of the area. Commercial logging is contributing to deforestation, threatening the region's diverse flora and fauna.

    While industrial growth creates environmental problems, it also provides much-needed jobs in a region plagued with widespread poverty. However, if the environment is not protected, the resources that provide jobs may be used up quickly.

South Asia

LESSON QUIZ 1

Matching

| 1. B | 2. E | 3. A | 4. D | 5. C |

Multiple Choice

| 6. C | 7. D | 8. B | 9. A | 10. C |

LESSON QUIZ 2

True/False

| 1. True | 2. False | 3. True |
| 4. True | 5. False |

Multiple Choice

| 6. A | 7. C | 8. D | 9. B | 10. C |

LESSON QUIZ 3

Matching

| 1. B | 2. E | 3. D | 4. A | 5. C |

Multiple Choice

| 6. B | 7. C | 8. D | 9. A | 10. C |

CHAPTER TEST, FORM A

True/False

1. False. South Asia forms a subcontinent.
2. True
3. True
4. False. India is the world's second most populous country today.
5. True

Matching

| 6. D | 7. C | 8. E | 9. A | 10. B |

Multiple Choice

| 11. C | 12. D | 13. C | 14. B | 15. B |
| 16. A | 17. D |

Short Answer

18. Students' responses will vary. Possible response: The forests are an important habitat in South Asia because they are home to South Asia's unique wildlife. Indian forests are home to three of Earth's most endangered mammals: the tiger, the Asian elephant, and the one-horned rhinoceros. South Asians are working to reverse some of the region's wildlife losses. They have created wildlife reserves and established laws controlling hunting and logging. These efforts have started to make a difference in protecting the wildlife.

19. Students' responses will vary. Possible response: Population trends are changing in India. More and more people are leaving the villages. Hoping to find better jobs, they migrate to the "metros," or big cities. In the 2011 census, for the first time, India's urban areas were growing faster than rural areas. India's biggest city, Mumbai, is now the fourth-largest city in the world.

Essay

20. Students' responses will vary. Possible response: Having lasted for nearly 1,000 years, the ancient Aryan civilization left behind two legacies. One was social; the second, literary. Each of these two legacies had a great impact on South Asians.

Discovering World Geography

Aryans believed that society benefited if people followed strict roles and tasks. They developed a system of social classes or castes, called *varnas*. At the top of the system were priests, next were warriors, followed by merchants, and then a bottom caste of peasants and laborers. These castes affected South Asians for thousands of years. Even if they had the talents and skills to do so, people born into a lower caste could not rise into a higher caste. In India, the caste system has been outlawed since the country won independence in 1947, but some effects of the system are still present.

The second legacy of the Aryans was literary. The Aryans composed long, poetic texts in the ancient Sanskrit language. These texts were religious hymns called the Vedas. Hindi, one of the most important languages in modern India, came from Sanskrit, which also played a significant role in the development of Latin and Greek. One of the poetic texts, the *Rig Veda*, provided some of the founding ideas of the Hindu religion.

Through these two legacies, the ancient Aryan civilization has influenced the culture and way of life for South Asians.

CHAPTER TEST, FORM B
True/False
1. True
2. False. The *Rig Veda* was part of a literary legacy left by the Aryans.
3. True
4. True
5. False. Arranged marriages are still allowed in South Asia, but are less common than in the past.

Matching
6. C   7. E   8. B   9. D   10. A

Multiple Choice
11. A   12. C   13. A   14. B   15. B
16. D   17. C   18. D   19. C

Essay
20. Students' responses will vary. Possible response: Having lasted for nearly 1,000 years, the ancient Aryan civilization left behind two legacies. One was social; the second, literary. Each of these two legacies had a great impact on South Asians.

Aryans believed that society benefited if people followed strict roles and tasks. They developed a system of social classes or castes, called *varnas*. At the top of the system were priests, next were warriors, followed by merchants, and then a bottom caste of peasants and laborers. These castes affected South Asians for thousands of years. Even if they had the talents and skills to do so, people born into a lower caste could not rise into a higher caste. In India, the caste system has been outlawed since the country won independence in 1947, but some effects of the system are still present.

The second legacy of the Aryans was literary. The Aryans composed long, poetic texts in the ancient Sanskrit language. These texts were religious hymns called the Vedas. Hindi, one of the most important languages in modern India, came from Sanskrit, which also played a significant role in the development of Latin and Greek. One of the poetic texts, the *Rig Veda*, provided some of the founding ideas of the Hindu religion.

Through these two legacies, the ancient Aryan civilization has influenced the culture and way of life for South Asians.

Central Asia, the Caucasus, and Siberian Russia
LESSON QUIZ 1
True/False
1. False   2. True   3. True
4. False   5. False

Multiple Choice
6. A   7. D   8. B   9. A   10. C

LESSON QUIZ 2
True/False
1. True   2. True   3. False
4. True   5. False

Multiple Choice
6. C   7. B   8. A   9. C   10. B

LESSON QUIZ 3
True/False
1. False   2. False   3. True
4. False   5. True

Answer Key *cont.*

networks

Multiple Choice

6. A   **7.** C   **8.** C   **9.** B   **10.** A

CHAPTER TEST, FORM A

True/False

1. True
2. False. Central Asia has few trees because of the region's arid climate.
3. False. The Central Siberian Plateau supplies most of Russia's coal.
4. True

Matching

5. F   **6.** C   **7.** E   **8.** A
9. D   **10.** B

Multiple Choice

11. B   **12.** D   **13.** B   **14.** A   **15.** C
16. A   **17.** D

Short Answer

18. The presence of these two large bodies of water makes the region's summers cooler and winters warmer than in Central Asia. They also influence the amount of rain in the region. For example, the Black Sea gives Georgia's coastal lowlands a humid subtropical climate, with up to 100 inches (254 cm) of rainfall per year.

19. Students' responses will vary. Possible response: Timur was a patron of arts and science. He made Samarkand, the capital of his empire, a cultural center by bringing in artists and scholars from other parts of the empire. It also became a major center for the study of astronomy and mathematics.

Essay

20. Students' responses will vary. Possible response: The Aral Sea was once the fourth-largest inland lake in the world, but it has shrunk to about 10 percent of its former size. The cause of this problem began in the 1960s. The Soviets built huge farms in the desert and steppes and needed water to irrigate those farms. They dug long canals from the Aral Sea to bring irrigation water to the farms. There were several effects from this situation. The sea shrank because there was not enough water flowing in from other seas to replace the water that was being lost to evaporation and irrigation. The shoreline receded as the level of the water shrank. Towns that were important fishing ports were no longer located on the sea. The seafloor dried up and the farm chemicals and salts that polluted the sea bed were carried away by the wind. These chemicals damaged the health of people living in the area and those who lived hundreds of miles away.

CHAPTER TEST, FORM B

True/False

1. False. The first humans in Siberia came from Europe or from central and eastern Asia.
2. True
3. True
4. False. Tajikistan is mainly rural, but the country's largely mountainous terrain causes its settled areas to be densely populated.
5. False. Most Azerbaijanis are Muslims, and most Armenians and Georgians are Christians.

Matching

6. A   **7.** C   **8.** B   **9.** D   **10.** E

Multiple Choice

11. A   **12.** B   **13.** C   **14.** B   **15.** A
16. C   **17.** D   **18.** C   **19.** B

Essay

20. Students' responses will vary. Possible response: The Aral Sea was once the fourth-largest inland lake in the world, but it has shrunk to about 10 percent of its former size. The cause of this problem began in the 1960s. The Soviets built huge farms in the desert and steppes and needed water to irrigate those farms. They dug long canals from the Aral Sea to bring irrigation water to the farms. There were several effects from this situation. The sea shrank because there was not enough water flowing in from other seas to replace the water that was being lost to evaporation and irrigation. The shoreline receded as the level of the water shrank. Towns that were important fishing ports were no longer located on the sea. The seafloor dried up and the farm chemicals and salts that polluted the sea bed were carried away by the wind. These chemicals damaged the health of people living in the area and those who lived hundreds of miles away.

Copyright © The McGraw-Hill Companies, Inc.

342   *Discovering World Geography*

Southwest Asia

LESSON QUIZ 1

Matching

1. D   **2.** A   **3.** C   **4.** E   **5.** B

Multiple Choice

6. B   **7.** D   **8.** C   **9.** A   **10.** A

LESSON QUIZ 2

Matching

1. E   **2.** B   **3.** D   **4.** A   **5.** C

Multiple Choice

6. D   **7.** B   **8.** D   **9.** B   **10.** A

LESSON QUIZ 3

True/False

1. False   **2.** True   **3.** True
4. True   **5.** False

Multiple Choice

6. C   **7.** D   **8.** B   **9.** A   **10.** C

CHAPTER TEST, FORM A

True/False

1. True

2. True

3. False. By about A.D. 800, Islam extended from north Africa into most of Spain and Portugal.

4. True

5. False. The population of Southwest Asia is slightly greater than that of the United States.

Matching

6. C   **7.** A   **8.** D   **9.** E   **10.** B

Multiple Choice

11. B   **12.** C   **13.** D   **14.** C   **15.** A
16. A   **17.** B

Short Answer

18. Students' responses will vary. Possible response: For many Southwest Asians, Islam plays a central role in their daily lives. They consider their religion as a complete way of life. Islam has rules regarding people's diets, hygiene, business practices, family relationships, and laws. During the holy month of Ramadan, Muslims fast and then celebrate the end of fasting with a three-day festival.

19. Students' responses will vary. Possible response: Deserts cover nearly the entire area of the Arabian Peninsula, and this area falls within a very dry, or arid, climate zone. As such the area receives less than 10 inches of rain during the year. The summers are brutally hot in the desert areas. In contrast, the mountainous areas in Turkey, Iran, and Afghanistan have continental climates. In those areas, temperatures vary greatly between summer and winter. Glaciers can be found among the mountain peaks.

Essay

20. Students' responses will vary. Possible response: The discovery of oil deposits in Southwest Asia has had a strong impact on the region's economy and social order.

The discovery of oil has brought great wealth to the oil-producing countries along the Persian Gulf. However, this wealth has not always been distributed evenly. A few people are extremely wealthy, but many remain quite poor. The revenues have sometimes been used to modernize countries but often this has not improved the daily lives of most of the people. There is a growing gap between the rich and poor countries. For example, oil-rich Kuwait is among the world's wealthiest countries, yet Afghanistan is among the world's poorest.

For some people, the discovery of oil deposits has brought changes in their way of life. Many of those who now live in cities grew up in remote areas and practiced traditional farming and herding. They now work in industries supporting the production of oil. The struggle to control oil has also led to tension and wars, along with intervention by foreign powers. Some Muslims believe that exposure to Western ways is corrupting the region's people.

Oil dependency also has issues. First, oil is not a renewable resource, so reserves are being used up. Second, prices of oil may rise or fall dramatically. When prices are high, the economy thrives; when they are low, the economy suffers. In the future, the market for oil may change even more drastically, especially if countries that now rely on oil find alternative energy sources. If demand for oil drops, it could damage the economies of the oil-producing countries in Southwest Asia.

CHAPTER TEST, FORM B

True/False

1. True

2. False. Most of Southwest Asia falls within an arid climate zone.

3. True

4. False. The Ottoman Empire was formally dissolved after World War I.

5. True

Matching

6. D   7. B   8. E   9. A   10. C

Multiple Choice

11. C   12. B   13. D   14. A   15. C

16. B   17. D   18. C   19. A

Essay

20. Students' responses will vary. Possible response: The discovery of oil deposits in Southwest Asia has had a strong impact on the region's economy and social order.

The discovery of oil has brought great wealth to the oil-producing countries along the Persian Gulf. However, this wealth has not always been distributed evenly. A few people are extremely wealthy, but many remain quite poor. The revenues have sometimes been used to modernize countries but often this has not improved the daily lives of most of the people. There is a growing gap between the rich and poor countries. For example, oil-rich Kuwait is among the world's wealthiest countries, yet Afghanistan is among the world's poorest.

For some people, the discovery of oil deposits has brought changes in their way of life. Many of those who now live in cities grew up in remote areas and practiced traditional farming and herding. They now work in industries supporting the production of oil. The struggle to control oil has also led to tension and wars, along with intervention by foreign powers. Some Muslims believe that exposure to Western ways is corrupting the region's people.

Oil dependency also has issues. First, oil is not a renewable resource, so reserves are being used up. Second, prices of oil may rise or fall dramatically. When prices are high, the economy thrives; when they are low, the economy suffers. In the future, the market for oil may change even more drastically, especially if countries that now rely on oil find alternative energy sources. If demand for oil drops, it could damage the economies of the oil-producing countries in Southwest Asia.

Africa

UNIT TEST

True/False

1. True   2. False   3. True   4. False   5. True

Matching

6. E   7. B   8. C   9. A   10. D

Multiple Choice

11. B   12. D   13. C   14. A   15. B

16. D   17. C   18. B   19. A   20. C

North Africa

LESSON QUIZ 1

True/False

1. True   2. False   3. True   4. False   5. True

Multiple Choice

6. A   7. D   8. C   9. B   10. B

LESSON QUIZ 2

Matching

1. D   2. A   3. C   4. E   5. B

Multiple Choice

6. B   7. A   8. D   9. C   10. D

LESSON QUIZ 3

True/False

1. False   2. True   3. True   4. False   5. True

Multiple Choice

6. D   7. B   8. C   9. A   10. A

CHAPTER TEST, FORM A

True/False

1. False. The easternmost country in North Africa is Egypt.

2. True

3. True

Matching

4. B   **5.** A   **6.** D   **7.** E   **8.** C

9. G   **10.** F

Multiple Choice

11. B   **12.** B   **13.** D   **14.** A   **15.** C

16. D   **17.** C   **18.** C   **19.** D

Essay

20. Students' responses will vary. Possible response: Water is the most precious resource in North Africa, because it is so scarce. Oil and natural gas are important to the economy, of course, but water is essential for living. In fact, many early North African civilizations, such as Egypt, developed around waterways. Available water gives people safe water for drinking, but also allows irrigation for agriculture and water for bathing, washing, and even recreation. Water is necessary for life.

Unfortunately, low rainfall and high temperatures in the region leave little freshwater on the surface. Outside of the Nile valley, most of the need for water in the region is met with water from oases and aquifers. However, increasing population threatens to empty available aquifers. If this occurs, people will not have enough water to drink, and the region's agriculture will suffer.

CHAPTER TEST, FORM B

True/False

1. False. Much of North Africa has either a desert or semiarid climate, but steppe, highland, and Mediterranean climates are also present.

2. True

3. False. In October 2011, Libyan rebels killed dictator Muammar al-Qaddafi.

4. False. North Africa's largest city is Cairo, Egypt.

5. True

6. False. Rapid population growth is a major concern in Libya and Egypt.

Matching

7. D   **8.** B   **9.** A   **10.** C

Multiple Choice

11. D   **12.** C   **13.** B   **14.** A   **15.** A

16. B   **17.** C

Short Answer

18. Students' responses will vary. Possible response: The rain shadow effect occurs when moist air on the windward side of a mountain rises and cools. This causes precipitation on that side of the mountain, but it leaves the other side of the mountain dry. The dry interior of western North Africa lies in the rain shadow of the Atlas Mountains.

19. Students' responses will vary. Possible response: The cities and towns of North Africa have grown haphazardly over many centuries. Narrow streets often curve here and there, with no evidence of planning. Industry and trade are centered in cities and make for lots of bustle and activity. Often cities sprawl outward into the rural farming areas that surround them.

Essay

20. Students' responses will vary. Possible response: Water is the most precious resource in North Africa, because it is so scarce. Oil and natural gas are important to the economy, of course, but water is essential for living. In fact, many early North African civilizations, such as Egypt, developed around waterways. Available water gives people safe water for drinking, but also allows irrigation for agriculture and water for bathing, washing, and even recreation. Water is necessary for life.

Unfortunately, low rainfall and high temperatures in the region leave little freshwater on the surface. Outside of the Nile valley, most of the need for water in the region is met with water from oases and aquifers. However, increasing population threatens to empty available aquifers. If this occurs, people will not have enough water to drink, and the region's agriculture will suffer.

East Africa

LESSON QUIZ 1

True/False

1. True   **2.** True   **3.** False

4. True   **5.** False

Multiple Choice

6. C   **7.** B   **8.** D   **9.** A   **10.** B

LESSON QUIZ 2

Matching

1. C   **2.** E   **3.** A   **4.** D   **5.** B

Multiple Choice

6. C   **7.** A   **8.** B   **9.** D   **10.** C

LESSON QUIZ 3

True/False

1. True   **2.** True   **3.** False

4. True   **5.** False

Multiple Choice

6. D   **7.** B   **8.** A   **9.** C   **10.** B

CHAPTER TEST, FORM A

True/False

1. True

2. True

3. False. Well-known wildlife reserves are located on the Serengeti Plain, an area of tropical grasslands larger than the state of Connecticut.

4. False. Until the late 1800s, most Europeans knew little or nothing about Africa.

5. True

Matching

6. C   **7.** E   **8.** A   **9.** D   **10.** B

Multiple Choice

11. C   **12.** B   **13.** D   **14.** B   **15.** D

16. C   **17.** A

Short Answer

18. Students' responses will vary. Possible response: The purpose of the Jonglei Canal project, begun in the 1970s, was to provide more water to Egypt and Sudan. The project was suspended in 1983 because civil war in Sudan made it too dangerous.

19. Students' responses will vary. Possible response: In the 1990s, the Hutus who dominated the government of Rwanda began an attack on the minority Tutsi. Hundreds of thousands of people were killed during the conflict, which amounted to genocide, or the slaughter of a whole people for ethnic reasons.

Essay

20. Students' responses will vary. Possible response: The countries of East Africa face major health issues, and these issues have greatly impacted the region's economy. First is the poor nutrition—even starvation—of many people in East Africa.

The many wars and conflicts since 1990 have not only blocked economic development but also caused widespread starvation, sending thousands of refugees pouring across international borders. Drought and famine in the region have also shortened many lives. Second is the spread of the serious and often fatal disease, HIV/AIDS. Efforts to combat this disease through medical education and treatment have put further strains on the economies of East African countries.

CHAPTER TEST, FORM B

True/False

1. True

2. True

3. False. The kings of Aksum adopted Christianity as their religion.

4. True

5. False. Agriculture is the main economic activity in East Africa.

Matching

6. E   **7.** B   **8.** C   **9.** A   **10.** D

Multiple Choice

11. B   **12.** D   **13.** C   **14.** B   **15.** B

16. D   **17.** C   **18.** A   **19.** B

Essay

20. Students' responses will vary. Possible response: The countries of East Africa face major health issues, and these issues have greatly impacted the region's economy. First is the poor nutrition—even starvation—of many people in East Africa. The many wars and conflicts since 1990 have not only blocked economic development but also caused widespread starvation, sending thousands of refugees pouring across international borders. Drought and famine in the region have also shortened many lives. Second is the spread of the serious and often fatal disease, HIV/AIDS. Efforts to combat this disease through medical education and treatment have put further drains on the economies of East African countries.

Central Africa

LESSON QUIZ 1

True/False

1. True   **2.** False   **3.** True

4. False   **5.** False

Multiple Choice

6. D   **7.** B   **8.** C   **9.** B   **10.** A

LESSON QUIZ 2

True/False

1. False   **2.** True   **3.** True   **4.** False   **5.** True

Multiple Choice

6. C   **7.** B   **8.** D   **9.** D   **10.** C

LESSON QUIZ 3

True/False

1. True   **2.** False   **3.** False
4. True   **5.** False

Multiple Choice

6. C   **7.** B   **8.** A   **9.** B   **10.** C

CHAPTER TEST, FORM A

True/False

1. True

2. True

3. False. Central Africans who flee war and conflict are known as *refugees*.

4. False. In rural Central Africa, most people work as subsistence farmers.

Matching

5. F   **6.** B   **7.** A   **8.** D
9. C   **10.** E

Multiple Choice

11. C   **12.** D   **13.** D   **14.** B   **15.** C
16. A   **17.** B

Short Answer

18. Students' responses will vary. Possible response: The Congo River is very important to Central Africa. For one thing, people use the river's water for their thirsty crops. Second, they catch and eat the fish that live in the river. Third, people use the river for travel and to transport goods from place to place. Fourth, they have built dams on the river that produce large amounts of hydroelectric power.

19. Students' responses will vary. Possible response: People use a variety of materials from the environment to construct their homes. Some use branches to build one-room houses. Others use mud to create bricks to build their homes.

Another group use tree limbs to construct walls, which are held together by mud and covered by palm fronds to make roofs.

Essay

20. Possible response: As Europeans colonized the Americas, they developed huge plantations that required a large workforce to run. The slave trade in Central Africa developed as European colonizers shipped people from Africa over to the Americas to meet the demand for workers.

The transport of slaves was part of the "triangular trade" during that time. This described the shape that the trade routes made on a map. During the first stage of the trade route, ships arrived in Africa with goods from Europe. These ships would then be used to transport slaves from Africa to the Americas during the second stage. In the final stage, the goods that were produced by slaves on the plantations were shipped from the Americas over to Europe.

CHAPTER TEST, FORM B

True/False

1. True

2. False. Central Africans make tapioca and flour from the root of the cassava.

3. True

4. True

5. False. In the Democratic Republic of the Congo, about half the people are Roman Catholic.

Matching

6. C   **7.** B   **8.** E   **9.** A   **10.** D

Multiple Choice

11. D   **12.** C   **13.** D   **14.** C   **15.** A
16. C   **17.** B   **18.** B   **19.** A

Essay

20. Possible response: As Europeans colonized the Americas, they developed huge plantations that required a large workforce to run. The slave trade in Central Africa developed as European colonizers shipped people from Africa over to the Americas to meet the demand for workers.

The transport of slaves was part of the "triangular trade" during that time. This described the shape that the trade routes made on a map. During the first stage of the trade route, ships arrived in

Africa with goods from Europe. These ships would then be used to transport slaves from Africa to the Americas during the second stage. In the final stage, the goods that were produced by slaves on the plantations were shipped from the Americas over to Europe.

West Africa

LESSON QUIZ 1

True/False

1. True   **2.** False   **3.** True
4. False   **5.** True

Multiple Choice

6. C   **7.** A   **8.** B   **9.** D   **10.** B

LESSON QUIZ 2

True/False

1. False   **2.** True   **3.** True
4. False   **5.** True

Multiple Choice

6. C   **7.** B   **8.** D   **9.** A   **10.** B

LESSON QUIZ 3

True/False

1. False   **2.** True   **3.** True   **4.** False   **5.** True

Multiple Choice

6. C   **7.** B   **8.** B   **9.** D   **10.** A

CHAPTER TEST, FORM A

True/False

1. True
2. False. In early times, the main barrier to contact between West Africa and North Africa was the Sahara.
3. False. In 1989, Charles Taylor led an invasion of Liberia to depose the president.
4. True
5. True

Matching

6. B   **7.** A   **8.** E   **9.** D   **10.** C

Multiple Choice

11. A   **12.** C   **13.** C   **14.** A   **15.** D
16. B   **17.** D

Short Answer

18. Students' responses will vary. One possible answer: Different parts of the Bantu culture spread throught Bantu migration. First, agriculture was spread as the Bantu cultivated bananas, taro, and yams. Second, language, as the Bantu spread their languages into new regions. Third, technology, as the Bantu smelted iron and created tools and weapons unlike any the non-Bantu people had ever seen.

19. Students' responses will vary. One possible answer: In both countries, those natural resources are being depleted. In the future, the hardwood industry of Benin and the iron ore industry of Mauritania will probably decline in economic importance.

Essay

20. Students' responses will vary. One possible answer: When the British combined two of their West African colonies to form the Nigerian Protectorate in 1914, they ignored traditional territories of the ethnic groups living in the region. Those groups were very different, and forcing them together into a single country created a great deal of tension between them—especially after Nigeria gained its independence in 1960.

Great Britain developed the southern part of Nigeria extensively, including building schools, so Nigerians in the south were better educated and became leaders of the new country. Many of them were from the mainly Christian Igbo people. The Hausa people of the north, who were Muslims, resented the power of the Igbo. Violent conflicts broke out among the Hausa, the Yoruba, and the Igbo. Up to a million Igbo fled their homes in northern Nigeria for fear of being massacred. In 1967, the eastern region withdrew and created the republic of Biafra. But Nigeria invaded Biafra and left it in ruins after two years of war. Ultimately, civil war claimed the lives of almost 1 million people.

From that point on the country was under military rule. Finally, in 1978, a new constitution was written and a democratic election was held. A new civilian government took office, ending the military rule in 1983. In 1999, a democratically elected president took office to rule Nigeria.

CHAPTER TEST, FORM B

True/False

1. False. Cape Verde and Tristan da Cunha are island nations of West Africa.

Discovering World Geography

2. True

3. True

4. True

5. False. The British government outlawed the slave trade in 1807.

Matching

6. D   7. B   8. A   9. E   10. C

Multiple Choice

11. D   12. A   13. A   14. D   15. B

16. C   17. C   18. B   19. C

Essay

20. Students' responses will vary. One possible answer: When the British combined two of their West African colonies to form the Nigerian Protectorate in 1914, they ignored traditional territories of the ethnic groups living in the region. Those groups were very different, and forcing them together into a single country created a great deal of tension between them—especially after Nigeria gained its independence in 1960.

Great Britain developed the southern part of Nigeria extensively, including building schools, so Nigerians in the south were better educated and became leaders of the new country. Many of them were from the mainly Christian Igbo people. The Hausa people of the north, who were Muslims, resented the power of the Igbo. Violent conflicts broke out among the Hausa, the Yoruba, and the Igbo. Up to a million Igbo fled their homes in northern Nigeria for fear of being massacred. In 1967, the eastern region withdrew and created the republic of Biafra. But Nigeria invaded Biafra and left it in ruins after two years of war. Ultimately, civil war claimed the lives of almost 1 million people.

From that point on the country was under military rule. Finally, in 1978, a new constitution was written and a democratic election was held. A new civilian government took office, ending the military rule in 1983. In 1999, a democratically elected president took office to rule Nigeria.

Southern Africa

LESSON QUIZ 1

True/False

1. False   2. True   3. False   4. True   5. True

Multiple Choice

6. B   7. A   8. C   9. D   10. B

LESSON QUIZ 2

Matching

1. D   2. B   3. E   4. A   5. C

Multiple Choice

6. B   7. A   8. C   9. C   10. B

LESSON QUIZ 3

True/False

1. True   2. False   3. False   4. True   5. True

Multiple Choice

6. A   7. C   8. B   9. A   10. C

CHAPTER TEST, FORM A

True/False

1. True

2. True

3. False. Great Zimbabwe, the capital city of the Shona people, was abandoned in the 1400s.

4. True

5. False. Malawi is Southern Africa's most rural nation.

Matching

6. E   7. A   8. C   9. B   10. D

Multiple Choice

11. D   12. C   13. D   14. B   15. A

16. B   17. C

Short Answer

18. Students' responses will vary. Possible response: Some countries in Southern Africa mine and burn coal to produce electricity. Mozambique, and Angola both have large deposits of natural gas. Angola is a leading oil producer in Africa. Namibia also has oil and natural gas deposits. Some use rivers and waterfalls to provide electric power. Zimbabwe, Zambia, and Malawi get electricity from their rivers and falls. However, some countries, such as Mozambique and Angola, have not made full use of their rivers to provide power.

19. Students' responses will vary. Possible response: When Britain gained control of Cape Colony in the early 1800s, the Boers resented the British. Thousands of Boers left Cape Colony in a

migration called the Great Trek. They settled north of the Orange River

Essay

20. Students' responses will vary. Possible response: After gaining its independence, mining and other industries in South Africa began to grow. These industries relied on the labor of black Africans. In order to stay in power, the white minority government limited the education and political rights of the blacks, who greatly outnumbered them. Protests by thousands of black miners scared white voters into electing an Afrikaner government in 1948, which began creating laws that developed the system of apartheid. These laws limited the rights of blacks and restricted them from voting.

The African National Congress (ANC) protested these laws by beginning a campaign of civil disobedience. While the protests were intended to be peaceful, the government responded violently and the ANC turned to armed conflict. Nelson Mandela, who led the ANC, was arrested in 1962 and sent to prison for life.

In the 1970s, other countries took notice of the struggles with apartheid and began placing embargos on South Africa. In 1989, the president of South Africa was forced to resign and a new president, F.W. de Klerk, was elected. Under his leadership, the government began repealing the apartheid laws and released Mandela from prison in 1991. Finally, a new constitution was written in 1993 that gave all races the right to vote. The following year the ANC won the election and Mandela became the new president.

CHAPTER TEST, FORM B

True/False

1. True
2. False. The largest lake in Southern Africa is Lake Malawi.
3. True
4. False. Most people in Southern Africa live in the countryside.
5. True

Matching

6. B   7. E   8. D   9. A   10. C

Multiple Choice

11. C   12. B   13. B   14. D   15. A
16. D   17. C   18. B   19. A

Essay

20. Students' responses will vary. Possible response: After gaining its independence, mining and other industries in South Africa began to grow. These industries relied on the labor of black Africans. In order to stay in power, the white minority government limited the education and political rights of the blacks, who greatly outnumbered them. Protests by thousands of black miners scared white voters into electing an Afrikaner government in 1948, which began creating laws that developed the system of apartheid. These laws limited the rights of blacks and restricted them from voting.

The African National Congress (ANC) protested these laws by beginning a campaign of civil disobedience. While the protests were intended to be peaceful, the government responded violently and the ANC turned to armed conflict. Nelson Mandela, who led the ANC, was arrested in 1962 and sent to prison for life.

In the 1970s, other countries took notice of the struggles with apartheid and began placing embargos on South Africa. In 1989, the president of South Africa was forced to resign and a new president, F.W. de Klerk, was elected. Under his leadership, the government began repealing the apartheid laws and released Mandela from prison in 1991. Finally, a new constitution was written in 1993 that gave all races the right to vote. The following year the ANC won the election and Mandela became the new president.

Oceania, Australia, New Zealand, and Antarctica

UNIT TEST

True/False

1. False   2. True   3. True   4. False   5. True

Matching

6. B   7. C   8. E   9. A   10. D

Multiple Choice

11. B   12. A   13. A   14. C   15. D
16. D   17. C   18. B   19. B   20. A

Australia and New Zealand

LESSON QUIZ 1

True/False

1. True   2. True   3. False   4. False   5. True

Multiple Choice

6. C   **7**. B   **8**. B   **9**. A   **10**. C

LESSON QUIZ 2

Matching

1. B   **2**. E   **3**. D   **4**. A   **5**. C

Multiple Choice

6. D   **7**. B   **8**. C   **9**. A   **10**. B

LESSON QUIZ 3

True/False

1. False   **2**. True   **3**. False   **4**. True   **5**. True

Multiple Choice

6. C   **7**. A   **8**. B   **9**. D   **10**. C

CHAPTER TEST, FORM A

True/False

1. False. Overall, Australia has a low elevation compared to other continents.
2. True
3. True
4. False. The British colonized Australia and New Zealand.
5. True

Matching

6. C   **7**. B   **8**. E   **9**. D   **10**. A

Multiple Choice

11. B   **12**. A   **13**. C   **14**. D   **15**. B
16. A   **17**. C

Short Answer

18. Students' responses will vary. Possible response: A drought is a long period with little or no rain. During a drought, water reserves become low and water quality becomes poor. The poor-quality drinking water may cause health problems for humans. Droughts also threaten the survival of wildlife, livestock, and farm crops.

19. Students' responses will vary. Possible response: Both Australia and New Zealand have low birthrates and low death rates. Families are having fewer children, which results in a lower birthrate. And both countries have high life expectancies, so people are living longer. This results in a low death rate. Since the countries have both a low death

rate and a low birthrate, their populations are aging. This means that more younger workers will be needed to support the older populations at a time when there are fewer younger workers coming along. Immigrants to Australia and New Zealand are filling some of these positions, which helps fill the need for care providers.

Essay

20. Students' responses will vary. Possible response: Animals that are not native to a country but are brought there from other places are called introduced species. Sometimes these species can harm a country's environment. Such is the case with Australia.

When people began settling Australia, they sometimes brought with them the animals they had in their home countries. For example, sheep ranchers brought their dogs with them to herd and protect their flocks. Although dogs in themselves did not harm the environment, other species introduced to Australia had more harmful effects. Wealthy people imported rabbits for the sport of hunting. These rabbits multiplied rapidly, often eating all the grasses and wildflowers in an area and leaving it bare. To protect their crops, especially sugar cane, from beetles, farmers introduced a toad to prey upon the beetles. They controlled the beetles, but these toads were poisonous to other species. Eventually, they crowded out and killed many native animals.

It is difficult to estimate the amount of damage introduced species have done to Australia's environment. Although some of these species are now under control, others still cause problems to both humans and native animals.

CHAPTER TEST, FORM B

True/False

1. False. Christianity is the most common religion in Australia and New Zealand.
2. True
3. False. Explorers from other European countries sailed around Australia and New Zealand before the British arrived.
4. True
5. True

Matching

6. D   **7**. A   **8**. E   **9**. B   **10**. C

Multiple Choice

11. B **12.** C **13.** D **14.** C **15.** D
16. C **17.** D **18.** A **19.** B

Essay

20. Students' responses will vary. Possible response: Animals that are not native to a country but are brought there from other places are called introduced species. Sometimes these species can harm a country's environment. Such is the case with Australia.

When people began settling Australia, they sometimes brought with them the animals they had in their home countries. For example, sheep ranchers brought their dogs with them to herd and protect their flocks. Although dogs in themselves did not harm the environment, other species introduced to Australia had more harmful effects. Wealthy people imported rabbits for the sport of hunting. These rabbits multiplied rapidly, often eating all the grasses and wildflowers in an area and leaving it bare. To protect their crops, especially sugar cane, from beetles, farmers introduced a toad to prey upon the beetles. They controlled the beetles, but these toads were poisonous to other species. Eventually, they crowded out and killed many native animals.

It is difficult to estimate the amount of damage introduced species have done to Australia's environment. Although some of these species are now under control, others still cause problems to both humans and native animals.

Oceania

LESSON QUIZ 1

True/False

1. False **2.** True **3.** True
4. True **5.** False

Multiple Choice

6. B **7.** D **8.** D **9.** C **10.** A

LESSON QUIZ 2

True/False

1. False **2.** True **3.** True
4. True **5.** False

Multiple Choice

6. D **7.** B **8.** D **9.** C **10.** A

LESSON QUIZ 3

True/False

1. True **2.** True **3.** False
4. True **5.** False

Multiple Choice

6. B **7.** C **8.** A **9.** D **10.** C

CHAPTER TEST, FORM A

True/False

1. False. The smallest inhabited island nation in Oceania is Nauru.

2. False. Once Europeans began colonizing Oceania in the 1600s, colonists and native people often clashed violently.

3. True

4. True

5. True

Matching

6. C **7.** B **8.** A **9.** E **10.** D

Multiple Choice

11. D **12.** A **13.** B **14.** C **15.** B
16. A **17.** D

Short Answer

18. Students' responses will vary. One possible answer: Basically, high islands are formed by eruptions of volcanoes on the ocean floor; lava forms volcanic rock that eventually reaches high above sea level. By contrast, the volcanic rock underlying low islands remains beneath the ocean's surface. The islands build up as a result of the growth of coral reefs on the volcanic base followed by a buildup of sand and sediment as the reef ages.

19. Students' responses will vary. One possible answer: A positive result of such diversity is that there is a wide variety of music, foods, clothing, and artwork in Papua New Guinea. However, negative effects such as ethnic discrimination and violent conflicts among tribal groups are also common.

Essay

20. Students' responses will vary. One possible answer: The high islands of Oceania are more likely to have prosperous economies than the low islands.

High islands tend to have more mineral resources. For example, New Guinea contains gold, copper, petroleum, and natural gas. High islands are also generally larger and greener than low islands. Rain forests grow on many high islands, providing valuable timber. In addition, many high islands have rich volcanic soil that is good for farming. Many products can be exported, benefitting the economies of high islands.

Low islands are small and therefore have limited land area. Also, they are based on coral and do not have rock foundations. Because large deposits of metal ores are found in deep layers of rock, low islands lack such natural resources. Vegetation is scarce on low islands as well; they have few trees to provide timber, rubber, and similar products. Besides, the poor, sandy soil of low islands makes farming difficult. The result is that low islands have few products to export.

CHAPTER TEST, FORM B

True/False

1. True
2. False. In general, the highland areas of Papua New Guinea have higher population densities than the lowlands and coastal plains.
3. False. A simplified language that is used for communication between people who speak different languages is called a pidgin language.
4. True
5. False. Most islands in Oceania import far more than they export.
6. True

Matching

| 7. A | 8. C | 9. D | 10. B |

Multiple Choice

| 11. B | 12. A | 13. C | 14. C | 15. D |
| 16. B | 17. C | 18. D | 19. A |

Essay

20. Students' responses will vary. One possible answer: The high islands of Oceania are more likely to have prosperous economies than the low islands.

    High islands tend to have more mineral resources. For example, New Guinea contains gold, copper, petroleum, and natural gas. High islands are also generally larger and greener than low islands.

Rain forests grow on many high islands, providing valuable timber. In addition, many high islands have rich volcanic soil that is good for farming. Many products can be exported, benefitting the economies of high islands.

Low islands are small and therefore have limited land area. Also, they are based on coral and do not have rock foundations. Because large deposits of metal ores are found in deep layers of rock, low islands lack such natural resources. Vegetation is scarce on low islands as well; they have few trees to provide timber, rubber, and similar products. Besides, the poor, sandy soil of low islands makes farming difficult. The result is that low islands have few products to export.

Antarctica

LESSON QUIZ 1

Matching

| 1. C | 2. E | 3. A | 4. D | 5. B |

Multiple Choice

| 6. D | 7. B | 8. C | 9. A | 10. B |

LESSON QUIZ 2

True/False

| 1. False | 2. True | 3. True |
| 4. True | 5. False | |

Multiple Choice

| 6. D | 7. B | 8. A | 9. C | 10. B |

CHAPTER TEST, FORM A

True/False

1. False. Antarctica is located in the Southern Hemisphere.
2. True
3. False. Antarctica has an extremely dry climate.
4. True
5. True

Matching

| 6. C | 7. E | 8. A | 9. D | 10. B |

Multiple Choice

| 11. B | 12. C | 13. A | 14. D | 15. C |
| 16. A | 17. B |

Short Answer

18. Students' responses will vary. Possible response: Most scientists only live in Antarctica during the summer months because the conditions are too harsh and dangerous during the winter. During the summer, the temperatures are cold but they are not deadly like they are in the winter. The sun also shines for 24 hours a day in the summer, which gives them longer days to work.

19. Students' responses will vary. Possible response: Because Antarctica is at a very high latitude, it never receives direct rays from the sun—not even in summer, when the Southern Hemisphere is tilted toward the sun. Because the sun's energy thus must spread over a wider area, very little of that energy reaches any one spot on Antarctica's surface. Also, because most of the continent is south of the Antarctic Circle, Antarctica receives no sunlight and remains completely dark for at least three months of the year.

Essay

20. Students' responses will vary. Possible response: Geographers have sought to measure climate change by using satellite imagery and taking local measurements. In this way, they have learned that the Antarctic ice sheet is shrinking. Many scientists are concerned that global warming is causing this shrinkage. Global warming not only affects Antarctica's ecosystems, but the whole of the planet Earth.

Melting ice and shrinking ice sheets tell scientists that global temperatures are rising, and rising quickly. The impact of global warming could permanently damage ecosystems in Antarctica. Also, because Antarctica is considered a "global barometer," conditions there are generally an indicator of what is happening to the climate around the world. With rising temperatures, chunks of ice break from the ice sheets of Antarctica, causing more icebergs to litter the seas. This makes travel on the seas even more difficult and dangerous. More serious, however, is the possibility that as more and more ice melts, sea levels worldwide will rise. In many low-lying areas throughout the world, survival would then be impossible for humans and other life.

Climate change is also affecting the food chain of the land and sea animals of Antarctica. Plankton and krill populations are decreasing. Plankton are a food source for krill, and krill are a food source for many of the fish that thrive in the seas of Antarctica. Without enough food, the fish population will either die or go elsewhere, leaving the seals and penguins without an adequate food supply. Such disruption of the food chain would have disastrous effects on Antarctica's animal life.

CHAPTER TEST, FORM B

True/False

1. True

2. False. Icebergs look smaller than they really are.

3. False. Antarctic hair grass and Antarctic pearlwort are the only flowering plants that grow in Antarctica.

4. True

5. True

Matching

6. C **7.** A **8.** E **9.** D **10.** B

Multiple Choice

11. C **12.** D **13.** B **14.** C **15.** A
16. B **17.** D **18.** C **19.** B

Essay

20. Students' responses will vary. Possible response: Geographers have sought to measure climate change by using satellite imagery and taking local measurements. In this way, they have learned that the Antarctic ice sheet is shrinking. Many scientists are concerned that global warming is causing this shrinkage. Global warming not only affects Antarctica's ecosystems, but the whole of the planet Earth.

Melting ice and shrinking ice sheets tell scientists that global temperatures are rising, and rising quickly. The impact of global warming could permanently damage ecosystems in Antarctica. Also, because Antarctica is considered a "global barometer," conditions there are generally an indicator of what is happening to the climate around the world. With rising temperatures, chunks of ice break from the ice sheets of Antarctica, causing more icebergs to litter the seas. This makes travel on the seas even more difficult and dangerous. More serious, however, is the possibility that as more and more ice melts, sea levels worldwide will rise. In many low-lying areas throughout the world, survival would then be impossible for humans and other life.

Climate change is also affecting the food chain of the land and sea animals of Antarctica. Plankton and krill populations are decreasing. Plankton are a food source for krill, and krill are a food source for many of the fish that thrive in the seas of Antarctica. Without enough food, the fish population will either die or go elsewhere, leaving the seals and penguins without an adequate food supply. Such disruption of the food chain would have disastrous effects on Antarctica's animal life.